scientific thought

scientific thought

cases from classical physics

J. A. EASLEY, JR.
and
MAURICE M. TATSUOKA
of the
University of Illinois

ALLYN AND BACON, INC., BOSTON

PREFACE

This book grows out of a lengthy struggle to bring into science instruction the spirit and methodology of scientific thought. No textbook, of course, can provide a complete solution of this problem, for the instructor and students must play their roles. However, a science textbook should clearly illustrate methodological principles.

Our text, developed during seven years of teaching at the Hilo Campus of the University of Hawaii, has gone through two mimeographed editions. We are much indebted to our students at Hilo and to several colleagues who participated in this development.

This book owes its inspiration to a number of sources, including *The Harvard Case Histories in Experimental Science*, edited by James Bryant Conant and Leonard Nash. Its cases, however, are much more abstracted from the historical context than the cases in that pioneering work and are more interconnected in their overall development. Its general conceptual framework derives in part from the Harvard course, Natural Sciences 1, taught by Phillippe LeCorbeiller, in which one of us (Easley) had the great pleasure of serving as teaching fellow. The notion that students should learn, by practical experimentation, to use simple apparatus to investigate physical phenomena stems in part from the laboratory of the Natural Sciences course developed in the 1940's by Joseph Schwab and his colleagues at The College, University of Chicago.

For most students, the characteristics of scientific thought will, in the long run, be a more significant aspect of physical science than its content. They will very likely find themselves either engaged in scientific inquiry in the social sciences or attempting to suppress its inroads into the humanities. In this book we develop our own view of the significant principles of method illustrated by the cases of classical physical science which are accessible to the student. We recognize that the philosophy of science we espouse is not (and indeed cannot be) acceptable to all philosophers nor to all scientists, but we must offer our answers to the philosophical questions about the nature of scientific knowledge and the manner in which it has been developed and substantiated. To avoid facing these questions would be to assume that there are no ground rules at all in science except that of reporting "the truth," and that would certainly be an error.

We should like to emphasize that there are many scientific methods (i.e., strategies of inquiry), but that there are not, as some would have it, different methods for different subject matters. Each method can be applied to any subject matter, but some are more useful at certain times in one science than in another, depending on the state and nature of available theory. The truly difficult problem of scientific inquiry is to find and master the appropriate method for the problem at hand. For this, a unified methodology, a theory of method, would be valuable, but such a theory does not yet exist. We are very much indebted to Professor Israel Scheffler, of Harvard University, for his continued encouragement to bring out a book in this field with a strong philosophical emphasis. We are also grateful to many others who have encouraged us or assisted us in revision of the manuscript.

The principles of method set forth here are demonstrably powerful in physical science and have some usefulness in other sciences. Our examples are deliberately classical, partly because the method can be more completely illustrated for the general student by the classical cases, and partly because the cases themselves serve as points of reference in developing new approaches and in the investigation of new areas of human knowledge.

We have not specified a program of laboratory instruction, but have incorporated experimental suggestions into the text as integral parts of the development. We tried out and shaped these suggestions ourselves with our classes in Hilo, where two-hours of laboratory work was required each week. (We should like to mention our special debt to Mr. Wolf Siegert of Hamburg, Germany, for several experimental ideas.) We hope that students will have the opportunity to see the physical phenomena in a context permitting experimental control. Some of the experiments can be performed outside of a laboratory, using everyday objects in a dormitory room, for example. Others are best performed under the supervision of an experienced instructor in a teaching laboratory. We leave to the instructors and students the decision of what organized laboratory work to perform.

Problems and annotated references to supplementary reading materials are provided at the end of each chapter. The problems can be solved by anyone who has grasped two years of high school mathematics. The same mathematical criterion applies to the theoretical development in the text. In the three or four places where a mathematical idea beyond that level is required, we develop the essential mathematics. Mathematics is the language of physical science and cannot be dropped. Moreover, it provides a needed correction to the simplistic empiricism that still prevails among the social sciences. We hope that students will appreciate the great contribution of Newton who showed that it is possible through mathematical reasoning to grasp nature intellectually.

J. A. EASLEY, JR.   MAURICE M. TATSUOKA
GENEVA   TOKYO

CONTENTS

MODELS OF THE UNIVERSE
BEFORE NEWTON

From the earliest written documents of all civilizations and from the most primitive tribes on the earth today, we find evidence of man's great interest in the stars and other celestial bodies. Part of primitive man's interest stemmed, no doubt, from the awe and mystification with which he viewed these brilliant objects in the skies. His mystification led to a belief that human events are somehow controlled by the stars, and that the future can be foretold by making observations of the heavens. Thus the occult "science" of astrology developed, which gave rise to such figures of speech as "being born under a lucky star." Although it is now completely discarded by scientists, astrology has had a *motivational* influence on the work of many of the founders of modern astronomy. We might say that modern science owes a certain debt to astrology, but the debt does not make astrology any more credible, for the *results* of a scientist's work are largely independent of his motivations. Along with the motivation founded in mysticism, however, there were more practical reasons for interest in the celestial bodies. The desire for calendars was one of these; the need for navigational guides was another.

Among those who helped establish patterns for modern astronomy, the Babylonians used the moon as a convenient reference for measuring periods of time longer than a few days. Therefore, they developed a calendar in lunar months, while the Egyptians based their calendar on the sun, and reckoned in years. Other achievements of these early astronomers include the discovery that the sun, moon, and planets stay within a narrow, beltlike strip of the sky as they revolve around the heavens. The naming of stars and drawing of maps showing their positions in constellations was another major contribution. The astrologer's concern to keep track of the sun, moon, and planets as they move through the belt of constellations, identified by the twelve signs of the zodiac, is based on early, detailed knowledge of planetary movement and a conception of the skies as a sphere. Astronomers and navigators still record the location of planets, sun, moon, and stars with reference to an imagined sphere as well as the astrologers.

The conception of the skies as a sphere is the basis for all work in mapping the sky and for the aiming of modern telescopes, even though it is well known that celestial bodies vary enormously in their distances from the earth. This conception also formed the basis for the first scientific theories of the universe, developed by Greek astronomers, who had little reason to suspect that the stars were not all the same distance away. The contributions of the Egyptian and the Babylonian astronomers were less conceptually unified, but they had accumulated a considerable body of observations, on the basis of which they would make predictions of eclipses and could draw celestial maps that helped them in navigation.

Theoretical exercise:

1.1 Give an argument to show why stellar positions on a sphere have value even though distances to the stars are not uniform. ▬

Observational explorations:

1.2 Observe two or three prominent natural objects in the night sky—e.g., the moon, bright stars or planets. Record, by a sketch, their positions at a given hour relative to two fixed objects on the horizon. Repeat your observations after two hours or more. (If the night sky is not observable, because of overcast or city lights, make your observations in a planetarium or use photographs.) Information on positions of planets can sometimes be found in local newspapers. ▬

1.3 Construct a physical model representing the night sky by partially filling a spherical flask with water and mounting it in a clamp as shown in Fig. 1.1, marking a 24-hour time scale on tape around the neck. Mark the first positions of the celestial bodies you observed in Ex. 1.2 with the pointer at the appropriate time, then rotate the flask in its clamp to the second observation time. Do the positions of the marked objects seem correct? If not, what adjustments of the flask model could you make to produce a more accurate representation of your observation? ▬

1.4 Repeat the observations of Ex. 1.2 two or three nights later, if the moon was included, or five to seven nights later if the moon was not included but the planets were. Determine if these observations are representable by the flask-model without changing the marks that worked best in Ex. 1.3. ▬

HOW THE ANCIENTS MEASURED THE SIZE OF THE EARTH

By the second century B. C., several Greek astronomers, including Eratosthenes and Poseidonius, working in Alexandria, the great center of Greek culture in Egypt, determined the circumference of the earth with considerable exactitude. This remarkable achievement, whose geographical implications were not followed up until the time of Columbus, deserves our attention as a striking example of the measurement of distances that could not be directly compared with standards of length. The development of a quantitative science of astronomy clearly depends on such indirect methods of measurement, as do most branches of quantitative science. The geometrical method of reasoning illustrated by this calculation is fundamental to the development of theoretical models of the universe which we shall consider in this chapter.

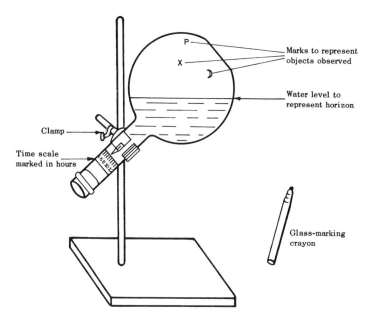

Figure 1.1 Flask-model of the Sky.

Figure 1.2 shows the relation between the lengths of shadows in two particular locations and the size of the earth, which forms the basis for this method of determining the circumference of the earth. Vertical posts of the same height in different places on the earth typically cast shadows of different lengths at the same time. Knowing the height of the two posts and the lengths of their shadows, one can draw them to scale, positioning them suitably on the circumference of some circle. On any drawable circle the distance between the posts must be on a different scale than the lengths of posts and shadows. Knowing the scale of distance between posts permits one to calculate the circumference of the earth.

It is convenient, as a first approximation, to assume that the sun's rays striking the earth are parallel; hence, the posts are positioned so that lines from their tops to the tips of the shadows are parallel. One may then construct a diagram of the earth with compass and ruler as shown in Fig. 1.2. It can be shown that angles A and B, made by the sun's rays with the posts at their tops, differ by angle C, the angle between the two posts. This follows because angles A and B are equal respectively to angles A'' and B'' at the center of the earth, and $\angle C + \angle B'' = \angle A''$. Once angles A and B and the distance between the posts have been determined, the circumference of the earth can be calculated. One has only to answer the question, *What* times angle C is 360°? He can then answer the question, *What* times the distance between the posts is the circumference of the earth?

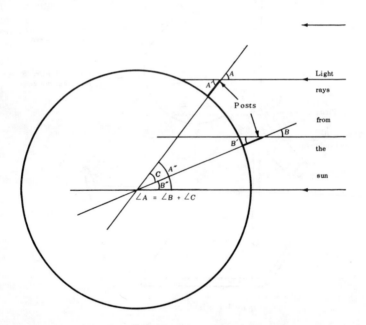

Figure 1.2 Angles Formed by Sun's Rays and Two Posts.

From the point of view of the philosophy of science, it is interesting to examine the sense in which the indirect measurement of the earth, described above, presupposes a *theoretical model*. For the time being, the term *model* will not be defined precisely, but the student may construe the term to stand for a scale model of an object or something like a scale model—even a verbal description of such a model—used to analyze the object itself. A more precise denotation of the word will be given later. Since some aspects of the theoretical model used in this calculation are not immediately susceptible to verification, the assumptions involved in the argument are listed below. It should be evident that, if any of these assumptions should turn out to be false, the resulting estimate of the earth's circumference would be in error by a commensurate amount.

(1) The earth is assumed to have a circular cross section. As evidence for this assumption, it had been noted that the earth's shadow on the moon (a lunar eclipse) was always at least approximately circular.

(2) The sun's rays striking the earth are assumed to be parallel. This was certainly in error, but by a very small angle.

(3) It is assumed that measurements of the shadows of the two poles are made simultaneously despite the considerable separation between the poles. The possibility of satisfying this assumption is better than one might suppose. (See Ex. 1.7.)

(4) The surface of the earth in the immediate vicinity of the two poles is assumed to be flat. (This assumption is necessary if angles A and B are determined by way of the shadow lengths. If another method of measurement were used, it would carry other assumptions with it.)

Classroom discussion problem:

1.5 The students should identify the particular point in the description of the procedure for measurement of the earth that hinges on each of these assumptions. ▄

The well-known ancient determinations of the earth's diameter were by Pliny (8720 miles), Poseidonius (7480 miles), Eratosthenes (7850 miles), and Al-Farghani (6500 miles). Recent determinations of the diameter through the poles are approximately 7900 miles.

It is impressive that, with so many assumptions and such limited means as the ancients had for checking them, their results came as near as they did to our current information. Is this merely a matter of chance? Do not modern scientists profit enormously by avoiding the making of so many wild assumptions? We shall see later that this is not necessarily so.

Theoretical explorations:

1.6 How far off might each assumption have been? How much difference would such error make in the result? ▄

Experimentation:

1.7 Measuring the length of shadow of some rigid object in the sunlight every 15 minutes between 11 a.m. and 1 p.m. and plot a graph of shadow length against time. Explain how Eratosthenes could have conducted his measurements so as to satisfy assumption (3) on the preceding page even if he had no clock. ■

PYTHAGORAS' MODEL OF THE UNIVERSE

Pythagoras and his school of Greek thinkers who lived in the sixth century B.C. placed great stock in numbers. The essence of things and phenomena, they said, lay in quantities and the interrelationships among quantities. For instance, the relative pitches of muscial notes produced by a vibrating string depend on the length of the string in a neat arithmetical manner. A harmonious series of notes, leading up to a sort of scale on a stringed instrument like a guitar or violin, is produced by shortening a stretched string to the following small, whole number ratios of the original length: 1/2, 1/3, 1/4, 1/5, 1/6, 1/7, 1/8, 1/9, ... , 1/16. The scale formed by the last eight ratios can be reproduced more conveniently if one multiplies them by 8. (See Fig. 1.3.) Multiplication of the ratios does not change the melodic character of the scale.[1]

Experimentation:

1.8 Measure the distances from the bridge to the nut and successive frets of a guitar, ukulele, or other fretted instrument as one plays a diatonic scale. Compute the fractions of the total string length which vibrate at each step of the scale and plot these ratios along the bottom line of Fig. 1.3. ■

1.9 Locate points corresponding to the ratios given in Fig. 1.3 along a taut wire and play this "Pythagorean" scale. Compare the Pythagorean and diatonic scales in musical quality and numerical structure. ■

The underlying reason for the existence of such simple arithmetical relationships, according to Pythagoras, was that nature was built on

---

[1] The scale described above is a portion of the harmonic sequence for stringed instruments. Pythagoras developed a slightly different scale by choosing string lengths of 1/2, 2/3, 3/4, and 1 (4/4) as four basic notes and then filling in four more notes of the following string lengths: 8/9 of 1, 8/9 of 8/9 of 1, 8/9 of 2/3, and 8/9 of 8/9 of 2/3. In this scale, the lengths of string for pairs of successive notes form ratios of 8/9 (whole steps) in five cases and $\frac{3 \times 9^2}{4 \times 8^2}$ (half steps) in two cases. In the harmonic scale above, the intervals are 8/9, 9/10, 10/11, 11/12, ... In contemporary music the tempered scale is used which does not have such neat arithmetic properties as these.

a simple numerical pattern. The basic simplicity of nature must then be reflected in the shapes of the earth and celestial objects, as well as in the motions of the latter. What could be more natural, he argued, than that the earth should have the same simple and perfect shape as the sun and the moon: that of a sphere? The motions of the sun and the moon, likewise, should describe that simplest and most perfect of all plane curves, the circle. In order to understand the theory he built on this assumption, we must first understand how the sun and the stars actually appear to move to observers on the earth. The simplest way to describe the motions of celestial bodies is to record the times and positions of their rising and setting.

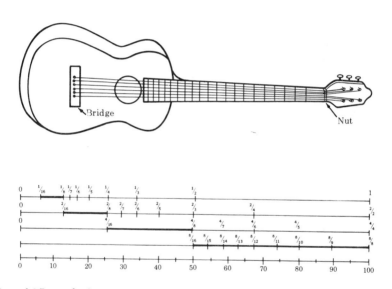

Figure 1.3 Parts of a Guitar and "Pythagorean" Ratios. (The heavy segments of each line correspond to the same scale in different octaves.)

Observations in Pythagoras' time were made with reference to a pillar erected on a flat surface. The surface was then marked off to indicate directions. We may imagine that a circle was drawn with the pillar as its center. The circle was then divided into equal units of angular measure, one mark being placed to point the direction of the pole star from the pillar. (See Fig. 1.4.) Even with such an elementary instrument, it could easily be determined that the sun rises and sets at slightly different points on the eastern and western horizons each day. The points of rising and setting shift southward during the period from June 21 to December 21 and shift back again during the period from December 21 to June 21 of the following year. On the other hand, each star rises in the east and sets in the west at exactly the same point each night.

Every night stars rise and set a few minutes earlier than they did the night before. By the time a year is half gone, stars that were rising at dawn now rise at sunset. So the time of rising of a star changes by 24 hours in a whole year.[2]

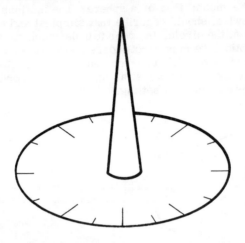

Figure 1.4 A Pillar and Divided Circle for Observing the Positions of Heavenly Bodies.

Since observations with the naked eye do not reveal the relative distances of celestial objects from the earth, the simplest representation of their observed positions would place them all at the same distance from the earth. A spherical map can be constructed showing the relative positions of all the stars whose positions could be observed—from some part of the earth at some time—as points on a sphere. The stars that can be viewed at one moment from one place all lie on one hemisphere. The great circle that divides this hemisphere from the other represents the observer's horizon.

Having constructed such a spherical map of the heavens, with a fixed circle representing the horizon, the rising and setting of the stars can be simulated by a rotation of the sphere. (See Fig. 1.5.) Since the one star in the heavens that does not appear to move appreciably is the North Star (or Pole Star), the axis of rotation of the sphere must pass through it. By properly tilting the axis relative to the fixed horizon, this model can be made to represent accurately the

---

[2] The length of a year may be defined approximately as the number of days between successive returns of the sun to its highest (or lowest) position in the sky. In the sense that the maximum height is not the same every year but diminishes slightly, 365 days is an approximation. Every fourth year takes 366 days, and the sun returns approximately to its highest point again.

apparent motion of the stars as seen from a given location. This representation of stellar motion, itself a great achievement, forms the foundation for the model by which Pythagoras sought to explain the apparent motions of all the heavenly bodies.

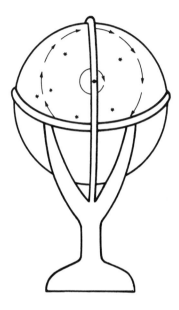

Figure 1.5 Stellar Sphere with Fixed Horizon.

We have noted that the stars rise and set a few minutes earlier each night. In terms of the stellar-sphere model, this means that slightly more than one complete rotation of the sphere must occur between two successive sunrises (or sunsets). Sunrise (or sunset) is represented by rotation of the stellar sphere carrying the sun-point across the horizon. In order that the next sunrise (or sunset) occurs after slightly more than one rotation, the sun's position must have moved a small distance on the sphere in a direction opposite to the sphere's motion. The amount of the sun's daily shift must be such that it goes completely around the stellar sphere in one year. This is so because the time of rising of any star changes by 24 hours in a whole year. When the observed daily shift in the direction of sunrise (or sunset) is considered, together with the daily backward shift just described, the annual path of the sun-point around the stellar sphere is determined. It turns out to be along a great circle, about 23° off from the equator. (See Fig. 1.6.)

Pythagoras' model thus represents celestial phenomena by a stellar sphere which rotates slightly more than once each day, carrying the sun around with it. The sun, however, is not fixed at a single point on the sphere (as each star is) but slowly creeps around it in approximately the opposite direction.

The length of the sun's journey across the sky between sunrise and sunset is longest on June 21 and shortest on December 21. Inspection of Fig. 1.6 shows that the predicted changes in day length are gradual, as observed. Pythagoras' model accounts also for the seasonal changes in the length of day.

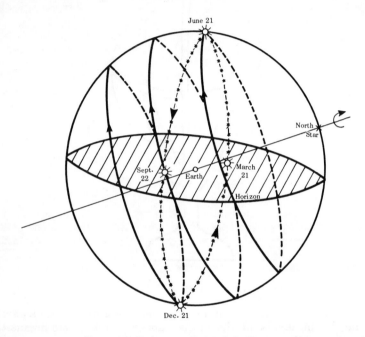

Figure 1.6 Pythagoras' Model of the Universe.

In an exactly analogous manner a moon-point can be added to the model so as to account successfully for the apparent motion of the moon. Having accounted, in this way, for the apparent motion of the "fixed stars" and two "wandering bodies," Pythagoras also tried to represent the motions of the other wanderers, Mercury, Venus, Mars, Jupiter and Saturn. These five, together with the sun and moon, were called planets in Pythagoras' day, the word *planet* meaning "wandering body." But with these five *other* planets he was unsuccessful. Their apparent motions are much more complex than those of the sun and the moon. For example, they periodically *reverse* the direction in which they "wander" through the sky. (At such times these planets are said to perform *retrograde* motion.) Nevertheless, his achievement was a momentous one for his day—and one whose influence was to hold sway for centuries. It is worthy of being called the first scientific theory in astronomy. It had the appealing simplicity of reducing many, more or less discrete observations to combinations of simple, circular motions. It not only systematized the paths of sun and moon against the background of stars, but also explained the well-known changes in length of day.

It is always easier to use the term *model* in retrospect than during the development of a theory. Pythagoras' thinking about astronomical problems may not have required the construction of any physical sphere, and we probably cannot say much about the degree of skepticism he may have felt concerning the limitations of his solution. Scientists typically have presented their theories as discoveries of reality. Use of the term *model*, with its implication of partial truth is a recent development. We can, however, appreciate his work today as a first major foothold in the tremendously exciting exploration of outer space.

Pythagoras' model successfully served to predict future positions of the sun, moon, and stars and to account for observations that had been made earlier, but an underlying question still demanded an answer: How can the motions of so many separate objects be so closely interrelated that the constellations preserve their shape for centuries? Why, indeed, don't the stars fall to earth?

Pythagoras, and other early astronomers, conceived of actual spheres to which the celestial bodies were physically attached. It is very likely that Pythagoras thought of an actual celestial sphere, because there was otherwise no means available to him to explain how the motion of one object could be related to the motion of another.

Theoretical explorations:

In the laboratory, construct or examine a ball or a clear glass or plastic globe marked off to represent the stellar sphere of Pythagoras' model with the path of the sun's annual journey marked on it. Use this model to answer the following questions:

1.10 How many times does the stellar sphere rotate in a year of 365 days? ▬

1.11 If star maps were made on the first night of successive months, at the same hour, in which direction would the constellations progress from one map to the next—east to west or west to east? Explain. ▬

1.12 At the North and South Poles, the sun shines for six months without setting. This period is followed by six months in which the sun does not appear. Explain. What would be the difference between the sun's behavior at the North and at the South Poles? ▬

1.13 Determine those regions of the earth where there are one or more days of the year on which the sun does not rise and set. ▬

1.14 Considering that a full moon rises in the east at sunset every 27 days, how much later does it rise each day? ■

ARISTOTLE'S AND PTOLEMY'S MODELS

Two other Greek models of the universe deserve consideration, although one, Aristotle's, was developed five centuries before the other, usually attributed to Ptolemy. Both sought to accomplish what Pythagoras' model failed to do: to account for the motions of the (other) five planets. This they did in two rather divergent ways, so they offer us an opportunity to compare and weigh the relative merits of different models which achieve more or less the same ends.

Aristotle, who lived in the fourth century B. C., was the outstanding scientist and philosopher of the Greek age. He organized and systematized knowledge in many fields including astronomy. His model is essentially an extension of Pythagoras' model for solar motion. With respect to the motions of the sun and the moon, Aristotle's model and that of Pythagoras are, in fact, equivalent. Both postulate an annual circular revolution of the sun, but in Aristotle's model this motion is imparted by the rotation of a sphere *within* the stellar sphere. The moon was likewise located by Aristotle on its own sphere inside the sphere of the sun.

His solution of the problem of planetary motion was to postulate for each planet a nested series of rotating spheres. For the outermost planet, the series terminated in the stellar sphere. Each sphere was connected to and carried around by its outer neighbor, while it rotated on its own axis. A planet was fastened on the innermost sphere of its series. (See Fig. 1.7.) By adjusting the speeds of many spheres, the observed motion of a single planet could be satisfactorily approximated.[3] To explain the motions of the other known planets, further series of nested spheres were inserted. Aristotle's explanation was obviously accomplished at the price of introducing enormous complexity into Pythagoras' theory. Did Ptolemy's theory fare any better?

Ptolemy, a Greco-Egyptian astronomer and mathematician (A. D. the second century) published a treatise on astronomy, later called the *Almagest*, which remained the authoritative work on astronomy for fourteen centuries. In it, he resolved one of the major shortcomings of Aristotle's model, namely, its failure to account for the ob-

---

[3] This development foreshadowed an extremely useful mathematical model for representing complex periodic phenomena as the sum of an indefinitely long series of simple periodic motions of suitable frequencies and magnitudes, that was demonstrated by J. B. Fourier in 1822.

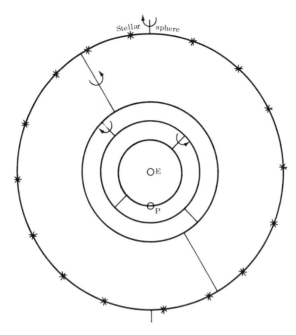

Figure 1.7 Aristotle's Model.

served variation in brightness of the planets because the spheres were all concentric around the earth.

In Ptolemy's model, each planet was moved by a sphere embedded within a spherical shell thick enough to permit considerable variation in the planet's distance from the earth. In the simplest form of the model, this variation took place as a uniform circular motion. (See Fig. 1.8.) This circle within the shell was named an *epicycle*. There were then two motions to be adjusted to fit observations: the motion of the center of the epicycle along a circular path, called the *deferent*, and the revolution of the planet on its epicycle.

This simple form of Ptolemy's model did not have enough flexibility to account for observed planetary motions accurately. Refinements were made by adding epicycles onto epicycles. That this was an ingenious theory cannot be denied. By using accumulated observational data on the paths described by each planet, Ptolemy was able to assign its deferent and epicycles their sizes and speeds and directions of rotation. In short, he attained a complete quantitative description of planetary motion from which a planet's position at any future time could be predicted. (However, his most precise model employed some 70 epicycles.) These predictions, it turned out, agreed quite well with observations made in succeeding years—agreed, that is, within the degree of accuracy that could be expected of the astronomical instruments of those days. So successful was the Ptolemaic system for all practical purposes, that no theory challenged it seriously for some 1400 years.

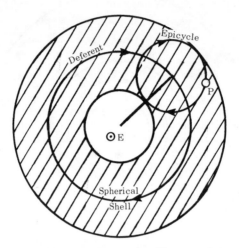

Figure 1.8 Ptolemy's Concept of an Epicycle.

How shall we compare the relative merits of the models of Aristotle and Ptolemy? We have raised the question of relative simplicity, but simplicity alone cannot enable us to judge one model better than another. Recall that Pythagoras' model was far simpler than either Aristotle's or Ptolemy's. However, its failure to account for the motion of planets may be described as a limitation of the scope of the model. In order to compare the relative simplicity of two models, it is necessary at the same time to consider their scopes. We have seen that Aristotle's model failed to account for changes in brightness of the planets; to do so, some additional device would have been required. At best, Aristotle's model cannot be regarded as simpler than Ptolemy's, because both used the same device of a series of circular motions to represent the motion of each planet. Ptolemy's model unquestionably had the greater coverage of data and is for this reason superior to Aristotle's.

The fact that adjustments had to be made in directions and speeds of rotation (and, in the case of Ptolemy's model, also the radii of circles) in order to fit the model to observational data, may lead one to think that these models accomplished no more than summarizing past observations. It should be noted, however, that from each of these models predictions could be made of other types of observations than those used for determining the properties of the model. For example, in Pythagoras' model, the seasonal variations in length of day could be determined from the model, once it was adjusted, although they were not needed in making the adjustments. Even if new types of observations could not have been predicted, it would still be true to say that these models accomplished more than just summarizing already observed data. For, by using a relatively few past observations to make the necessary adjustments, the models served to predict an indefinite number of future observations of the same sort.

THE COPERNICAN REVOLUTION

Copernicus is rightfully credited with turning men away from a geocentric conception of the universe and thereby paving the way for the development of our modern view. But in order to appreciate fully the boldness of Copernicus' proclamation that the sun (and not the earth as Ptolemy's model would have it) was fixed at the center of the universe, we must consider the intellectual climate prevailing in Europe toward the end of the fifteenth and the dawn of the sixteenth century.

This was an age in which the Christian church reigned supreme over all Europe, posing itself as the authority not only in religious and moral matters, but also in political, philosophical, and even scientific matters. Theologians had effected a union of the philosophy and science of ancient Greece with the Christian doctrine of salvation. In particular, the thesis that the earth was at the center of the universe—held by Pythagoras, Aristotle and Ptolemy alike—was taken as evidence that man occupied a place of supreme concern in the eyes of God. The general antagonism of fifteenth-century churchmen toward a theory that would deprive the earth of its central position in God's design can be readily imagined.

Actually, the heliocentric[4] hypothesis was not original with Copernicus. Some ancient Greek thinkers, notably Aristarchus of Samos (c. 250 B. C.), had realized that the observed motions of the sun, moon and planets could just as readily be accounted for by a heliocentric as by the prevailing geocentric theories. But the ideas of these early thinkers remained largely speculation. It was Copernicus who first carried out detailed calculations based on a sun-centered system and produced arguments that made its eventual adoption inevitable.

Copernicus published his theory in 1543 in a book entitled *De Revolutionibus Orbium Celestium* (On the Revolution of the Heavenly Spheres). In it he showed by calculations based on numerous observational data of planetary positions—some ancient, some recent, some of which he collected himself—that the following model would satisfactorily account for the planetary motions.

Instead of assuming a daily rotation of the stellar sphere, as was the traditional view, Copernicus held that it was stationary. The daily rising and setting of the sun, moon, planets, and stars he explained by assuming a daily rotation of the earth itself. The sun's apparent

---

[4]Derived from *helios*, the sun.

shifting with respect to the stars, he explained, was due to a second motion of the earth, its annual revolution around the sun in a circular orbit. The earth became one of the planets, and the sun became a fixed body. The moon accompanied the earth in its journey around the sun, revolving around the earth as though on an epicycle.

In the basic Copernican model (see Fig. 1.9), the other planets describe circular orbits around the sun. The radius of each planetary sphere and the rate of its motion were adjusted to fit observational data. These values in turn enabled Copernicus to compute approximately the apparent position of any planet against the background of the stars at any given time in the past or future. To demonstrate the retrograde motions of the planets, his model did not require the device of deferents and epicycles; just one circular orbit was needed for each planet. It was the moving "platform" of the observer on the orbiting earth, as it overtook a slower-moving planet, that made the latter appear to move backward.

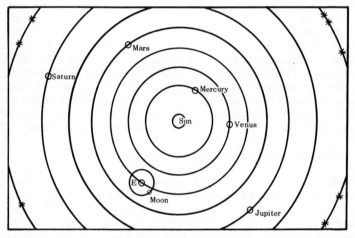

Figure 1.9 Copernicus' Model.

It is true that to achieve greater accuracy, Copernicus did make use of epicycles. He was not satisfied with the approximate agreement between calculated and observed planetary positions that could be attained without epicycles. In his most accurate model, he was forced to use about 30 epicycles. For Ptolemy's model, however, epicycles had been essential even to attain so much as a rough, qualitative description of planetary motions, in particular their retrograde motions.

In comparison with earlier models, it should be noted that, not only were the statuses of the earth and sun interchanged, but the daily motion of all the celestial bodies was also replaced by a daily rotation of the earth alone. In this way Copernicus' model accounted for the same scope of observations as did the Ptolemaic model, but did it in a considerably simpler manner.

The arguments just presented point out another consideration which must be borne in mind in applying the criterion of simplicity to scientific theories. It is not enough to speak of "simplicity relative to the scope of observational data represented," but the phrase, "for a given degree of precision" must be added. In general, in order to increase their precision, theories have to be made more complex. It is the revolutionary theory that takes a step in the other direction.

Theoretical explorations:

To understand better the gains made by Copernicus the student should carry out the following exercise:

1.15 First, construct a diagram according to the simple Ptolemaic model showing the earth, the planet Mars, and the stellar sphere. Draw an epicycle at eight positions evenly spaced around the deferent. Make the radius of each drawing of the epicycle the same—at least one-third of that of the deferent. Mark the positions of a planet that revolves around the epicycle twice during the time the epicycle takes to go around the earth once, both revolutions being counterclockwise.

Next, construct the orbits of the earth and the planet Mars, according to the simple Copernican model. Use as radii, 1 inch for earth and 1.5 inches for Mars. Also represent the celestial sphere by a circle 5 inches in radius. Mark eight evenly spaced positions of the planets on their orbits. Let the earth revolve twice around the sun while Mars goes around once, both planets revolving counterclockwise.

In both diagrams draw straight lines from the earth through Mars to the circle representing the stellar sphere and number the successive positions where this line intersects the circle. Compare the wandering path of Mars through the stars in the two cases. If they do not agree, determine what changes would be needed to make them agree.

Running counter, as it did, to the deeply entrenched beliefs of the times, Copernicus' theory understandably met with violent and prolonged opposition. It was exceedingly difficult for him to convince his opponents because he had to rest his case solely on simplicity. He did not have any of the modern evidence supporting his conclusion that the earth spins on its axis and revolves annually about the sun. Very precise telescopic measurements, Newton's theory of tides, the general pattern of atmospheric circulation and much other evidence now lead to the inescapable conclusion that the earth spins on its axis. These were not known to Copernicus and his contemporaries. He defended his theory by means of subtle and penetrating arguments, but it could not, at that time, be rigorously supported by observational evidence.

Two of the arguments brought against Copernicus were the following: (1) If the earth is rotating at such a rapid rate as once in 24 hours, why aren't all objects on its surface flung into space just as mud is thrown from the rim of a wheel in motion? (2) If the earth revolves around the sun, why don't the stars appear to change their positions relative to one another in accordance with our changing perspective?

Without an adequate theory of gravity and a theory of the dynamics of rotation, the first question could not be answered conclusively, and it remained in the realm of speculation until Newton's time. The second argument, however, appears subject to precise measurement and could well have been considered fatal to the Copernican theory. The earth, if it revolves in an orbit, must annually approach and recede from any given group of stars. The observed angle between any two stars in the group should then increase and decrease once each year as the earth moves nearer and farther.[5] Although such an effect was sought, no such changes in angle were detectable. Therefore, the opponents of Copernicus concluded, the earth does not move.

Copernicus was undaunted and replied that the distance from the earth to the fixed stars was evidently much greater than anyone had supposed—so great, in comparison to the diameter of the earth's orbit, that the parallax, though present, was too small to be observed. But since this supposition of the enormity of the stellar sphere could not be checked by the means of astronomical measurement available in those days, Copernicus' answer seemed to the Ptolemians merely to beg the question.

The argument as to whether failure to observe parallax was conclusive evidence against its presence is an example of a type of argument frequently encountered in science. Opponents in such disputes cannot be reconciled so long as they fear different types of errors. Copernicus feared missing an important advance. His opponents feared making fools of themselves by changing their present view to a false one. Scientific research is not generally as objective as is commonly supposed. It always involves a similar gamble, and it usually reveals scientists of both progressive and conservative concerns. The progressive fears missing an opportunity to advance knowledge, and the conservative fears taking a step that might be wrong.

A laboratory exercise on parallax:

1.16 Before performing a quantitative experiment on parallax, the student may get the general idea of parallax by the following simple

---

[5] Such angular variation due to a motion of the observer is called *parallax*.

procedure. He may hold up two fingers together at arm's length, close one eye, and find some object at the other end of the room that is just barely covered by the fingers. Now, with arm steadily outstretched, he should move toward the object he sighted. It will be noticed that the edges of the object now extend beyond the width of two fingers. This increase in apparent width of the object is an example of parallax.

In the laboratory a quantitative investigation of parallax may be conducted using very simple apparatus to simulate that used by astronomers of Copernicus' time. The apparatus consists of a movable table with a pinhole sight at one edge and two pins near the opposite edge standing on movable wooden blocks. Across the room against a light background two cross marks are placed to represent stars. (See Fig. 1.10.) ■

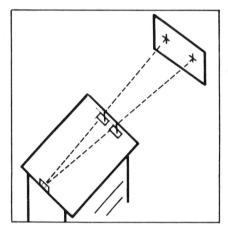

Figure 1.10 A Parallax Experiment.

The experiment consists in observing the separation of the "stars" from several different points of observation, successively moving the table toward or away from the "stars." At each observation point, observe the angle made by the two lines of sight from the pinhole to the two "stars," respectively. As a measure of this angle, compute the ratio of the distance between the pins to their distance from the pinhole. The placement of the pins is difficult to do precisely, so it should be repeated several times with the table at one position; then the table should be moved, and the whole process repeated.

The measure just described of the visual angle separating two "stars" will be found to vary from one trial to another at the same observation point. This variation is caused primarily by errors of measurement unavoidable with this apparatus. Consequently the measures taken with the table at two successive positions may overlap one another considerably. It is interesting to determine by experiment the smallest movement of the table required for the two sets of measures to show virtually no overlap with each other.

When there is no overlap in two sets of observations taken at different times, the data show, with little chance of error, that a movement toward the "stars" has occurred. However, if insistence is made on complete separation before concluding that a movement has occurred, the chances of falsely accepting the view that no motion has occurred are increased. To conclude from the data above either that the table has moved or that it has not, it becomes necessary to place ourselves at some definite point along a progressive-conservative continuum. However, the progressive may find it nearly impossible to convince the conservative of his conclusion, just on the basis of available evidence. One often requires an appeal to simplicity to support his case in the face of ambiguous evidence.

Once we are satisfied that parallax has been observed between two positions, our data may be used for estimating the distance to the "stars" from either of the two observation points. The method of parallax had been used successfully by astronomers before Copernicus' time for measuring distances from the earth to the moon and to nearby planets. The procedure is illustrated below by simple calculation.

In Fig. 1.11, S and T represent the two "stars," which we assume to be fixed. L_1 and R_1 are the left and right pins respectively, when the table is in the first position, and E_1 is the pinhole sight where the observer has his eye. L_2, R_2 and E_2 represent the same objects when the table is in the second position.

Let the distance between the pins L_1 and R_1, measured in centimeters, be p_1, and let the length of the perpendicular from E_1 to the line L_1R_1 be d cm. The measure of the visual angle of the stars from the first observation point is given by the ratio p_1/d. In practice the measure will be the average of many such ratios, each obtained independently from separate observations made at the first position of the table. Of course, only p_1 needs to be measured over and over again; a single value is used for d, since the variability is small compared with the values themselves.

Similarly, let the distance between the pins, when lined up with the stars from the second observation point, be designated by p_2 cm. The measure of the visual angle of the stars from this point is the ratio p_2/d—or rather, the average of many such ratios.

The foregoing quantities can all be actually measured. We now introduce the quantities that we could not measure if this were an astronomical experiment. These are the distances, s_1 and s_2, from the two observation points, respectively, to the line connecting the two stars. We now use the facts that the triangle $E_1L_1R_1$ and E_1ST are similar to each other, and that triangles $E_2L_2R_2$ and E_2ST are, likewise, similar to each other. Under these conditions, the following proportionality relationships are true: $p_1/d = \overline{ST}/s_1$ and $p_2/d = \overline{ST}/s_2$.

Solving each of these equations for $\overline{ST}$ and equating the two results, we get

$$s_1(p_1/d) = s_2(p_2/d) \tag{1.1}$$

Now, although the distances s_1 and s_2 themselves are not measured,

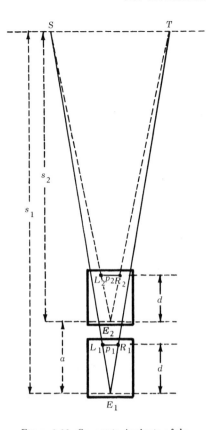

Figure 1.11 Geometric Analysis of the
Parallax Experiment.

the difference between them, being the distance by which the table has
been moved in going from the first to the second position, is readily
measured. Let this difference be a cm. We then have the equation,

$$s_1 - s_2 = a \qquad (1.2)$$

The two equations, (1.1) and (1.2), enable us to calculate the distances s_1 and s_2. To illustrate, let us suppose we had, from our measurements, $p_1/d = 0.0606$, $p_2/d = 0.0627$ (each of these ratios being the
average of several similar ratios), and $a = 30$ cm. Substituting these
values in the two equations, we obtain:

$$s_1(0.0606) = s_2(0.0627)$$

and

$$s_1 - s_2 = 30$$

Solving these two equations simultaneously, we get

$$s_1 = 895 \text{ cm}$$

and

$$s_2 = 865 \text{ cm}$$

We have been able to estimate the distances from the two points of observation to the "stars."

The numerical values used above were actually obtained in an experiment of the sort just discussed. In that experiment, it took a minimum of 30 centimeters' change in point of observation to yield a reliably noticeable parallax for objects located at an estimated average distance of 880 cm. (The actual average distance, incidentally, was 875 cm.) A change in observation point was first clearly discerned at about 3.4% of the average distance to the "stars."

In the debate between the Ptolemains and Copernicans, assume that somewhat more precise observations might have been made by skilled astronomers of those days. It seems reasonable to assume that a shift in observation point of about one percent of the distance to the stars would have been required before any stellar parallax could have been detected. (Remember, the telescope had not yet been invented.) If this is correct, Copernicus' argument would have implied that the distance to the stars was at least 100 times the diameter of the earth's orbit. That the distance to a visible object could have such a magnitude must have seemed inconceivable to most of his contemporaries. Today it is known that the distance to the closest star, Proxima Centauri, is approximately 25 million million miles, more than 100,000 times the diameter of the earth's orbit.[6] Our shift in point of observation is only about one hundred-thousandth, or *one-thousandth of one percent*, of our average distance to the closest star. No wonder that stellar parallax could not be detected in Copernicus' day.

Although scientific theories must always ultimately meet the test of observational evidence, the conflict of Copernicus' theory with the apparent nonexistence of parallax is a striking example of a circumstance often found on the frontiers of science. The point is that observational evidence, as of any given time, is necessarily incomplete and cannot be presumed to decide theoretical issues with absolute finality.

TYCHO BRAHE, JOHANNES KEPLER, AND GALILEO GALILEI

The controversy surrounding the Ptolemaic and Copernican theories continued unabated for almost three-quarters of a century before the

---

[6] 186 million miles.

work of three men—Tycho Brahe, Johannes Kepler and Galileo Galilei—produced evidence which decided most astronomers in favor of Copernicus' heliocentric system.

The first of these scientists, Tycho Brahe, is noted for his accurate and extensive observations which eventually contributed greatly to the establishment of Copernicus' theory. Ironically, he was a staunch opponent of the heliocentric school of thought. He undertook to collect a large body of accurate data that would establish the geocentric hypothesis once and for all. To his observatory in Denmark he brought the best available astronomical instruments from all over Europe and also built still better ones for himself. The vast collection of astronomical data accumulated by Tycho and his staff were unsurpassed for their accuracy in those days before the telescope was invented.

When he began comparing these data with the predictions of the Ptolemaic model, however, Tycho found that he could not obtain a good agreement without introducing still more epicycles. He realized that this process could go on indefinitely if he wanted to make the motions of planets in the theoretical model agree precisely with their observed motions. Discouraged by the complexities of the Ptolemaic model, but at the same time unwilling to shake off his belief that the earth stood still at the center of the universe, Tycho ended up by proposing a compromise theory of his own. The planets, he postulated, revolved around the sun, while the sun and the moon each described a circular orbit around the earth, taking, respectively, one year, and 27.3 days for one cycle. (See Fig. 1.12.) Death overtook him before he had completed very much of the detailed calculations needed to fit his theory to his observations. We nevertheless speak of the model

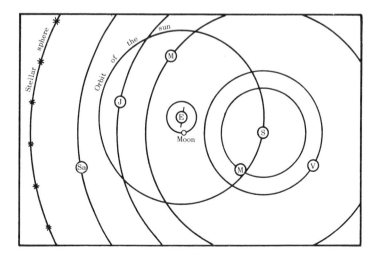

Figure 1.12 Tychonic Model of the Universe.

summarized above as the "Tychonic model." Since, in it, the sun is the center of motion of all planets, this model represents a compromise between the Ptolemaic and Copernican models. This model constituted recognition, by a proponent of the geocentric view, that Copernicus' simplicity argument holds theoretical weight.

Theoretical exploration:

It will be instructive for the student to compare the two competing theories by constructing diagrams according to the models of Tycho Brahe and Copernicus showing the earth, the sun, and the planet Mars as described in the following exercises:

1.17   In drawing the Tychonic diagram, let the radius of the sun's orbit around the earth be 1 inch and that of Mars around the sun be 1.5 inches. Mark eight evenly spaced positions of the sun, labeling them A–H in counterclockwise order. Draw the orbit of Mars around sun-point A, and locate the planet on it at the opposite end of the diameter passing through the earth. Draw each of the other seven orbits successively and locate the planet on it, noting that Mars makes one half of a revolution in its orbit around the sun while the sun revolves once around the earth. For each of the positions of Mars labeled B–H on the diagram, draw the triangle it makes with the corresponding sun-point and the earth. ■

1.18   In constructing the Copernican diagram, follow the relevant procedures described in Ex. 1.15 (except that no celestial sphere need now be represented). Label the earth-points A–H in counterclockwise order, and locate Mars-point A on its orbit diametrically opposite earth-point A. Draw the triangles formed by the seven succeeding Mars-points (B–H), the corresponding earth-points, and the sun. ■

1.19   Compare the corresponding triangles in the two diagrams. What can be concluded with respect to the possibility that observations of the relative positions of the three bodies would decide between the Copernican and Tychonic models? What would the situation be with respect to the other planets? ■

At Tycho Brahe's death, one of his assistants, Johannes Kepler, took over the accumulated data and took up the task of theoretical investigation of the controversial question. Kepler was a diligent worker with a passion for accuracy, and he tried out numerous modifications of both the Ptolemaic and Copernican models. He did, in fact, succeed in fitting a theoretical model (which could have been interpreted either way, and was replete with such devices as epicycles and eccentric circles) to Tycho's detailed data on Mars with a heretofore unequaled degree of agreement.[7] Yet Kepler had such great faith in the accuracy of Tycho's data that he was unwilling to attribute a discrepancy of even this much to observational error. He decided that models based on circular motions could not be made to fit the data well enough—at least within the capability of calculation methods available—and therefore should be discarded.

It is a tribute to Kepler's mathematical versatility combined with his indefatigable persistence that he decided to scrap the results of four tedious years of calculation and start a completely new attack. The essential creative leap he took was to free himself of the traditional preconception that the orbits of the heavenly bodies were *circular* in shape. He postulated that the orbits were *elliptical*, and it worked like magic. He was able to construct an ellipse for each planet that fitted Tycho's data with remarkable precision. Kepler achieved this remarkable agreement by a mathematical model, the main postulates of which have come to be known as Kepler's three laws of planetary motion.

In this model, the sun was not located at the center but at one of the two foci of each ellipse (Kepler's First Law). Moreover, the rate of motion of each planet was not made uniform, but was made greater in places closer to the sun and smaller in places more remote. This relation of speed to position in Kepler's model is illustrated in Fig. 1.13. More precisely, he found that best agreement with data was achieved when the speed was such that, as a planet moves along its elliptical orbit, the line connecting it to the sun sweeps out equal areas in equal times (Kepler's Second Law). If it takes a certain length of time, say one month, for planet P to move from position P_1 to P_2 and takes the same time to move from P_3 to P_4, or from P_5 to P_6, then the shaded areas in the figure are all equal.

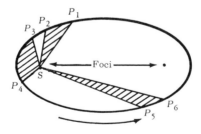

Figure 1.13 Illustration of Kepler's Second Law.

Kepler's triumphs did not end here. Momentous as these achievements were, he scored an even greater success: he was able to formulate a law linking the motions of all the planets. His third law states

---

[7] The largest discrepancy was no more than one quarter of the apparent diameter of the full moon.

that the ratio of the cube of the average distance from the sun to the square of the period has the same value for all planets.

Kepler's Third Law has a more general theoretical status than his first two. To understand this point, note that his third law involves a constant ratio applicable to all planets of the solar system. Once this ratio has been determined from data concerning one planet, the law enables one to predict, prior to making any observation on another planet, that the ratio for the second planet will have the same numerical value. Or, knowing either the average distance or the period, one can predict the other quantity. In order to apply the first two laws more than one quantity must be measured in each planet. The lengths of the largest and smallest diameters of the elliptical orbit are specific to each planet, as is the magnitude of the constant area swept out by the line from the sun to a given planet in a given length of time. Numerical values of these quantities determined for one planet will in no way enable us to predict the values of the same quantities for another planet. The relationship embodied in Kepler's Third Law has the distinction of being the first statement about planetary motions that involves a constant common to all planets. It will help in understanding this relationship if we examine the numerical calculations tabulated in Table 1.1. In addition to the average distances, D, and the periods, T, and their respective cubes and squares, D^3 and T^2, there is also a column of the calculated ratios, D^3/T^2. It can be seen that these ratios have approximately the same value for all planets (including the three that were unknown to Kepler).

Table 1.1 Data Demonstrating Kepler's Third Law

Planet	D^*	D^3	T (years)	T^2	D^3/T^2
Mercury	36	46,656	.24	.06	778,000
Venus	67	300,763	.62	.38	791,000
Earth	93	804,357	1.00	1.00	804,000
Mars	142	2,863,288	1.88	3.53	811,000
Jupiter	483	112,678,587	12.00	144.00	782,000
Saturn	886	699,050,456	29.50	870.25	804,000
Uranus	1780	5,639,752,000	84.00	7056.00	751,000
Neptune	2790	21,717,639,000	165.00	27225.00	797,000
Pluto	3670	49,430,863,000	248.00	61504.00	804,000

$^*D$ is measured in millions of miles.

To summarize Kepler's model, we may state his three laws as follows:

I. *Law of Elliptical Orbits*: Each planet moves in an elliptical orbit with the sun at one of the two foci.

II. *Law of Constant Areal Speed*: A line connecting the sun with a given planet sweeps out equal areas in equal times as the planet moves around the sun.

III. The cube of the average distance, D, of a planet from the sun, divided by the square of its period of revolution, T, yields the same quotient for each planet.

In view of the great success of Kepler's three laws of planetary motion—so simple and so accurate—it might be expected that no one could any longer doubt the superiority of Copernicus' heliocentric idea to Ptolemy's earth-centered notion. But such was not the case. Many people regarded Kepler's model as a mere mathematical device and still refused to budge from their preconception that the earth was at the center of the universe.

In order for the heliocentric theory to be generally accepted, some direct observational evidence seemed needed. The first man to supply such evidence was the great Italian astronomer and physicist, Galileo Galilei.

Galileo heard, in 1609, that a Dutch lensmaker had invented a device for enlarging the apparent sizes of distant objects. He could not obtain an exact description of the instrument, which was a jealously guarded secret, but was nevertheless able to construct several similar instruments for himself. He lost no time in pointing these telescopes to the heavens, thus converting a toy into a scientific instrument. His observations were revealing and exciting. Some of his most important discoveries are described below. In order to appreciate fully why these discoveries were damaging to the geocentric theory, however, it must be realized that the geocentric viewpoint was firmly embedded in the general cosmology of Aristotle which included descriptions of the substance of the celestial bodies. Aristotle had asserted that they were made of a "sublime, ethereal principle" forming perfect spheres free from any defects or flaws such as characterize terrestrial objects. Any evidence pointing against these supposed properties of celestial objects, therefore, would deprive the geocentric thesis of much of its authoritative status.

First to come under Galileo's scrutiny was the moon. This he found to have a rugged surface covered with mountains and craters—far from being a "perfect, heavenly sphere," as Aristotle had described it.

Turning his attention next to the sun, he found its brilliant face blemished with numerous small dark spots. Noting that these spots move from day to day, Galileo determined that the sun was rotating on its own axis, and that its period was about twenty-five days. This was striking evidence against the belief that the celestial bodies were flawless spheres that were unchanging except for their revolutions around the earth.

The planets Jupiter and Venus were the next objects of Galileo's observations. Around Jupiter he found four small bodies revolving. We now know these, together with eight similar objects, as the *satellites* (or moons) of Jupiter; but Galileo, not unnaturally, called them planets. Here, he pointed out, was direct and indisputable evidence that there *were* celestial bodies that did not "pay homage" to Earth by revolving around her—a deathblow to the geocentric doctrine. By watching Venus over a period of several months, he found that this planet showed changes in phase, as the moon does, and also underwent great variations in size—appearing largest when crescent and smallest when full. These findings were readily explainable in the Copernican model, which postulated that Venus follows an orbit inside that of the earth. (See Fig. 1.9, p. 16.)

When the stars were viewed in Galileo's telescope they remained mere points of light, unlike the planets which were magnified into small disks. This indicated that the stars were much farther away than had ever been dreamed. Here was evidence to support the Copernican explanation for the lack of detectable stellar parallax.

All these and many more observational evidences were put forth by Galileo in favor of Copernicus' heliocentric theory. It is small wonder that he made bitter enemies of some of the churchmen. An anecdote has it that, when Galileo invited several leading theologians to look through his telescope and see with their own eyes the four additional "planets" that revolved around Jupiter, the latter flatly refused to look; they preferred to close their eyes to the evidence and persist in their beliefs.

The story of Galileo's last days is tragic. An invalid close on seventy, he was brought before the Inquisition and required to recant his belief in Copernicus' theory that the earth revolves. The story is told that, as he was leaving the chambers of the Inquisition after this forced submission, he muttered under his breath, "But still it moves."

Galileo is remembered today not only for his astronomical work described above, but also for his extensive researches in the theory of mechanics. The famous (though probably fictitious) anecdote about his dropping two weights from the Leaning Tower of Pisa is too well known to be repeated. But it does serve to remind us that Galileo performed a great deal of pioneering work on the motion of falling bodies. He paved the way for Isaac Newton, who was born in the same year that Galileo died, 1642.

METHODOLOGICAL REVIEW

Before going on to the next phase in the development of astronomy, it is well to recapitulate the major points covered so far in the matter of scientific methodology, and in so doing also clarify some new points. Having studied the best known pre-Newtonian models of the universe, we are now in a position to consider the nature of theoretical models more generally and their relation to observations. As a point of departure, the question which has been discussed briefly in the foregoing sections, "What are the criteria by which we compare the merits of one scientific model over another?" may now be taken up.

To persons living in the twentieth century, the statement that the observable implications of a scientific theory are expected to be in close agreement with empirical evidence may seem very trite. This view has not always been commonplace, as we saw in the case of the theologians who refused to look through Galileo's telescope. This statement, also, is not so simple as it may seem at first sight. Because of the inevitable incompleteness of experimental evidence at any given time, human judgment of its significance is required. There are always two sides to the question of how reliable the evidence must be to warrant a change in theory. Copernicus could have been completely dissuaded from the heliocentric theory had he accepted the observational evidence against parallax as being sufficiently precise to rule out the possibility of parallax. On the other hand, Kepler may never have hit upon the idea of elliptical orbits if he had dismissed as observational error the relatively minor discrepancies between Tycho's data on Mars and the best-fitting epicyclic model which he (Kepler) had been able to devise for them. While personality differences may affect such judgments to some extent, a great deal also depends on what alternative theories can be produced.

We have considered the related criteria of simplicity, scope, and precision. Judging theoretical models by these criteria is, in fact, one of the basic characteristics of scientific thought. Kepler's turning from epicyclic models cannot be regarded as only a quest for greater accuracy. For with the addition of sufficiently more epicycles, any motion could in principle, if not in practical computation, have been represented to any given degree of accuracy. It seems probable that he was unwilling to increase the complexity of a model unduly and thus treat it as merely a mathematical device. Such a "brute force" method of accounting for the data is not at all appealing aesthetically, but Kepler's elegant solution is.

In Kepler's Third Law we can note an important advance in the generality he achieved over earlier theories. Recall (p. 10) that, in Pythagoras' model, the sun's motion could be adjusted using a few types of data (e.g., positions of sunrise and sunset and daily changes in the time of "star rise") and that predictions could be made about data of other kinds (e.g., length of day, regions where sunrise and sunset are periodically interrupted). Similarly, any scientific model must do more than merely summarize the data used to construct it. It must permit some additional inferences. However, the additional inferences permitted by different models may vary considerably in scope. In pre-Keplerian models, without some data on a given planet, no quantitative information about it could be obtained. By means of Kepler's Third Law, however, measurements made on one planet may be used to predict the ratio D^3/T^2 for all the others. If one knew the period of revolution and average distance from the sun for, say, Mars, and knew either one of these data for, say, Jupiter, he could predict the other datum.

The predictive power of Kepler's Third Law was further demonstrated when, as new planets (Uranus, Neptune and Pluto) were discovered long after Kepler's time, measurement of their distances from the sun permitted calculation of their periods, which were subsequently confirmed by observation. Most people would agree that confirmation of such quantitative predictions compels us to a greater degree of belief in a law than does the confirmation of a qualitative prediction such as the prediction that the orbits of the new planets will be elliptical in form (Kepler's First Law). The basis for this different psychological impact lies, no doubt, in the fact that a quantitative prediction implies a greater commitment: the chances of its being falsified are immensely greater than in the case of a qualitative prediction. We may summarize this state of affairs by saying that Kepler's Third Law, when confirmed, has greater "surprise value" than does his first law.

Another point of interest in connection with the theoretical models studied is the changing meaning of the word *planet*. Originally, this word meant "wandering body," and was applied to any heavenly body whose apparent position with respect to the fixed stars was observed to change from day to day. For Pythagoras, Aristotle, Ptolemy, and Tycho Brahe the seven planets were the sun, the moon, Mercury, Venus, Mars, Saturn and Jupiter. Copernicus and Kepler, for whom the sun was fixed, put the earth in place of the sun in the list of planets. In these models, the term had shifted in meaning from the original sense of "wanderer" (whose wandering was apparent to an observer on earth) to "wanderer within a theoretical model." For Galileo the term had the same meaning as for Copernicus and Kepler, but his list of planets was increased by the four moons of Jupiter that he discovered.

In modern times, the word *planet* has been given a more specific meaning: "a body which revolves around the sun." The modern list of planets is hence the same as that for Copernicus except that the earth's moon is omitted and Uranus, Neptune, and Pluto are added. It should be mentioned that a few contemporary astronomers make a further stipulation that a planet must *not* originally have been a satellite (a body revolving around a planet), in addition to the requirement that it is currently revolving around the sun. The status of Pluto then becomes controversial, for it is supposed by some astronomers today that Pluto was once a satellite of Neptune. Such changes that occur in the meanings of words, as one theoretical model replaces another, serve as an indication of the pervading effects that a few changes in basic postulates can have.

In this chapter we have seen the background and successful development of a revolution in astronomy that in some sense serves as a model for revolutions in other sciences. Although we have highlighted the shift from a geocentric to a heliocentric theory, this should not be permitted to obscure the even more far-reaching change that took place in the course of this shift. This is the shift from mechanistic models of the universe to abstract mathematical models. We can note this change from mechanistic to purely mathematical models exemplified in Kepler's work. The mechanistic conceptual models had flexibility enough to accommodate many centuries' accumulation of moderately accurate data. The price paid for this flexibility, however, was an excessive degree of complexity. As more accurate measurements accumulated, the added complexity that would have been required became so great that the use of mechanical models had to be given up. That Kepler made the decision to abandon mechanical conceptions was probably his greatest contribution to theoretical astronomy. When his contemporaries criticized his elliptical orbits as mere mathematical devices, they little suspected that a new era in scientific theory was being launched precisely by these "devices." Kepler's abandonment of the mechanical simplicity of compound circular motions for the mathematical simplicity of elliptical orbits gave him far greater flexibility to accommodate accurate data and, at the same time, the opportunity to discover fundamental relationships that could not have been revealed in a maze of epicycles.

PROBLEMS

1. Which of the following concepts were ones concerning which Copernicus may be regarded as assuming a conservative position? (More than one, or none, may be selected.)

    Epicycles, parallax, circular motion, perceptibility of the earth's motion.

2. Complete the following statements by choosing one or more relevant items from the list on the right.

    a. _____was (were) regarded as planets by Ptolemy, Copernicus and Galileo, but are not so regarded now.

    b. _____was (were) regarded as planets by Ptolemy, Copernicus and Galileo, and are still regarded as planets.

    c. _____was (were) regarded as planets by Ptolemy but not by Galileo or by modern astronomers.

    Earth

    Earth's moon

    Jupiter's moons

    Mars

    Pluto

    Venus

3. With many man-made earth satellites in orbit, together with the moon and a number of small, stone-sized natural satellites of the earth recently discovered, the earth may very well be regarded as the center of a miniature "solar system" of its own. It would therefore be interesting to determine whether or not Kepler's Third Law, which works so well for the planets revolving around the sun, might apply, at least approximately, to the satellites revolving around the earth.

    The following table gives some approximate data for the moon and a hypothetical smaller satellite X. Determine whether these data are consistent with Kepler's Third Law.

Satellite	Period of Revolution	Average Distance from Center of the Earth
Moon	27 days	234,000 miles
Satellite X	1 day	26,000 miles

4. Imagine that you are a Martian astronomer studying a planet called X. The Xian year is half as long as yours, and is divided into 16 phobs. That is to say, X's period of revolution around the sun is 8 phobs. (The word *phob*—corresponding to our word *month*—is derived from *Phobos*, the name of one of Mars' satellites; one phob is the approximate period of revolution of Phobos around Mars.)

Figure 1.14 shows the orbits of Mars and Planet X around the sun, the positions of the two planets on the first day of the first phob of a Martian year, and the stellar sphere.

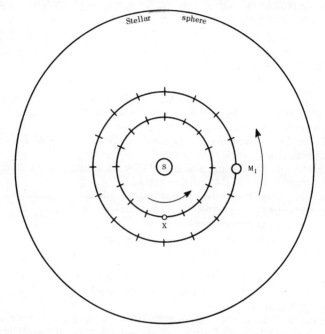

Figure 1.14 Diagram for Problem 4.

   a. By plotting the positions of the two planets in as many successive phobs as you may find necessary, determine whether or not you will observe X to undergo a retrograde motion. If your answer is affirmative, determine in which phobs (1st, 2nd, 3rd, etc.) it would be possible to observe X's retrograde motion.

   b. Since X is an inner planet to you, you should be able to observe changes of phase (crescent, "half-X," "full-X," etc.). Determine in which three of the eight phobs you would see X full or nearly full.

5. Although astronomers, as a result of recent planetary probes, have lost what was left of their hope to find intelligent life on Mars, science fiction writers have not. A recent publication depicts two

diagrams of the solar system (Figs. 1.15 and 1.16), allegedly found on Mars.

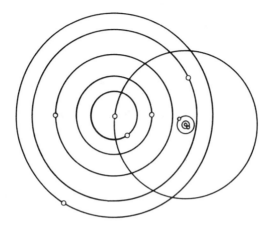

Figure 1.15 Diagram for Problem 5.

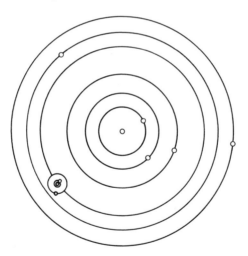

Figure 1.16 Diagram for Problem 5.

a. Suppose these diagrams represent theories of two Martian astronomers: determine to which Earthian astronomer they would correspond, taking into account the different perspectives of the two planets.

Bodies with which Martians are all familiar are listed below with the abbreviations that you are to use. Phobos and Deimos are the two Martian moons, Phobos being nearer to Mars than Deimos.

Phobos . . . . P	Venus V
Deimos . . . . . . D	Mercury . . . . Mer
Saturn . . . . S	Sun . . . . Su
Jupiter . . . . J	Mars . . . . Ma
Earth . . . . E	

   b. Label each body on each diagram with the appropriate abbreviation for its name.

   c. Indicate which of the bodies depicted would never be visible to the Martians at midnight.

   d. A Martian astronomer, Rasgothapy, whose views were said to correspond with those of the Earthian astronomer Pythagoras, was able to represent the motions of only some of the bodies listed in his model. Which bodies could he not represent?

6. In each part of Fig. 1.17, two sets of measurements of angles between stars are summarized by bar graphs. Between the two sets of measurements making each pair, a certain period of time has elapsed. For each pair of bar graphs, choose one of the numbers below to indicate which of the conclusions listed best fits the given data. That is, choose the best answer to the question whether the observer moved relative to the stars between the two sets of measurements constituting a pair. (The same conclusion may be used more than once.)

Symbol	Conclusion
+ 3	The evidence definitely shows a change in position; it is impossible that no motion occurred.
+ 2	There is clear evidence of a change in position; the possibility that no movement occurred seems slight.
+ 1	There is strong suggestion of a change in position, but the evidence for it is not conclusive.
0	It is not possible to tell whether there was a change in position or not from this evidence.
- 1	There is a strong suggestion that there was no change, although the possibility remains that there was a slight change.
- 2	There is no evidence of a change in position; if there was such a change, it was smaller than the errors of measurement.
- 3	It is impossible that any change has occurred in position; the evidence definitely shows the same value.

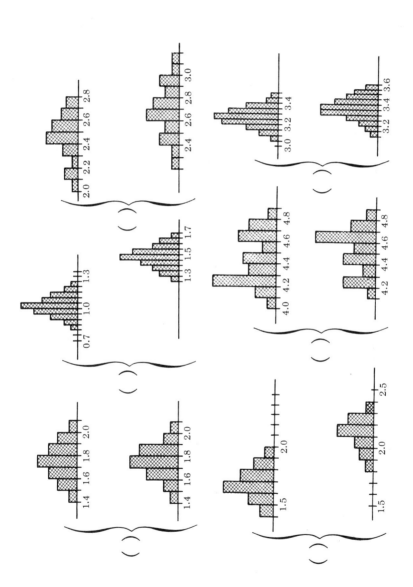

Figure 1.17 Diagram for Problem 6.

SUPPLEMENTARY READINGS

Armitage, Angus. *The World of Copernicus (Sun Stand Thou Still)*. New
York: New American Library of World Literature (A Mentor Book),
1951.
Gives a survey of Greek astronomy, describes the life and work of
Copernicus (including many interesting anecdotes) and the se-
quence of events leading to general acceptance of the heliocentric
theory.
Cohen, I. Bernard. *The Birth of a New Physics*. Garden City, N. Y.:
Doubleday (An Anchor Book), 1960.
A nontechnical survey of the work of Copernicus, Kepler, and
Galileo viewed as a chain of developments leading to the "grand
design" of Newton's "new physics."
Holton, Gerald and Roller, Duane H. D. *Foundations of Modern Physical
Science*. Reading, Mass.: Addison-Wesley, 1958.
A general physics text with an unusual amount of scientific history
and philosophy. Chapter 9 ("Kepler's Laws") and Chapter 10
("Galileo's Contributions to Astronomy"), besides giving addi-
tional details of the work of these two men, include several inter-
esting excerpts from their writings.
Hoyle, Fred. *Astronomy*. New York: Doubleday & Company, 1962.
A beautiful book by a noted astronomer; contains many fascinating
illustrations of historical and modern astronomical instruments
and observations.
Kuhn, Thomas S. *The Copernican Revolution: Planetary Astronomy in
the Development of Western Thought*. New York: Random House
(A Modern Library Paperback), 1959.
A detailed analysis of the intellectual background of the Copernican
revolution. Includes especially valuable material on the models of
Pythagoras, Ptolemy, and Copernicus; presents selected excerpts
from Copernicus' writings.
Munitz, Milton K. *Theories of the Universe from Babylonian Myth to
Modern Science*. Glencoe, Ill.: The Free Press, 1957.
A collection of original and secondary writings including selections
from most of the men whose theories were studied in this chapter.
Reichen, Charles-Albert. *A History of Astronomy*. (New Illustrated
Library of Science and Invention, Vol. 5), New York: Hawthorn
Books, 1963.
Especially valuable for its beautiful reproductions of original
documents and drawings.
Rey, H. A. *The Stars—A New Way to See Them*. Boston: Houghton
Mifflin Company, 1962.
For the star gazer. Unusually clear diagrams of the constellations
and the solar system.
Sarton, George. *A History of Science: Volume I, Ancient Science
through the Golden Age of Greece*. Cambridge, Mass.: Harvard
University Press, 1952.

The work of a leading historian of science. Chapters VIII and XX give the main biographical events and intellectual backgrounds of Pythagoras and of Aristotle as an astronomer.

Schwartz, George and Bishop, Philip W. (eds.). *Moments of Discovery, Vol. I, The Origins of Science*. New York: Basic Books, 1958.

A valuable collection of brief statements on the nature of science and carefully selected and annotated excerpts from scientific writings. See especially selections from Copernicus, Tycho Brahe, Galileo, and Kepler in the section on "The Scientific Revolution."

Toulmin, Stephen and Goodfield, June. *The Fabric of the Heavens, the Development of Astronomy and Dynamics*. New York: Harper & Row, 1965.

An exciting account; for the student who wants richer historical and philosophical material.

2

THE MECHANICS OF LINEAR
MOTION: GALILEO'S MODEL

Kepler's laws, the culmination of our study of astronomy, provided a precise, quantitative description of the planetary motions. To achieve this, Kepler was forced to dispense with the "machinery" of the celestial spheres that had earlier provided astronomers with a comfortable sense of structure in the universe. The contact between the objects that moved and something (even a hypothetical something) that moved it was now lost. Without the spheres, the intellectual world was left with the uncomfortable picture of a system of free objects with nothing to move them and keep them in their orbits. Do the planets just happen to move around the sun, and the satellites around the planets, or is there some explanation of the uniformity of their behavior?

In Chapter 3, we will examine the answer Newton was able to give to this question which makes use of an analogy between the motions of projectiles, such as a ball fired from a cannon, and the motions of satellites and planets. The description of the curved motions of projectiles is derived, in turn, from a mathematical model of motion in a straight line. The latter was largely developed by Galileo but reorganized and refined by Newton. This model is the subject of the present chapter.

DEVELOPING A LANGUAGE FOR DESCRIBING
LINEAR MOTIONS

Suppose we wanted to describe the motions of a man running, of a ball rolling down a slope, and of a stone dropped from the top of a tall building. What are the ways in which the motions of these different objects can be compared? We might think first of the direction of these motions. The man moves horizontally; the ball moves obliquely downward; and the stone moves vertically downward. We might also compare these motions in terms of smoothness and speed. The stone moves more smoothly than the other two objects and also faster. We begin to develop a theory of motion when we undertake to analyze these comparisons in detail.

Note also what was omitted. The man is propelled by the movement of his own legs against the ground, the ball moves in contact with a surface, the stone touches nothing from the time it is dropped until it strikes the earth. The man is soft-bodied, the ball is firm and spherical, and the stone hard and irregular. Most of these facts are relevant to the motion, in the sense that they affect it. For example, if we rolled the stone down the incline, its motion might be more irregular than that of the ball. We discard this information only in the interest of obtaining the simplest possible language for describing the motions themselves. Scientists, who looked at such systems of objects in all their complexity, long ago decided that all motions could be described by focusing attention on speed, distance, direction, and time. Today we have prior knowledge that these variables constitute a useful abstraction from the complex set of descriptive terms that could have been used. The first person who made this decision may have gambled somewhat on his choice of terms. However, he succeeded in separating effects from their causes—a very useful though probably not universally workable strategy in scientific thought. Whatever put an object into motion or modified the motion after it began can be neglected for the moment as one describes the resulting movement of the object in terms of its spatial position, its direction, and its speed at various times.

How does one describe speed? To find the **speed** of an object, we could observe the time it takes for it to cover a certain distance (or, conversely, measure the distance it covers in a specified time). Speed is a ratio. **Distance** and **time** seem to be more basic concepts in the description of motion. Once we measure these, we can easily calculate speed by dividing distance by time. We may start out tentatively by setting up the following definition:

$$\text{Speed} \underset{\text{(by definition)}}{=} \frac{\text{distance moved}}{\text{time taken for the motion}}$$

Should we, then, define *distance* and *time* as well? Trying to do so will soon convince us that the task is not as easy as it might seem. Even if we succeeded in defining these terms, the definitions themselves would involve new terms that require clarification. Defining these new terms would introduce more new terms to be defined; and so on. If this process is kept up, we would—since the natural vocabulary of any language is finite—eventually come to a point where we are forced to use the words *distance* and *time* themselves in the definitions, thus leading us around in a circle.

The only way to avoid such circular definition is to leave certain basic terms undefined. This is not as bad as it may sound. One thing that may be done with these undefined terms is to describe how to perform the measurements usually associated with them. The absence of definitions for these terms will cause us little trouble if the concepts are more or less familiar to us. Such is certainly the case with distance and time. Let us agree to leave them undefined, and simply indicate that distance is measured by a yardstick or meterscale, and time is measured by a stopwatch or similar timepiece. Such undefined terms are called the **primitive terms** of a scientific theory.

We have earlier indicated that we are confining our attention to motion in a straight line. It should be made clear what we gain by so doing. In a motion along a curved or jagged path, the direction of the motion would always be changing and the speed may well be changing also. We are looking now at simpler cases in which the direction is constant but in which the speed may vary. Changes in the observable characteristics of motion are more easily studied one at a time. Although changes in direction are certainly obvious and important aspects of many motions, and although direction is measurable (e.g., by a compass), the relationship of direction with distance, time, speed, and other variables is complex. Holding direction constant for the present will enable us to derive some useful consequences of our definition of speed. We will find these consequences useful when studying changes in direction in the next chapter.

In calculating speed, we must specify the units for distance and time. For instance, if a car traveled 80 miles in 2 hours, we compute its speed as 80 miles/2 hours = 40 mph (miles per hour). Again, if a man ran 100 yards in 12 seconds, his speed was 100 yards/12 seconds = 8.33 yards per second. In order to distinguish our definition of speed from the somewhat looser common-sense idea of speed, we introduce the term **velocity** in place of *speed*. The term *velocity*, as used by physicists, incorporates the direction of motion as well as the "rapidity" of motion—thus, 40 mph north is a velocity. We will be discussing linear motions only, and once a straight path has been specified, only two directions are possible. If the direction is unimportant, we need not always explicitly refer to the direction of motion. We will, however, use the term *velocity* rather than *speed*, as a reminder that we are working on linear motion and that it is used in the strict sense of our definition rather than in some common-sense way.

In scientific work (and, in most parts of the world, for everyday use) the **centimeter** (cm) is a customary unit of distance, supplemented by auxiliary units such as the millimeter (1 mm = 0.1 cm), meter (1 m = 100 cm), hectometer (1 hm = 100 m), and kilometer (1 km = 1000 m), depending on the magnitude of the distance in question. We shall adopt the scientific convention and avoid the arithmetic complications of inches, feet, and miles. For measuring time, there is no dispute: the basic unit is customarily the second (sec), with the minute and hour used as auxiliary units. Using the units centimeter and second for distance and time respectively, and introducing convenient abbreviations, we may write our definition of velocity in both verbal and mathematical forms. The following sentence gives us a context for using the word *velocity*.

If an object, moving on a straight path covers d cm in t sec, its *velocity* (v) is d/t cm/sec (read "centimeters *per* second") in the direction of motion.

That is what we are to understand when stating the definition in the form of an equation, thus:

$$v =_{Df} \frac{d}{t} \qquad (2.1)$$

The symbol "Df" to the lower right of the equality sign makes it explicit that this is an equality *by definition*. (In practical application, where this fact need not be emphasized, the "Df" is usually omitted.)

If we multiply both sides of Eq. (2.1) by t and interchange them, we get

$$d = vt \qquad (2.1a)$$

The "Df" must be dropped since this equation is not a definition of d.

Next, if we divide both sides of Eq. (2.1a) by v and interchange them, we obtain

$$t = \frac{d}{v} \qquad (2.1b)$$

The two equations just written, of course, express exactly the same relations as (2.1); they are merely algebraic consequences of (2.1). They are useful, respectively, for finding the distance covered when velocity and the time taken are known, and for finding the time taken when the distance covered and velocity are known.

GRAPHICAL REPRESENTATIONS OF LINEAR MOTION

Let us see how we can construct a diagram or graph to represent the relation between distance and time that is expressed by Eq. (2.1) for a given velocity. In drawing a graph it is helpful first to make a table. Suppose we measured the distance covered by an object, which is moving with a velocity of 2 cm/sec, during the first 5 sec, the first 10 sec, the first 15 sec, and so on. If we construct a table of these measurements, it should look something like Table 2.1.

To represent these data graphically, we first draw horizontal and vertical axes. We choose the horizontal axis to represent time, and scale it off in suitable units. Similarly, the vertical axis, representing distance, is scaled off. When this is done, we can plot a point for each pair of numbers in Table 2.1. This may be done by first determining the appropriate time point along the horizontal axis and then measuring off the corresponding distance-value in the vertical direction. The points are shown in Fig. 2.1 as dots through which a line has been drawn, suggesting the continuous, uniform motion of the object. Such a line is called the **graph** of the motion. A graph together with the two axes is called a **diagram**.

Table 2.1

Time in seconds	Distance in centimeters
5	10
10	20
15	30
20	40
25	50

The simplest graph through the points plotted from Table 2.1 is a *straight* line. That is, the points representing the pairs of numbers all fall on a single straight line. This is how the uniformity of the motion shows itself geometrically. A *d-t* **diagram** gives all the information concerning the motion of our object that our equations do; that is, distance, time, and velocity. But it may not be immediately obvious just how a d-t diagram shows the velocity. Let us go back to the definition of velocity and check its value. Substituting any of the d-t pairs of Table 2.1 in Eq. (2.1), we get $v = 10/5$ (= $20/10 = \ldots = 50/25$) = 2 cm/sec. What aspect of the graph of Fig. 2.1 corresponds to this constant velocity of 2 cm/sec? The student should draw a graph for a motion with a greater velocity, say 4 cm/sec, in order to see that the graph is steeper. In general, the greater the velocity, the steeper is the graph.

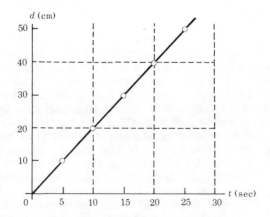

Figure 2.1 d-t Diagram for Table 2.1.

We could measure the steepness of a sloping line, for instance line c in Fig. 2.2, in several ways:

(1) the angle between lines b and c,
(2) the length of line segment a divided by the length of line segment c,
(3) the length of line segment c divided by the length of line segment b,
(4) the length of line segment a divided by the length of line segment b (the slope of line segment c).

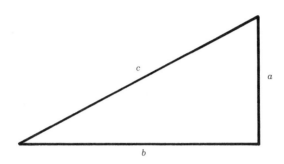

Figure 2.2. Analysis of the Slope of a Line.

The student can readily convince himself, by drawing sloping lines of various steepnesses, that as each of these quantities becomes larger, the line is made steeper. Any of the four quantities above could serve as a measure of steepness, but the last one has at least one advantage over the others. When applied to the graph of a d-t diagram, this measure is precisely the velocity of the motion represented. It is technically called the **slope** of a straight line. This gives us another way of stating our definition of velocity:

Velocity $=_{Df}$ the slope of the graph in a v-t diagram

Up to this point we have discussed only the case of constant velocity. In actual motions, more often than not, the velocity cannot be regarded as constant. The rate of motion may be increasing (as in the case of a ball rolling down an incline) or decreasing (as in the case of a car coming to a gradual stop), or may alternately increase and decrease (as a roller coaster moving along its tracks with many ups and downs). In such cases the d-t graph would not be a single straight line, but could be represented approximately by a series of straight-line segments, each segment having a slope different from the preceding one. The successive line segments would become steeper in a d-t diagram representing a motion that is getting faster and faster; they would become less and less steep if the motion depicted were getting slower and slower. As a simplified, hypothetical illustration, let us consider the case of an object moving in the manner depicted in Fig. 2.3.

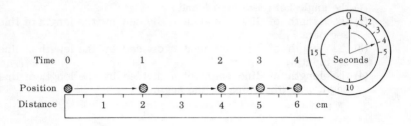

Figure 2.3 Positions, at One-Second Intervals, of a Hypothetical Moving Object.

The time and distance measurements have been entered in Table 2.2. These data are represented by the points A, B, C, D in Fig. 2.4.

Table 2.2

Time in sec (t)	Total distance in cm (d)	Velocity during each second, in cm/sec (v)	Velocity during first t sec in cm/sec
1	2	2	2
2	4	2	2
3	5	1	5/3
4	6	1	3/2

Note that, unlike the points in Fig. 2.1, these points do not fall on a single straight line. This indicates that the velocity is not uniform.

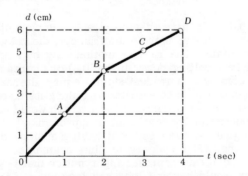

Figure 2.4 d-t Diagram for Table 2.2.

Points A, B, and the common zero-point of the axes (known as the **origin** of the diagram) lie on one straight line; B, C, and D lie on another stright line.

Since the velocity is not uniform throughout the motion, we must speak of the velocities during time intervals, for example, during one-second intervals. Velocities for successive one-second intervals have been calculated and entered in the third column of Table 2.2. Note that if the total distances and times were substituted directly into Eq. (2.1), the figures in the fourth column would result. When this is done, we obtain velocities during time intervals which all begin at the time zero. However, the use of these values to represent the successive velocities would be somewhat confusing in the case of the time intervals from 0 to 3 sec and 0 to 4 sec. Although these velocities do accurately reflect the total distance traveled in the first 3 and 4 seconds respectively, they obscure the fact that the velocity is not uniform throughout.

In order to compare their slopes, the student should sketch in separate dashed-line segments from the origin to points C and D. These straight-line graphs provide less accurate descriptions of the motion than does the bent-line graph, so we may conclude that the procedure of dividing the total distance by the total time should be used only when the velocity is uniform throughout, or when it is unimportant to pay attention to changes in velocity. The procedure used for calculating the values in the third column of Table 2.2 is a more general one than that used in calculating the fourth column. To take cognizance of this observation we should modify our definition for velocity as follows:

$$v =_{Df} \frac{d_f - d_i}{t_f - t_i} \qquad (2.2)$$

In Eq. (2.2) t_i and t_f are the initial and final values of the time interval in question; hence, their difference is the duration of the time interval. Similarly, d_i and d_f are the distances traveled from some common reference point at the beginning and end of the time interval; hence, their difference is the distance traveled during the time interval. Note that this definition reduces to Eq. (2.1) in case d_i and t_i are both zero. Equation (2.1) defined velocity during an interval, as does Eq. (2.2), but in order to apply Eq. (2.1) to any given time interval in question it requires, in effect, resetting the clock to zero.

It is customary to denote *the difference between two distances* by Δd (read "delta of d" or simply "delta-d"), Δ being the Greek upper case letter corresponding to our "d," the initial of the word "difference." Similarly, $t_f - t_i$ may be written as Δt. Using these symbols, Eq. (2.2) may be written more compactly as

$$v =_{Df} \frac{\Delta d}{\Delta t} \qquad (2.3)$$

Obviously, in an actual motion like that of a ball rolling down an incline or of a car coming to a gradual stop, the velocity does not remain constant even for an interval of two seconds, as was the case in the motion represented by Fig. 2.4. In fact, naturally changing velocities are not constant even within intervals that are small fractions of a second in duration. The velocity is likely to be changing *continuously* from one instant to the next. We have seen that such motions can be represented approximately by a series of line segments with successively changing slopes. The shorter we make the time intervals, the more line segments we use and the better approximation to the motion the graph will be. But such a graph would still be only an approximation no matter how small a time interval we might take (1/10 sec, 1/100 sec, or even smaller) for the straight-line segments.

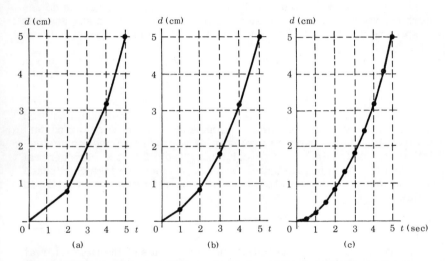

Figure 2.5 Three approximate *d-t* Diagrams for a Motion with Continuously Changing Velocity.

Examine the sequence of three *d-t* diagrams in Fig. 2.5. They may be regarded as approximate graphs of the same motion—a motion in which the velocity is continuously increasing. Note that (a) is less smooth than (b) and that (b), in turn, is not as smooth as (c). This is because the line segments cover successively smaller time intervals. In (a) each line segment (except the last) covers a time interval of two seconds; in (b) each line segment covers an interval of one second; while in (c) each interval has a duration of only 0.5 sec.

In our imagination we could continue this sequence of *d-t* diagrams, successively halving the time intervals for the line segments: 0.25 sec, 0.125 sec, 0.0625 sec, and so on. As the series progressed, each graph would appear smoother than the preceding one, although all such graphs would actually consist of line segments. If we could continue this process indefinitely, we could make a graph as smooth as we pleased. A perfectly smooth graph, although not attainable in principle by this process, could actually be approached as closely as desired by making the time intervals small enough. We may take such a hypothetical smooth graph as a model of motion in which the velocity is changing continuously. A smooth-curve graph which is approached in this way by a sequence of line-segment graphs is called the **limit** of the sequence. In Fig. 2.6 a smooth curve is shown which represents the limit of the sequence of graphs begun in Fig. 2.5.

One new problem raised by such a smooth $d-t$ diagram is that our procedure for the calculation of slope, and hence velocity, does not apply to a smooth curve. The definition for velocity applies over some definite time interval and cannot be used when the velocity changes from instant to instant.

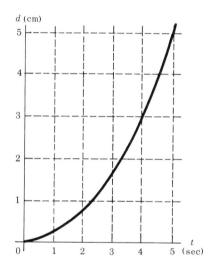

Figure 2.6 Smooth-curve Limit of the $d-t$
Diagrams in Fig. 3.5.

INSTANTANEOUS VELOCITY

As a step toward obtaining a definition of velocity which would be applicable to the continuously changing case, it should be helpful to examine the relation between velocity and time in various motions. To do this, it is desirable to employ another kind of diagram for representing motions: one in which *velocity* instead of distance is plotted against time. In order to become acquainted with this new type of diagram, let us first represent the uniform motion described in Table 2.1 by this means.

Since the velocity in this simple example is 2 cm/sec throughout the motion, the graph of velocity against time is a horizontal line, intersecting the vertical (or velocity) axis at the point $v = 2$ in Fig. 2.7(a). Such a diagram is called a **v-t diagram**. Similarly, the v-t diagram of the motion already diagrammed in Fig. 2.4 would consist of two horizontal lines, one (extending from $t = 0$ to $t = 2$ sec) at the height of 2 cm/sec and the other from $t = 2$ sec to $t = 4$ sec) at the height of 1 cm/sec. This new diagram is shown in Fig. 2.7(b).

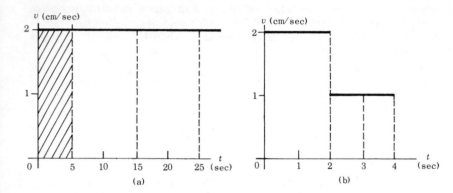

Figure 2.7 v-t Diagrams for (a) Table 2.1, and (b) Table 2.2.

Just as a distance-time diagram also represents velocity, so in a velocity-time diagram distance can be found. We recall from Eq. (2.1a) that $d = vt$. Since v is represented by the height of the graph and t by the graphical distance along the horizontal axis, we see that vt is the *area* of the rectangle whose height is v and whose base is t. In Fig. 2.7(a), the *distance* covered by the object during the first five seconds of its motion is represented by the *area* of the shaded rectangle, the product of 2 cm/sec (height) by 5 sec (base). The result, 10 cm, is in agreement with the first entry in Table 2.1. Similarly, the area of the unshaded rectangle in the figure represents the distance covered in the subsequent 20 sec, (2 cm/sec) · (20 sec) = 40 cm. The total distance is 50 cm, which also agrees with Table 2.1.

In the slightly more complex situation of Fig. 2.7(b), the distances covered during the first second and during the first two seconds of motion are obtained in exactly the same way as in the foregoing example, but for time intervals from zero to more than two seconds, we have to add the areas of two rectangles. The distance covered during the first three seconds of motion is represented by the sum of two areas: the area of the large rectangle extending from the vertical axis to the dotted line through $t = 2$, *plus* that of the smaller rectangle from $t = 2$ to $t = 3$. Their areas are 2×2 and 1×1 respectively, which total 5 and thus agree with the distance entry for $t = 3$ in Table 2.2 (5 cm). In general, we will have to combine the areas of as many rectangles as there are different velocity values in the time interval for which we want to find the distance covered.

Theoretical explorations:

The student should work out the following exercises to make sure he has grasped the idea of d-t and v-t diagrams. They will also serve as preparation for later laboratory work concerned with measuring velocities.

2.1 An object moves a distance of 6 m in 2 sec at constant velocity. If its velocity remains constant, how far will it move in a period of 5 sec? What is its velocity? Represent all of these facts on both d-t and v-t diagrams. ▬

2.2a A man and his wife drove from City A to City C, a distance of 45 miles, in 1.5 hours. Represent this trip by both d-t and v-t diagrams.
   b. The man's wife noticed that, 45 minutes after their departure, they reached an intermediate town, B, located 30 miles from City A. Represent the two parts of their trip—before and after town B—on a v-t diagram. ▬

2.3 Let us now reexamine with our new conceptual tool the more realistic case of motion exemplified in Fig. 2.5, in which the velocity is continuously changing. The v-t diagram of Fig. 2.8 (a) corresponds to the d-t diagram of Fig. 2.5 (a). There is a horizontal step in the v-t diagram corresponding to each line segment in the d-t diagram, and the height of each step represents the velocity in the corresponding time interval. In similar fashion, the first few steps of the v-t diagrams corresponding to the d-t diagrams of Fig. 2.5 (b) and (c) have been drawn in Fig. 2.8 (b) and (c). The first few steps of another graph (Fig. 2.8 (d)) have also been drawn, each step covering 0.25 sec. The student should complete diagrams (b), (c) and (d). In each of these v-t diagrams, the student should also find the distance covered from the beginning of the motion ($t = 0$) to some later instant ($t = 3$, 4, or 5) by computing the sum of the areas of rectangles up to the chosen point in time and verify that the result agrees with the distance calculated by using Eq. (2.1a). ▬

2.4 If the student connects the midpoints of the steps in each of the four v-t diagrams of Fig. 2.8, he will see that in each case they lie on a straight line passing through the origin. These straight lines are called the median lines. Observe that the four median lines are identical in position. Comparing the successive step-graphs, (a), (b), (c), and (d), we see that they progressively deviate less from the median line. The successive graphs could be confined in narrower and narrower strips surrounding the median line. ▬

Closely following the arguments leading to a smooth-curve d-t graph (p. 47), we can imagine continuing a sequence of v-t diagrams, using smaller and smaller time intervals for the steps. Each successive graph would be confined in a narrower strip surrounding the median line than was the preceding one. If we could continue this

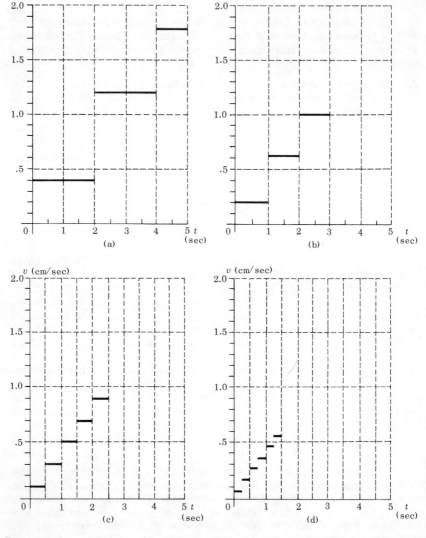

Figure 2.8 Four v-t Diagrams for a Motion with Continuously Changing Velocity. (The first three correspond to the d-t diagrams of Fig. 2.5.)

process indefinitely, we could make a graph that was confined to as narrow a strip surrounding the median line as we pleased. The limit of such a sequence of step-like v-t graphs would be the median line itself. As an ideal model of an apparent smooth motion which, when measured, yielded a step-wise v-t diagram like those in Fig. 2.8, we will take the median line as the v-t graph.

Figure 2.9 shows the step diagram of Fig. 2.8 (b) with the limiting straight-line graph superimposed. An important point to note about the median line is that one can still use areas for finding the distance covered in any interval of time. One computes the area under the straight-line graph, which is no longer a rectangular area, but a triangular one. This rule may be checked by using Fig. 2.9. Note that the area of any of the right-angled triangles bounded by one of the vertical broken lines passing through the points, t = 1, 2, 3, 4 or 5 sec, is equal to the sum of the areas of all the rectangles formed by the steps up to the one just to the left of the same dashed line. This is because the median line cuts the step diagram in such a way that, for each part of a rectangle that lies above the line, there is a corresponding and equal area under the line that is not a part of the rectangle.

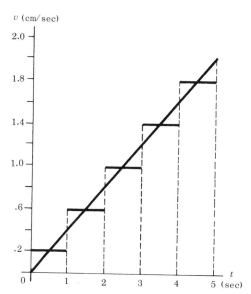

Figure 2.9 Median Line and Step v-t Diagrams for a Motion with Continuously Changing Velocity.

To give a numerical example, the distance covered during the first three seconds of motion is given by the area of the triangle that is bounded on its right side by the dashed vertical line at t = 3. This area is 1/2(1.2 cm/sec) · (3 sec), which is 1.8 cm. The same result is also obtained if we add the areas of the first three rectangles of the step diagram: (.2) · (1) + (.6) · (1) + (1.0) · (1) = 1.8. (The student should also check that this result is in agreement with the distance read off from the d-t diagram of the same motion, Fig. 2.5 (b).)

It is not always true that a motion with continuously changing velocity can be represented by a *straight-line v-t* diagram. (We will later see under what conditions this *is* the case.) However, it is always possible to construct a *step-graph v-t* diagram representing measurements made on a motion with continuously changing velocity. Whenever a motion can be represented by a straight-line graph, we then have a graphical means of determining the velocity at any instant.

The motion of a stone dropped from a height may be very closely represented by a straight-line *v-t* graph. This means that its velocity is continuously and uniformly increasing. From a straight-line *v-t* graph of such a motion, we can read off the velocity at any instant. A *v-t* diagram, then, gives meaning to the concept of the velocity at any instant. Since this concept was not covered by our earlier definition of velocity, it will be useful to construct a formal definition of it.

The limit of a sequence of uniform step diagrams is the median straight line. The height of any step on a *v-t* diagram measured from the base represents the velocity in that time interval in accordance with our previous definition. Referring to Fig. 2.8 (a)-(d), we see that, as the time intervals are made narrower, the step graph becomes closer to the straight line graph, the median line. But the height of the median line is the velocity at a particular instant. Therefore, it can be shown that, as the intervals are made smaller, the velocity at any instant can be approached as closely as desired by the interval velocities. The instant is contained within each one of a nested set of intervals that approach the velocity at that instant.

The mathematical problem is to generate such a nested set of intervals that all contain a given instant. In step diagrams, we have specified the beginning and end points of each time interval. To avoid overlapping, however, we should consider that each interval either contains the first of these end points and not the last, or vice versa. Conventionally, the earlier point is included. Starting with an interval bounded by a given instant at the beginning, halving it, and continuing to halve successively the first of the two halves yields a nested series of intervals that all contain the beginning point of the original interval. The velocity at a given instant (instantaneous velocity) can be defined as the limit of this kind of sequence of interval velocities for which all intervals contain the given instant.

Examination of Fig. 2.9 will show that, for any time interval, the distance given by the area under the steps is equal to the distance given by the area of the trapezoid under the portion of the straight-line graph that lies within that interval. With respect to the measurements of distance and time, then, it is as though the velocity were constant (the interval velocity) throughout the interval of time measured. The interval velocity we have been computing is the **average velocity** for the interval, because an average value is that one value which can be used in place of each member of an entire set of different values without changing the total. The student can see from the graph that the average velocity over an interval, so defined, is also the numerical average of the instantaneous velocity at the beginning of an interval and the velocity at the beginning of the next interval.

Since it is conventional to denote an average value by means of a horizontal bar placed above the symbol, we may now rewrite Eq. (2.3) as follows:

$$\bar{v} =_{Df} \frac{\Delta d}{\Delta t} \qquad (2.4)$$

The velocity at an instant clearly has more general applicability than average velocity, $\bar{v}$. Accordingly, we shall reserve the use of the symbol, v for this new concept and write $\bar{v}$ whenever we wish to refer to average velocity. In cases of uniform velocity, $\bar{v} = v$ at every moment, and we may use either symbol. In order to introduce the new concept of instantaneous velocity into our mathematical model, we shall adopt, as its definition, the following:

$v =_{Df}$ the limitng value of $\bar{v}$ for a sequence of time intervals beginning at time t, as these time intervals are made smaller and smaller indefinitely.

(A calculational formula for v will be derived in a subsequent section.)

Theoretical explorations:

The student should work out the following exercises to make sure he has grasped the ideas in this section.

2.5 Light from the sun requires about 8.3 minutes to reach the earth, a distance of about 150 billion meters. What is the velocity of light in m/sec? in cm/sec? ■

2.6 A motion picture sequence of an automobile coming to a stop from a speed of 45 feet per second (about 30 mph) was analyzed. The individual pictures, taken at the rate of five pictures each second, showed the distances traveled by the car every 0.2 sec from the instant the brakes were applied. These distances are shown in Table 2.3.

Table 2.3 Data for Exercise 2

t (sec)	d (feet)
0.2	8.6
0.4	16.2
0.6	23.0
0.8	28.0
1.0	33.8
1.2	37.8
1.4	41.0
1.6	43.2
1.8	44.6
2.0	45.0
2.2	45.0

a. Plot a d-t diagram of the motion of the car represented by these data.

b. Next, calculate the average velocity during each 0.2-sec time interval, and plot a v-t diagram superimposed on the d-t diagram. Plot the average velocity for each time interval at the midpoint of that interval and draw the median line. Comment on the shape of the median line. ■

2.7 Motion pictures of a falling steel ball taken at a rate of 15 frames every second showed the following distances between the successive positions of the ball: 2.2 cm, 6.4 cm, 10.7 cm, and 15.2 cm. Calculate $\bar{v}$ for each interval and plot a v-t diagram of the motion. What can you say about the uniformity with which the velocity is changing? What sources of error can you think of in such an experiment? ■

PROPORTIONALITY CONSTANTS

To characterize succinctly relationships in our mathematical model such as that between distance and time for uniform linear motions, it is useful to introduce the language of proportionality constants. It will also be useful in other areas of science to have a tool with which to study graphical relationships in general. In our present study, it will enable us to investigate more effectively the conditions under which a motion with continuously changing velocity can be represented by a straight-line v-t diagram.

We begin by reexamining an already familiar example of uniform linear motion. The data of Table 2.1 are reproduced (in slightly modified form) in Table 2.4. The constant velocity can be calculated by dividing any one of the d values by its corresponding t value. That is,

$$\frac{10}{5} = \frac{20}{10} = \frac{30}{15} = \frac{40}{20} = \frac{50}{25} = 2\left(\frac{\text{cm}}{\text{sec}}\right)$$

Table 2.4

Time	Distance
$t_1 = 5$	$d_1 = 10$
$t_2 = 10$	$d_2 = 20$
$t_3 = 15$	$d_3 = 30$
$t_4 = 20$	$d_4 = 40$
$t_5 = 25$	$d_5 = 50$

Using the subscripted variables in place of the particular numbers of the table, we may write

$$\frac{d_1}{t_1} = \frac{d_2}{t_2} = \frac{d_3}{t_3} = \frac{d_4}{t_4} = \frac{d_5}{t_5} = v$$

Whenever the ratios of corresponding pairs of values of two quantities (d and t in this example) are all equal, a **proportionality relationship** exists between the two quantities. To express such a relationship, the above series of equations is insufficient. For the subscripts denote only a few of the possible pairs of values of the two quantities. We wish to imply that all possible pairs of corresponding values are proportional. To suggest this, we omit subscripts altogether, and simply write

$$\frac{d}{t} = K \tag{2.5}$$

where K stands for the common value of all d/t ratios. K is called the **proportionality constant**. In this case, it is the velocity, 2 cm/sec.

The concept of proportionality is familiar to everyone, even though the way of expressing it in Eq. (2.5) may be new. We know, for instance, that the amount of money we pay for gasoline is proportional to the amount of gasoline we get from the pump. We have also encountered a scientific example of proportionality in the previous chapter: Kepler's third law of planetary motion: D^3 divided by T^2 is constant for all planets. The task here is to study the handling of a proportionality relationship mathematically and to associate it with its graphical representation. To use even more general variables than d and t, consider the equation

$$\frac{y}{x} = K$$

as representing the mathematical relationship underlying Eq. (2.5). Multiplying both sides of this equation by x, we obtain

$$y = Kx \tag{2.6}$$

which is a customary way of stating that y is proportional to x. For instance, x may stand for the number of gallons of gasoline we buy, and y for the total price we pay; in which case K is the price per gallon.

Mathematical exploration:

2.8 As an exercise, substitute in Eq. (2.6) T^2 (the square of the period of revolution) for y, and D^3 (the cube of the average distance from the sun) for x, and check that it expresses Kepler's third law. ■

Note that if y is proportional to x, x is also proportional to y. This means that whenever a proportionality relationship exists, there are two constants of proportionality as shown in the following equations:

$$y = K_1 x \quad \text{and} \quad x = K_2 y$$

The student should prove that the product of the two proportionality constants is one, i.e., that $K_1 K_2 = 1$. This shows that these constants are reciprocals of each other. Writing it differently,

$$K_1 = \frac{1}{K_2} \quad \text{and} \quad K_2 = \frac{1}{K_1}$$

In order to understand how a proportionality relationship is expressed graphically, consider again the d–t diagram of a motion with constant velocity. As shown in Fig. 2.1, the graph was a straight line, and the velocity was represented by the slope of the line. Generalizing these ideas to proportionality relationships in general, we can say: A proportionality relationship, $y = Kx$, is graphically represented by a straight line passing through the origin of the diagram (x being the horizontal axis and y the vertical axis). The proportionality constant K is represented by the slope of this line. Conversely, if we have a graph which is a straight line passing through the origin, we say right away that there exists a proportionality relationship between the two quantities represented by x and y, and the slope of the line gives us the value of the proportionality constant. As we continue with our studies, we will encounter proportionality relationships frequently and find it useful to express them both in mathematical and graphical forms.

ACCELERATION

Let us now apply the language of proportionality relations to a study of straight-line v–t diagrams such as the one shown in Fig. 2.9. Since the graph is a straight line passing through the origin, we infer that the instantaneous velocity v at any time t after the start of the motion is proportional to t. The equation relating v and t is, therefore, of the form of Eq. (2.6):

$$v = Kt \tag{2.7}$$

where K is the proportionality constant and also the slope of the v–t graph.

Recall the equation relating d and t in the case of motions with constant velocity,

$$d = vt \tag{2.1a}$$

We see a striking similarity with Eq. (2.7). This suggests that the K

in Eq. (2.7) can be interpreted as the *rate of change of velocity with time*, just as v is the rate of change of distance with time. We can see that this is true by solving Eq. (2.7) for K:

$$K = \frac{v}{t}$$

and noting that v is actually the amount by which the velocity changed, since we started from $v = 0$ at $t = 0$. To indicate this fact explicitly, we can write

$$K = \frac{v - 0}{t - 0}$$

If we are to include cases in which time is measured from some arbitrary starting point other than the beginning of the motion, we may write,

$$K = \frac{v_2 - v_1}{t_2 - t_1} \quad \text{or} \quad K = \frac{\Delta v}{\Delta t} \tag{2.8}$$

which are analogous to Eqs. (2.2) and (2.3) defining velocity.

The proportionality constant of Eqs. (2.7) and (2.8), or the slope of a straight-line v-t diagram, represents an important concept in mechanics: the rate at which the velocity changes. The term for this concept is **acceleration,** a term which is already more or less familiar to us in everyday speech. For instance, we speak of the gas pedal of a car as the accelerator. In technical usage the word *acceleration* is used irrespective of whether the change in velocity is an increase (positive acceleration) or a decrease (negative acceleration). Since velocity implies a direction, the term *acceleration* is also appropriately used, as will be illustrated in the next chapter, when only the direction—and not the speed—of a motion undergoes change. Using the symbol a for acceleration, let us define it as

$$a =_{\text{Df}} \frac{\Delta v}{\Delta t} \tag{2.9}$$

A motion whose v-t graph is a straight line, then, is one whose acceleration is constant, or equivalently, a motion that is uniformly accelerated. For the motion depicted in Fig. 2.9 (p. 51), for example, the constant acceleration may be calculated by dividing any change in instantaneous velocity Δv by the corresponding time interval Δt. We may take $\Delta t = 2$ sec, $\Delta v = 0.8$ cm/sec; or $\Delta t = 3$ sec, $\Delta v = 1.2$ cm/sec, etc. Any ratio we pick gives us

$$a = 0.4 \text{ cm per sec per sec}$$

The unit of acceleration, "centimeter per second per second," may sound awkward at first, but when we realize that the numerator of the expression for acceleration is a velocity-value, with the unit cm/sec, while the denominator has the unit of time, sec, it is natural that the unit for acceleration should be so. The customary notation for this acceleration unit is cm/sec/sec, or, more briefly, cm/sec^2 (read "centimeter per second-squared"). Strictly speaking, Eq. (2.9) defines acceleration only for a time interval. Since we will not deal with motions whose acceleration changes, this definition will suffice for our purposes, but it would be a simple matter to develop a definition of instantaneous acceleration similar to the definition of instantaneous velocity.

The following practical example may further clarify the concept of acceleration and the use of Eq. (2.9). Suppose a car was braked at an instant when its velocity was 18 m/sec (approximately 40 mph) and it came to a stop 1.5 sec later. Referring to Eq. (2.8), since $v_1 = $ 18 m/sec and $v_2 = 0$, we have $\Delta v = -18$ m/sec. We do not know t_1 and t_2 separately, but we do know that their difference, Δt, is 1.5 sec, which is what we need to compute the acceleration. Substituting in Eq. (2.9), we obtain

$$a = \frac{-18}{1.5} = -12 \text{ m/sec}^2$$

a negative acceleration. This is as it should be, since there was a decrease in the velocity of the car. Consider the v-t diagram for such a motion, which is the slanting straight-line graph shown in Fig. 2.10. Recall that the area under the graph gives us the distance covered during the interval. Applying the formula for the area of a triangle, we obtain the relationship,

$$d = \frac{1}{2}(t_2)(v_1)$$

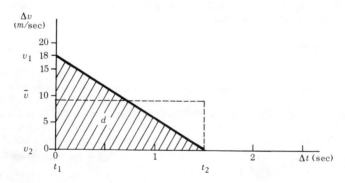

Figure 2.10 v-t Diagram Representing an Automobile Coming to a Stop.

In a case of positive acceleration, such as depicted in Fig. 2.11, the same equation holds.

Solving this equation for v_t, we get the general equation

$$v_t = \frac{2d}{t} \qquad (2.10)$$

This equation tells us that in Fig. 2.11 the instantaneous velocity t seconds after the start of the motion is equal to *twice* the distance covered in that time divided by the length of the time interval—*provided* the acceleration is constant. Note that v_t will be exactly twice the average velocity during the first t seconds. Note that the rectangular area in Fig. 2.11 under the line at the height $\bar{v}$ and bounded by the vertical line at t also gives the distance covered during the first t seconds of motion.

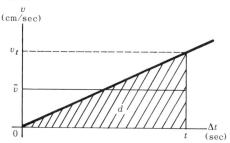

Figure 2.11 *v-t* Diagram for a Motion with Constant Positive Acceleration.

Substituting from Eq. (2.10) for v_t in the equation $a = v_t/t$, a computational formula for the acceleration of a uniformly accelerated motion is obtained:

$$a = \frac{2d/t}{t}$$

or

$$a = \frac{2d}{t^2} \qquad (2.11)$$

where d is the distance traveled during the first t seconds after the motion started. To illustrate the use of this formula, consider a ball rolling down a slope that travels 120 cm in the first two seconds. Its acceleration is

$$a = \frac{(2)(120)}{(2)^2} = \frac{240}{4} = 60 \text{ cm/sec}^2$$

Theoretical explorations:

As an exercise, the student should work out the following problems. (Assume acceleration to be constant in all cases.)

2.9 If an object is moving with an instantaneous velocity of 20 cm/sec exactly 5 seconds after the start of its motion, what is its acceleration? ▬

2.10 If an object is moving with a velocity of 16 cm/sec at a certain instant, and its acceleration is 3 cm/sec^2, what is its instantaneous velocity 4 seconds later? ▬

2.11 If a car is braked so that it has an acceleration of − 15 m/sec^2 beginning at an instant when it is traveling at 30 m/sec, how many seconds will it take to come to a standstill? Also, how many meters will it have traveled from the moment of braking? ▬

2.12 A stone dropped from a height of 44 meters reached the ground in 3 seconds. What was its acceleration? ▬

2.13 Given that the acceleration of any freely falling object near the surface of the earth is 9.8 m/sec^2, approximately how many seconds will an object take to reach the ground after being released from a height of 80 meters? ▬

FORCE AND MASS

The model we have developed so far has been used primarily in representing observed motions and filling in gaps between discrete measurements. We can also use the same concepts to make a prediction about the continuation of a motion whose beginning has been measured. In the example of the ball rolling down a slope we calculated the acceleration (assumed to be constant) from a single observation made 2 seconds after it began to roll. Once this constant has been determined, we can predict how far the ball will travel in, say, 4 seconds after it is started rolling again under the same conditions. We first substitute the determined value of a, i.e., 60 cm/sec^2, in Eq. (2.11) and write,

$$60 = \frac{2d}{t^2}$$

If we let $t = 4$ sec in this equation and solve it for d, we obtain

$$d = 480 \text{ cm}$$

This prediction can then be checked by experiment. If there is a sizeable difference, we would probably conclude that the acceleration was not constant after all and that conditions were not uniform.

If we had a high speed computer and an automatic means of making and feeding it measurements of distance and time, we could have the computer make predictions for a single motion and check them as the object moves. It could use Eq. (2.11) to predict and check the successive positions at certain times or the successive times at which the moving object reached given positions.

The task from here on is to develop the model for linear motions so that predictions may be made in cases in which the conditions of the motion are changing. To do so, we need to answer such questions as, "What makes an object move?" The commonsense answer to this question is that some force must be acting on an object to make it move. We all have an intuitive idea of the concept of force; but, like distance and time, force turns out to be a rather difficult concept to define. We can, however, resort to the expedient of introducing **force** as another primitive or undefined term of our model. As with distance and time, it will be helpful if we know how to measure it.

What is the most common and ubiquitous type of force? Some may immediately think of the muscular force we exert when we move or lift heavy objects; but we soon realize that it would be most unsatisfactory to try to use our subjective sensation as a basis for measuring force. The weight of an object itself seems a much more likely candidate for our purpose. When we let a heavy book rest on the palm of our hand, we "feel its weight." The sensation is the same as though someone were exerting a downward push (muscular force) on our palm. Weight, then, is a type of force which is very common in our experience—so common, indeed, that we perhaps do not bother to think of it as a force. It is a special type of force in one sense: it acts only in the vertical direction. If we can find a way to measure weight, we may be able to use the same device for measuring forces in general, regardless of the direction of their action.

Springs have a property which makes them suitable for measuring weights within certain limits. If a spring is suspended vertically and an object of suitable weight is attached to its lower end, the spring will be stretched by a certain amount. If another object, attached in place of the first, stretches the spring by that same length, then, with both objects attached simultaneously, the spring will be stretched twice as much. If three objects show equal individual effects on a spring, their joint effect is three times as great; likewise for four objects and so on—provided that the spring does not undergo *permanent* deformity because of excessive weight. The same holds true when, instead of stretching a vertically suspended spring, we compress a vertically standing spring (such as a mattress spring) by placing objects on its upper end. We may state this property of a spring in the following manner: The deformation (stretching or compression) of a spring—so long as its shape is not permanetly changed—is proportional to the number of equivalent weights (objects that individually produce equal deformations) acting on it. This is a form of Hooke's Law, named for Robert Hooke who formulated it *c.* 1660.

We can easily perform this experiment and construct a table or graph showing the lengths of deformation (the changes in overall length measured from the length without any weights) owing to different numbers of equivalent weights. Once such a graph (which may be called a **calibration chart** for reasons that will be made clear later) has been constructed, there is no reason the spring cannot be used for measuring forces other than weight, acting in an arbitrary direction.

One would simply measure the deformation in the length units of the graph and read off the corresponding number of equivalent weights. Care must be taken to orient the spring so that it is parallel to the direction in which the force is exerted.

For all practical purposes, we may use springs, together with their calibration charts, as the basic devices for measuring forces in any direction. Different springs will be needed to measure forces of various magnitudes, for the range of forces that can be measured by any one spring is necessarily limited by the amount of force that produces a permanent deformation. There is a lower limit also, namely, the force that does not noticeably change the length of the spring.

It still remains to decide on a suitable standard unit of weight before springs and their respective calibration charts can be used to provide interchangeable measures of force. There are many such units in use today—the gram-weight, kilogram-weight, pound, ton, and several others. However, the ones just mentioned are apt to be confused with units of mass—a concept to be discussed presently. To avoid such confusion, a unit somewhat less well known outside of scientific circles called the **newton** is used for standardizing measures of force. This is a convenient size for laboratory experiments. A weight of one newton is equal to 10/98 of the weight of the standard kilogram in Paris, or about one-fifth of a pound. It will become clear later how this particular unit is conveniently related to the international standard for length.

By hanging several one-newton weights on a vertically suspended spring and measuring the amount of stretch, the constant of proportionality k for that spring can be determined. If we let f be the force in newtons, and d be the length in cm by which the spring is stretched, Hooke's Law states that

$$f = kd$$

hence, $k = f/d$ newtons/cm. After determining the spring constant from the measured distortion by a given weight, this constant can be used to determine the magnitude of any force (that does not permanently distort the spring) from the resulting change in length. As we have suggested, it may sometimes be more convenient to construct a table or a graph. Commercial spring scales have force units already marked on the support or the housing and a pointer to indicate the scale reading.

Since we have specified a means of measuring force, this concept can now be admitted as another primitive term in our model. However, it becomes an integral part of the model only if we can find how it is related to some other terms in the model.

A simple but instructive experiment on the effects of force on motion, uses an apparatus known as Atwood's machine (see Fig. 2.12). This machine consists only of two objects of equal weight suspended by a string over a pulley. They are set in motion by adding small weights to one side. The force producing the motion can be measured by holding back one of the objects with a calibrated spring. The motion resulting when one of the objects is released can be studied by determining the time required for it to travel a measured distance. This information permits calculating the average velocity by Eq. (2.1). When we perform this experiment, we find that the motion is accelerated quite uniformly. So it is more informative to calculate the acceleration of the motion rather than just the average velocity. Since we have no means for computing instantaneous acceleration, we may assume the acceleration to be constant throughout the time interval, as we did in computing average velocity. Equation (2.11) applies on the assumption of uniform acceleration, and we can either interpret the result as an average or this assumption can be checked later in a manner described on page 67.

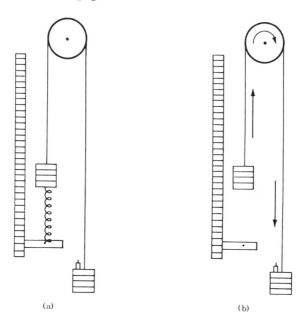

(a)

(b)

Figure 2.12 Atwood's Machine, Used to Measure Acceleration.
In (a) a spring is attached to measure force; in (b) the spring is
removed and the weights are in motion.

In the experiment, weights of various magnitudes are added to the object on one side of the machine. For each weight, the time required for the objects to move through a specified distance is measured. These time and distance measurements may then be substituted in Eq. (2.11) to calculate the acceleration resulting from each weight.

In order to examine the relationship between force and acceleration, we can then plot the measurements of force and acceleration on a graph. The x-marks in Fig. 2.13 represent the results obtained from an experiment of this type. Note that acceleration is here measured in m/sec^2, rather than cm/sec^2.

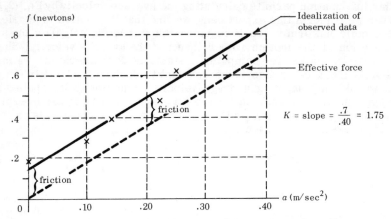

Figure 2.13 Accelerations Produced by Forces of Various Magnitudes in Experiment with Atwood's Machine.

We see that the x-marks lie moderately well along the solid straight line which was drawn to fit them as closely as possible. For purposes of developing our theoretical model we may ignore the deviations and take the straight-line graph as representing an ideal relationship between force and acceleration.

The graph reminds us of one representing a relationship of direct proportion. (See pp. 54-56.) There is one difference, however: the line does not pass through the origin. This reflects the fact that a certain amount of force (0.15 newton in the idealization graphed in Fig. 2.13) must be applied before any acceleration is produced at all. How should we interpret this fact? A reasonable interpretation is that this much force is used up just in overcoming the *friction* which resists the movement of the pulley wheel. So the forces actually contributing to the motions are this much less than the measured forces. (The surmise that there is a constant amount of force that does not contribute to the motion of the Atwood machine can be checked by further experiment. If it is so, then employing a pulley with less friction in the bearings would result in a graph that comes closer to passing through the origin.) On this interpretation, it seems appropriate to subtract this "wasted" part of the force from each of the measured values of force. Carrying out this subtraction for the idealization of the data is equivalent to moving the graph downward by the appropriate amount so that it passes through the origin. Therefore, we draw a line through the origin *parallel* to the best fitting straight line and interpret this new graph (dashed line) as representing the ideal relationship between acceleration and *effective* force—that is, the force which is actually responsible for the motion, after the resistance of friction has been overcome.

This new graph, then, *does* represent a proportionality relationship: the acceleration of a motion and the effective force producing the motion are proportional to each other. Referring back to Eq. (2.6), we see that the relationship between force and acceleration can be expressed by the equation

$$f = Ka \tag{2.12}$$

where f stands for the effective force measured in newtons, a the acceleration in m/sec^2, and K is the proportionality constant. The value of this constant (in this case 1.75) can be determined by calculating the slope of either line in a force-acceleration diagram like Fig. 2.13.

We saw in two previous cases of proportionality (between distance and time when velocity is constant, and between velocity and time when acceleration is constant) that the proportionality constant carried has a concrete physical meaning. Can we interpret the constant of proportionality in the present case? Under what circumstances would the constant (the slope of the graph) differ? In the laboratory, if we repeat the experiment using a pair of objects which are more massive than the two used in the first experiment, the objects would then move more sluggishly, i.e., the acceleration produced by each added weight would be *smaller* than that produced by the same weight in the first experiment. Such experiments verify the suggestion that the f-a graph for more massive objects has a greater slope (or proportionality constant) than the graph for the first experiment.

It may be easier to think of the situation in this way: to produce a certain acceleration, a larger force is needed if the objects being moved are more massive. Conversely, if less massive objects are set in motion, a smaller force than before will suffice to produce a given acceleration, and the proportionality constant will be smaller than before. We infer that the proportionality constant in Eq. (2.12) is directly related to the massiveness of the objects that are set in motion by the force.

If we had no measure of massiveness, but only a rough way of comparing two objects by hefting them, we would be interested in adopting a procedure, such as the Atwood machine experiment, that attached numerical values to objects in such a way that the "heftier" of two objects always had the higher value. However, it may be asked why we need a separate measure of massiveness—wouldn't its weight (in force units) suffice to represent the massiveness of any object? Gallileo evidently felt satisfied with force units for measuring the massiveness of objects.

However, a technical difficulty arises today, especially in geophysical studies. The weight of an object varies when measured by spring balances at differing distances from the center of the earth. Newton had another consideration in introducing this concept. He distinguished sharply between force and mass. Force is an interaction between two or more bodies, while mass is an invariant characteristic of a given body of matter. It is encouraging to learn that, at a given point on the earth's surface, weight and mass are directly proportional.

(We will later discuss the more conventional way of measuring mass, which is usually more convenient and accurate, but is conceptually more difficult to distinguish from weight.)

What would be the consequences of assuming Eq. (2.12) as the basis for the definition of **mass** in our model? To follow out the above suggestion, we replace the symbol K for the proportionality constant in Eq. (2.12) by m, standing for mass, and write, $f = ma$. Both sides of the equation are then divided by a, yielding for our definition,

$$m =_{\text{Df}} \frac{f}{a} \tag{2.13}$$

When force is measured in newtons and acceleration is measured in m/sec², the unit for mass, thus defined, turns out to be the *kilogram*. Mass, in this conception, sometimes called inertial mass, is the property of an object which determines the amount of force required to impart a unit amount of acceleration to the object. When mass of an object is measured in kilograms, its numerical value will be the same as the number of newtons of force required to give the object an acceleration of 1 m/sec².

Now that we have defined mass by Eq. (2.13), we may occasionally revert to the form of Eq. (2.12), and write it as

$$f = ma \tag{2.13a}$$

which is often the more convenient form for practical application. However, to avoid circularity, we can only use this equation to define one of the three terms. This form of the equation is commonly identified as Newton's Second Law of Motion and used to predict the amount of force required to produce a given acceleration in a given object.

An interesting consequence of this law is found by considering motion with constant velocity. In this case the acceleration is zero, since there is no change in velocity. According to Eq. (2.13a), the force must also be zero. This means that no *effective force* is required to keep the motion going at constant velocity, and the only force needed is that required to overcome friction. This means that an object moving on a perfectly frictionless surface without any external force would keep moving indefinitely at the same velocity. This conclusion is known as Newton's First Law of Motion.

Another consequence of Newton's Second Law is that we can now state the physical condition under which an object will be uniformly accelerated: namely, whenever the force propelling it is constant.

Our analysis of the Atwood machine experiment led to the introduction of a new theoretical concept, inertial mass. It would not be warranted to introduce a theoretical concept if it were only tied to a single type of experiment, and we have already implied that such is not the case. It may therefore give us a feeling of greater confidence to conduct another type of experiment which also yields results that point to the same definition of mass as the one above.

Laboratory exploration:

2.14 A study of the motion of an object sliding down a smooth, inclined plane provides an experiment parallel to the one discussed above. In this case the force acting on the object is varied by varying the steepness of the incline and can be measured by holding back the object with a calibrated spring balance before allowing it to start sliding. Just as in the pulley experiment, we find the motion to be accelerated. We can measure the acceleration, *under the assumption that it is constant*, by determining the time required for the object to slide down a measured distance and then using Eq. (2.11). The rest of the procedure is just the same as with the Atwood machine. Plot the force (in newtons) against the acceleration (in m/sec^2) which results from each measured amount of force. The graph may be compared to that for the pulley experiment (Fig. 2.13).

Again, by repeating the experiment with more massive (or less massive) objects, we can obtain a series of force–acceleration graphs from which the relation of slope to inertial mass may be examined. ■

One point requires further comment. In both the pulley experiment and the inclined plane experiment, we *assumed* the acceleration of the motion to be constant. We cannot check this assumption in the sense of providing absolute proof. If the motion were filmed by a high speed movie camera, we would have evidence which most persons would accept as a conclusive test, but even so the gaps between frames of the film would be relatively large compared with that portion of the motion photographed. But, as will be seen in succeeding chapters, it is rare that assumptions in science can be checked as well as in this case. More frequently one can only find out whether certain consequences of the assumption, often somewhat removed from it, are consistent with experimental evidence. In this sense, the assumption of uniform acceleration can be checked as follows: keeping the force constant, we use various distances through which to allow the suspended objects (in the pulley experiment) or the sliding object (in the inclined plane experiment) to travel. We measure the time taken for each of these distances traveled, and calculate the acceleration in each case, using the assumption of its constancy and Eq. (2.11) for the calculation. If the resulting accelerations for the different distances traveled are all equal within expected experimental error, we say that the assumption of constant acceleration has been verified. We see that no *circularity* of argument is involved; for the use of Eq. (2.11) requires that we assume constant acceleration only for *each one* of the several distances traveled, and we have no *assumption* of constancy of acceleration from one distance to another. If the latter assumption *had* been made, or if we had compared measurements for the same distance, we would have been guilty of circularity, since we would have assumed just what we wanted to verify.

Theoretical explorations:

The student should test and develop his grasp of the material in this section by working out the following exercises. (Assume no friction in all cases.)

2.15 If an effective force of 10 newtons is applied to an object of 20-kg mass, what acceleration should the object undergo? ▬

2.16 What effective force must an object of 15-kg mass receive in order to undergo an acceleration of 2 m/sec^2? ▬

2.17 What effective force is being exerted on a 5-kg object if it travels 8 meters in 2 seconds from the moment of onset of the force? ▬

2.18 How long should it take for a 10-kg object to travel 8 meters from the onset of a continuous 10-newton push? ▬

2.19 If a 5-kg object receives a continuous 12-newton push, how far should it have traveled 3 seconds after onset? ▬

A SHIFT IN PRIMITIVE TERMS

In the foregoing section, we have achieved the ability to predict distance and velocity in linear motions resulting from the application of a uniform force. In our theoretical model of linear motion, we introduced three primitive terms: *distance*, *time*, and *force*. For each of these concepts, measurement procedures have been specified, and definitions are not necessary as the concepts are familiar ones. Every theory must have some undefined terms, for otherwise circularity of the total set of definitions would result. But there is no *logical* reason one set of terms should be taken as the primitives rather than another set; the particular choice depends partly on convenience and degree of familiarity of the chosen terms. The chief goal in the logical organization (or possibly reorganization) of a theory is that of clarity and explanatory power.

We chose *distance* and *time* as two of the primitives because they seemed difficult to define, were familiar to everyone, and because they could be easily measured. But our choice of *force* as the third primitive has disadvantages. The accurate measurement of force is a rather delicate process, requiring the calibration of spring balances which, until quite recently, were quite unreliable. Moreover, the range of values of force that can be measured by any single spring balance is very small. The force must be strong enough to produce an appreciable deformation, but not so strong as to produce a *permanent* deformity of the spring. The calculation of distance, time, mass, and other quantities on the basis of force measurements would be less reliable than the calculation of force on the basis of these other measurements. A more basic difficulty arises from the fact that the weight of an object varies somewhat from one geographic location to another (for reasons which will later become clear). This means that the calibration of spring balances carried out at one place will not be *exactly* equivalent to a similar calibration performed at another place.

With all these disadvantages, the choice of force as a primitive term can hardly be called an ideal one. The principal advantage is that it enabled us to define the concept of inertial mass. Having once defined inertial mass in terms of force, it is a simple matter to reverse the statuses of these two terms, taking *mass* as a primitive and defining *force* in terms of it. The principal reason mass was not chosen as a primitive from the outset was that the concept of mass is difficult to separate from the concept of weight. We are now in a position to give a rationale for measuring mass and hence to adopt *mass* instead of force as the third primitive of our system.

It turns out that the mass of any object may be measured in terms of the mass of a standard object, taken as the unit of mass, in two ways: (1) by accelerating the two separately, as in an Atwood machine, under known forces and computing the slope of the f-a graphs (this is called inertial mass); and (2) by determining what multiple (or what fraction) of the *weight* of the standard object exactly balances the weight of the object to be measured (this is called gravitational mass). Fortunately, the two concepts of mass agree. If two objects, having equal inertial masses, are located *at a given place* on the earth, then their weights are equal and they will balance. Consequently, their gravitational masses are also equal. By *comparing* two weights in measuring mass, we circumvent the difficulty owing to geographic variations in weight of a single object that attends the measurement of weight. What may not be so obvious is that the two methods of measuring the mass of an object should give the same result. Extensive investigations with the most sensitive of instruments have shown agreement within .0001 of a gram. There is little evidence on which to raise a doubt about the issue. However, it remained something of a mystery until Einstein, in his general theory of relativity, argued that one could not distinguish from inside a spacecraft between an acceleration of the whole craft and a gravitational attraction for every object in it. It is not our concern here to develop this theory in detail but simply to indicate the general approach Einstein took in eliminating the conceptual distinction between inertial and gravitational concepts of mass.

The most common instrument for measuring mass by comparison of weights is the *pan balance*. The object whose mass is to be measured is placed on one pan. On the other pan are placed objects, whose individual masses are known multiples or fractions of the standard mass, to effect a balancing of the two sides. The standard object that defines the unit of mass is the **standard kilogram,** made of platinum and kept in the Pavillion de Breteuil, at Sevres near Paris, for international reference. Other units of mass are defined in terms of it. The commonly used auxiliary unit, the **gram** (g), is one-thousandth of a kilogram (= .001 kg). It is clear that a spring balance can be used to determine mass as well as a pan balance. For example, the weight of an unknown object and a standard set of objects of known mass could be compared in separate weighings. If the spring shows the same extension in both cases, they have the same mass. The difference between the measurement of weight and the measurement of mass is this: the spring balance is stretched (or compressed) by the gravitational force acting on the object being weighed (that is, by its weight). The pan balance, on the other hand, depends on the *balancing* of the gravitational pulls on two objects: that on the object whose mass is being determined with that on a standard object. It is the balancing of *two* gravitational pulls against each other that is utilized here, instead of the balancing of *one* gravitational pull against the elasticity of a spring. Thus the same object weighed on a pan balance and a spring balance in two different locations would be expected to yield different results on the spring balance but the same result on the pan balance.

Besides the invariance of mass measurements as one moves from place to place, another desirable feature is the wide range of masses that can be used on a pan balance, as compared with a spring balance. A typical spring balance can be used for weighing objects up to about 150 or 200 times the minimum weight it can reliably measure, whereas a typical pan balance can easily measure the masses of objects up to 2000 times the minimum mass measurable.

The advantages cited above of making *mass* a primitive term appear sufficient to outweigh the disadvantage of its relative unfamiliarity. Since we have already developed a model of linear motion with d, t and f as the primitives in which mass was defined ($m = f/a$), we are really no longer unfamiliar with the concept of mass. Such being the case, there is no longer any reasonable objection to taking *mass* as one of the primitives and defining force in terms of it. Our definition of force, then, will be

$$f =_{Df} ma \qquad (2.13b)$$

As is evident from the fact that this equation is identical to one which we had in the previous model (i.e., Eq. 2.13a), the two models are identical in all their equations. Nothing is changed from the standpoint of practical application. The difference lies only in the conceptual statuses of force and mass. Our emphasis is now on the dynamic aspect of force, since it is defined by the actual acceleration imparted by it to an object of given mass. In contrast, the Hooke's Law measurement of force utilized its static aspect: the deformation of a spring balance represented a force *capable of* (but typically not then *in the process of*) producing an acceleration.

In the case of a falling body, when acceleration actually occurs, the force acting on the object is proportional to its mass, and the constant of proportionality is the acceleration. For all objects falling freely near the surface of the earth, the acceleration is about 9.8 m/sec² —subject to small variations depending on locality and altitude. This constant acceleration (exactly constant for a given point on earth; approximately constant all over the earth) is denoted by the letter g, and is called **the acceleration due to** (the earth's) **gravity**. In order to call special attention to the relationship between weight (w) and g, we may rewrite Eq. (2.13b) as follows:

$$w =_{\mathrm{Df}} mg \tag{2.14}$$

where w is measured in newtons, m in kilograms, and g equals 9.8 m/sec^2.

METHODOLOGICAL REVIEW

Before going on to Chapter 3 in which the mathematical model we have developed for linear motion will be extended to include certain types of curved motion, it is desirable to consider more formally what kind of thing a mathematical model is.

It has often been suggested that mathematics provides a special language for science. This suggestion must be taken somewhat metaphorically, for it is clear that the language of science incorporates far more than purely mathematical terms and relations. For instance, *mass*, *force*, and *acceleration* have physical as well as mathematical connotations, while =, /, and + are ordinarily interpreted mathematically. A mathematical model combines both mathematical and nonmathematical terms, and can usefully be likened to a language—a precisely constructed artificial language. Although this analogy should not be pressed too far, it will help us in giving a summary description of the rather abstract mathematical model we have developed.

In undertaking to describe a language, one might, as a first step, make a list of the words most commonly used in the language, a basic vocabulary list. Then one could undertake the more difficult task of writing down the rules governing the use of these words. In a similar fashion, we may summarize our accomplishment in this chapter by listing the special terms (or vocabulary) used in our model and reviewing some of the most important rules adopted for their use. Our special vocabulary consists of the terms represented by the following symbols: d, t, $\bar{v}$, v, a, f, m, w and g. We have also used a number of mathematical symbols, including the fraction bar, multiplication sign, =, +, − and Δ. We have also used the numbers of arithmetic, the decimal point, and proportionality constants.

The basic rules governing the use of the terms listed above are the formal definitions adopted for the nonprimitive terms. These definitions include, in the latest version of our model (in which d, t and m are the primitives),

$$\bar{v} =_{\mathrm{Df}} \frac{\Delta d}{\Delta t}$$

$$v =_{\mathrm{Df}} \text{ the limit of } \frac{\Delta d}{\Delta t} \text{ as } \Delta t \text{ approaches } 0$$

$$a =_{\mathrm{Df}} \frac{\Delta v}{\Delta t} \quad \text{and}$$

$$f =_{\mathrm{Df}} ma$$

Besides the formal definitions which are parts of the model as such, we have made free use of standard rules of mathematics, such as algebraic rules for transforming equations and expressions and geometrical theorems and formulas. It was the use of such rules that enabled us, for instance, to write definitions and laws in more than one form. For example, $d = vt$, $f = ma$, and $a = 2d/t^2$ were obtained algebraically from definitions and laws.

However, we could not have used the model to describe the motions of actual physical objects unless we also adopted rules for procedures of measurement. Rules of measurement are the only rules expressly governing the use of the primitive terms of the model, but measurement procedures can be specified for defined terms as well. In contrast to the above-mentioned rules of mathematics, which are used in developing the internal structure of the model, rules of measurement serve to link the model to the physical world. Such rules are commonly known as rules for **interpretation** of the model.

It might have appeared that we have been using the terms *model* and *theory* somewhat interchangeably. We can now make a distinction between them and clarify their relationship. The term *theory* is probably the more familiar to the student. He has heard of "relativity theory," "atomic theory," and so on. A scientific theory makes statements (explanations or predictions) about the physical world. A mathematical model consists of statements linking its terms in precise relationships. These statements then function partly as rules that govern correct usage of the terms. We prefer to think of a mathematical model as that part of a theory *exclusive of* the rules of interpretation. Hereafter, when we use the word *theory* we will mean a system consisting of a model (mathematical or otherwise) together with a set of rules that link it to the physical world, thereby enabling predictions and experimental testing of the theory.

If we refer to the astronomical theories of Chapter 1, we can see that in addition to the models used, which prescribed relationships between position and time of the planets, the astronomers had to have rules or understandings how they would measure position and time. Instruments for measuring angles, crude clocks for measuring time, and the calendar were employed. These instruments and the knowledge of their proper use constituted the "interpretation" of the astronomical models, making it possible to test them and thereby adjust them to represent the observed motions of the celestial bodies more accurately. These models, supplemented by rules of interpretation, came to be scientific theories.

Against this conception of theory and model it is sometimes argued that theories claim to tell the truth about something whereas models do not. By identifying the mathematical, or general, part of a theory as a model, we hope to communicate a more skeptical view than is usually presented, recognizing that no theory in science can justifiably claim to have reached the truth. Looking backward at the history of science it is easy to see that theories are incomplete representations of phenomena. It is not easy to accept the idea that all present-day theories are sure to be changed in the future. Creativity may sometimes be hampered by such a skeptical view, but acceptance of this idea should relieve the scientist of an unrealistic burden and may actually make it easier for him to move boldly into new areas of research where every conceivable formulation of theory is recognizably inadequate but some may nevertheless be quite useful.

PROBLEMS

1. A 200 kilogram sacrificial pig was dropped into Halemaumau (the fire pit of Kilauea Volcano in Hawaii) and fell 450 meters to the bottom in 10 seconds.
   a. Draw a d-t diagram for the fall and calculate the average velocity of the pig during the fall.
   b. Assume the acceleration to have been uniform and draw a v-t diagram.
   c. Calculate the average acceleration during the fall.
   d. Suppose the pig had been weighed on a spring balance and found to weigh 1960 newtons. Calculate the acceleration which gravitational force (its weight) should have produced acting on the mass of the pig given.
   e. What factor might account for the difference between the two values of acceleration?
2. A man hits a golf ball with a force of 500 newtons.
   a. If the golf ball has a mass of .1 kg, what acceleration does it receive?
   b. If the golf club continues to exert the same force until the ball reaches a velocity, v, equal to 50 m/sec (see Fig. 2.14), how long a time does it push on the ball?
   c. Through what distance does the ball travel before attaining the velocity 50 m/sec?
3. In a drag race, a car was accelerated uniformly from standstill to 120 ft/sec (slightly more than 80 mph) in 20 seconds.
   a. Construct the v-t diagram for this motion.
   b. Construct the d-t diagram for this motion, assuming uniform velocity within successive 5-second intervals.
   c. Referring to the two diagrams constructed in (a) and (b), draw a *velocity-distance* diagram by plotting the estimated instantaneous

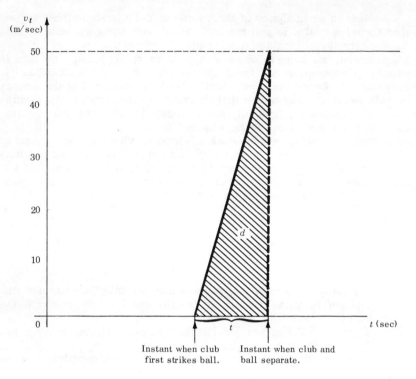

Figure 2.14 Diagram for Problem 2.

velocities at 200, 400, 600, 800, 1000 and 1200 feet from the starting point.

4. Equation (2.11) can be solved for d so that one can calculate the distance traveled, given the acceleration (uniform) and the time. The resulting formula, $d = at^2/2$, like Eq. (2.11) is applicable only when v_0 (the instantaneous velocity at $t = 0$) is zero.

The task in this problem is to derive a more general formula which is applicable even when v_0 is not zero and regardless of whether the acceleration is positive or negative.

It would be helpful to pattern the derivation on the numerical example below, using the steps that are outlined.

Example: An object moves with a uniform acceleration of 10 cm/sec^2. Its velocity at time zero was 20 cm/sec. What is the total distance it travels during the first three seconds of its motion?

a. Construct a v–t diagram of the motion described above.
b. Draw a vertical line through the point representing the velocity at $t = 3$ sec, and determine the distance traveled. (Hint: Find the area of the trapezoid.)
c. Label the relevant lengths in your v–t diagram (i.e., those that you needed in calculating the area of the trapezoid) using the

letters v_0, a and t instead of the numerical values of the particular example. By analogous calculations, find the relevant area in terms of these letters.

5. A traffic sign is to be placed near the end of a 45 mph zone to warn motorists that a 30 mph zone lies ahead. Assuming that the normal rate of deceleration of a car is 5.5 feet per second per second, how many feet before the beginning of the 30 mph zone must the warning sign be placed in order that a motorist traveling at exactly 45 mph can start slowing down the moment he reaches the warning sign and attain the speed of 30 mph just as he enters the reduced-speed zone? (Use *feet* and *seconds* as the units for distance and time. A speed of 15 mph is the same as 22 feet per second.)

SUPPLEMENTARY READINGS

Bixby, William. *The Universe of Galileo and Newton*. New York: American Heritage Publishing Co., 1964.
A beautifully illustrated history of the contributions of two giants to the Copernican revolution.

Dantzig, Tobias. *Number, the Language of Science*. Garden City, N. Y.: Doubleday (An Anchor Book), 1956.
A survey of many important mathematical ideas and their relation to science.

Holton, Gerald and Roller, Duane H. D. *Foundations of Modern Physical Science*. Reading, Mass.: Addison-Wesley, 1958.
Chapter 4 gives a treatment of Newton's laws of motion that reviews the topics covered in this chapter from a somewhat different perspective.

Kline, Morris. *Mathematics and the Physical World*. New York: Crowell, 1959.
Chapters 12 and 13 give a more historical treatment of linear motion than we have.

Lindsay, Robert Bruce and Margenau, Henry. *Foundations of Physics*. New York: John Wiley & Sons, Inc., 1936 (Reprinted in paperback by Dover, 1959).
Pages 1–29 give a valuable discussion of the nature of theories in physics.

Physical Science Study Committee. *Physics*. (2nd edition) Boston: D. C. Heath & Co., 1965.
Chapters 1–7 cover the same material with interesting extensions into modern treatments of space, time, motion, and mass, and stimulating supplementary problems.

Wiener, Philip P. *Readings in Philosophy of Science*. New York: Scribner's, 1953.
Articles 2 (Peirce), 4 (Duhem), and 6 (Hempel) discuss the relationship between mathematics and scientific theories.

3

NEWTON'S SYNTHESIS OF ASTRONOMY AND MECHANICS

The theory of mechanics presented in the preceding chapter was developed informally by Galileo and served as the foundation for the formal theory of mechanics worked out by Sir Isaac Newton (1642-1727) and the many applications which followed it. The use of Newton's theory in astronomy is our present concern, but we shall examine, farther on, some additional applications of Newtonian mechanics, as the theory is generally known. New applications will probably continue to be made for a long time to come despite the fact that relativistic and quantum mechanics have replaced Newtonian mechanics in many areas of physics.

The greatness of Newton's contribution lay in putting the principles of mechanics into concise mathematical form and showing how to apply them to the problems of astronomy raised by the Copernican revolution. Newton's work was a turning point in science. Not only did the theory he established find multifarious applications, but his method was also copied in diverse fields where no direct application could be made. The contrast between pre-Newtonian and post-Newtonian science has moved the poet to say, in Biblical parody,

"And God said, 'Let Newton be,' and there was light."

Newton himself, on the other hand, credited his predecessors, saying that if he had been able to see farther than other men, it was only because he had stood on the shoulders of giants.

The study of mechanics so far has been confined to linear motion. According to Kepler the planets move in ellipses. In order to follow Newton's synthesis of the Galilean–Newtonian mechanics and Copernican–Keplerian astronomy, we must first extend the theory of linear motion of Chapter 2 to include motions of objects in curved paths.

TRAJECTORIES OF PROJECTILES AND UNIFORM CIRCULAR MOTION

One of the key insights which permitted Newton to apply his theory of mechanics to astronomical problems was his recognition that the orbits of planets and satellites could be analyzed in the same way as the paths, or **trajectories,** of projectiles. Let us begin with an analysis of the trajectories of projectiles and then undertake to analyze uniform circular motion in the same way.

To make a record of the motion of a projectile in the laboratory, a high speed movie camera is often used to photograph the projectile in motion against a grid of horizontal and vertical lines. After the film is developed, the positions of the projectile on successive frames are transferred to a sheet of graph paper. When a smooth curve is drawn through these points we have a scale diagram of the trajectory. Knowing the time interval between the successive frames on the film, the time at which the projectile reached each position represented on the graph can be determined.

Each point on the graph may be located by measuring its horizontal and vertical displacements from the origin of the diagram. These displacements are called the **horizontal** and **vertical coordinates** of each point. Since we know the time at which the projectile reached each point, we know the time corresponding to the horizontal and vertical coordinates. Imagine that we construct one table showing the changes in the horizontal coordinates with time and another table showing the changes in the vertical coordinates with time. The first table could be taken to represent a motion along the horizontal axis, and the second table a motion along the vertical axis. These two imaginary linear motions may, in a theoretical model, be regarded as two *component motions* which, together, make up the actual motion of the projectile. The advantage of breaking down a curved motion in this way into two hypothetical linear motions is that we already have a theory of linear motion. A double application of this theory, once for each component motion, should then suffice to describe the curved motion of a projectile.

Experimental and theoretical explorations:

3.1 In the following experiment, the two hypothetical component motions of a projectile can be given a concrete, physical interpretation. First, arrange to set two balls in motion simultaneously from the same height—one being ejected horizontally while the other is simply released to fall vertically. (A simple apparatus to perform this experiment is shown in Fig. 3.1.) The paths of the two balls are shown in Fig. 3.2 by the curved line *AC* and the vertical straight line *AB*. It is an interesting fact that the two balls reach the floor at the same time irrespective of how high (within wide limits) the starting point is. This means that the two balls cross simultaneously any given horizontal line cutting their paths. At each instant throughout the motion, the horizontally ejected ball, or projectile, is at the same height as is the vertically falling ball, which therefore represents the vertical component motion of the projectile.

Next, imagine a third ball started with the same velocity as the projectile but moving with uniform velocity along a horizontal,

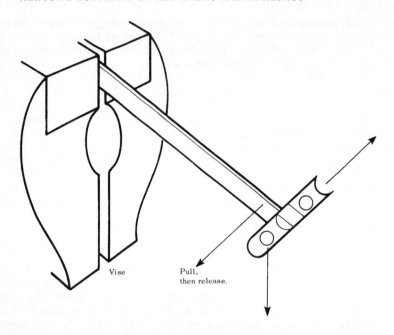

Figure 3.1 Simple Flat-spring Device for Simultaneously Ejecting One Ball Horizontally and Dropping a Second Ball Vertically.

frictionless track represented by the line AB' in Fig. 3.2. It would, moment by moment, be found directly above the projectile; that is, it would perform exactly the horizontal component motion of the projectile. In order to carry out this part of the experiment, slightly more

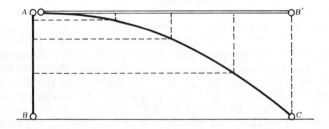

Figure 3.2 Components of the Motion of a Projectile.

elaborate apparatus is required. A double trough on the spring device of Fig. 3.1 will permit two balls to be ejected horizontally. A suitable track (though not frictionless) can be made of two parallel meter

sticks separated slightly. Positioning the track is a delicate opera-
tion which requires some experimentation.

In this experiment (whether actually conducted or only imagined
as a "thought experiment"), each component of the projectile's motion can then be identified with a separate physical process: the vertical component motion is the uniformly accelerated fall owing to the
influence of gravity, and the horizontal component motion is the continuing forward motion with uniform velocity, resulting from an initial
horizontal push.

If our purpose were solely to describe a curved motion, the choice
of the directions of component motions would have been a matter of
convenience. If we are to attach physical meaning to the components,
their directions must be the same as those of identifiable physical
processes—such as the horizontal motion due to inertia and the vertical free fall due to gravity.

In order to observe the relationships between a curved motion and
its components, a modification of the above experiment can be carried
out. A ball can be set in motion on a smooth-topped table, tilted toward
one side, so that its path describes a curve similar to the trajectory
of a projectile. (See Fig. 3.3.) If the ball is started off at right angles
to the direction in which the table tilts, it is possible to arrange for
two other balls to carry out the component motions. ∎

Now let us turn our attention to a case of circular motion, as Newton did when he analyzed the motion of the moon, and attempt to
analyze it in terms of linear components that have physical meaning.
Consider a small object attached to one end of a piece of string and
twirled around steadily on a smooth horizontal surface. If we should
let go of the string, the object would fly off at a tangent to its circular
path, much as mud is thrown off tangentially from the rim of a rapidly
spinning tire. Letting go of the string removes the "curving" force,
and we can observe a straight-line motion continuing across the flat
surface. On the other hand, if the object lies motionless on the surface and we pull it by the string, the object responds with a straight-
line motion in the direction of the string.

These considerations suggest that we should try to analyze the
circular motion we observe into the following two components: one
in the direction of the tangent to the circle at a given point and the
other in line with the string, corresponding to the effect of a string
pulling on an object. A diagram for this sort of analysis is shown in
Fig. 3.4. Such an analysis differs from the previous analysis of projectile motion in that the directions of the two component motions
cannot be fixed but change from moment to moment. However, Fig.
3.4 depicts a small enough portion of the circular motion so that the
similarity between the two kinds of curved motions can be seen by
comparison with Fig. 3.2. In each diagram, the points on the curved
paths may be located by moving first in accordance with one component and then in accordance with the other. Let us consider whether

the two analyses are sufficiently analogous that we may use a mathematical model for circular motion similar to that we used for a projectile. This, we have intimated, was Newton's idea. In particular, let us see whether the component motions in Fig. 3.4 are of the same kinds as those in Fig. 3.2, i.e., one with uniform velocity and one with uniform acceleration.

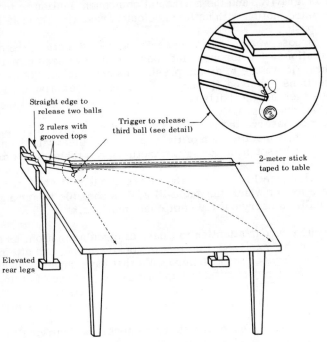

Figure 3.3 Table Arranged for Experiment on Component Motions.

In Fig. 3.4, a small portion of the circular motion is indicated by points along the circle, marked $A, P_1, P_2, \ldots, P_{10}$, adjacent pairs of which are separated by two degrees each. These equally spaced points represent the positions which the object takes after successive equal intervals of time. The motion begins at A and proceeds clockwise.

The line tangent to the circle at point A, is drawn as the direction of the tangential component motion. Corresponding to the points P_1, $P_2, \ldots, P_{10}$ on the circle, points $Q_1, Q_2, \ldots, Q_{10}$ on the tangent line are drawn at the intersections of that line with the extensions of radii drawn through the object positions. The points $Q_1, Q_2, \ldots, Q_{10}$ are analogous to the successive positions in Fig. 3.2 as the ball performs the horizontal component of the projectile's motion. The points along

acceleration since their spacing is reasonably uniform. To make use of this component motion we only need to know the instantaneous component velocity at point A, so we may ignore the extension of the horizontal line.

The other component motion, being directed toward the center of the circular path, O, may be called the **centripetal** component. If we take it to be represented by the successive line segments, $\overline{Q_1P_1}$, $\overline{Q_2P_2}$, ..., $\overline{Q_{10}P_{10}}$, we find that these segments are all in the direction of the string. Examination of the figure shows that such segments lose their physical significance also for points on the circle too far away from point A. (In fact, no segment could be constructed at a point 90° or more around the circle from A.) Again restricting our attention to points close to A, let us tentatively consider these segments to represent the successive amounts of the centripetal component motion.

Inspection of Fig. 3.4 clearly shows that the successive line segments $\overline{Q_1P_1}$, ..., $\overline{Q_{10}P_{10}}$, do not increase in length by equal amounts as they would if the motion they represent were one with constant velocity—even in the vicinity of point A. Considering that the string exerts a force on the object at all times along its circular motion, we may conclude from the law, $f = ma$, that there must be an acceleration of the centripetal component motion. If the force is constant, the acceleration should also be constant. Let us examine the motion of this component in detail to see if its acceleration is constant.

In order to plot d-t and v-t diagrams of the centripetal component motion represented by the successive line segments just referred to, we must specify the rate at which the circular motion proceeds. Then we can determine the successive lengths of the segments representing the distances covered by this motion in successive time intervals. Suppose that the object takes 1.8 sec to complete one revolution; i.e., that the **period**, T, of the motion is 1.8 sec. Since the angle between successive points is 2°, which is 1/180 of 360°, the time taken for the object to move from one point to the next is 1.8/180 or 0.01 sec.

We must then measure the distances represented by the line segments, $\overline{Q_1P_1}$, $\overline{Q_2P_2}$, etc., of Fig. 3.4. This may be done by accurately reproducing the figure on a much larger scale and actually measuring the distance of each deviation from the straight line. For greater precision, we may apply a trigonometric relationship to each of the right triangles, $\triangle OAQ_1$, $\triangle OAQ_2$, etc., and, with the help of a table of trigonometric functions, calculate the lengths of the hypotenuses, $\overline{OQ_1}$, $\overline{OQ_2}$, etc. By subtracting $\overline{OP_1}$, $\overline{OP_2}$, etc. (each of which is 100 cm in length), we find the distances sought. We have obtained these distances by the trigonometric method, and have shown them in the fourth column of Table 3.1 as values of d.

The distances (just obtained) by which the object successively departs from the tangential direction, together with the time measurements supposed in the paragraph before last (shown in the third column of Table 3.1) permit us to construct the desired d-t and v-t diagrams of the centripetal component motion. These are shown in

Table 3.1 Data Corresponding to Figure 3.4

Angle of revolution O	t as a fraction of T	t in the special case when $T = 1.8$ sec (sec)	d in the special case when $r = 100$ cm (cm)	k [in $a = kr/T^2$] (see p. 86)
$2°$	$\frac{1}{180} T$	0.01	0.06104	39.55
$4°$	$\frac{1}{90} T$	0.02	0.2445	39.60
$6°$	$\frac{1}{60} T$	0.03	0.551	39.67
$8°$	$\frac{1}{45} T$	0.04	0.983	39.81
$10°$	$\frac{1}{36} T$	0.05	1.542	39.97
$12°$	$\frac{1}{30} T$	0.06	2.23	40.14
$14°$	$\frac{7}{180} T$	0.07	3.06	40.47
$16°$	$\frac{2}{45} T$	0.08	4.03	40.80
$18°$	$\frac{1}{20} T$	0.09	5.15	41.20
$20°$	$\frac{1}{18} T$	0.10	6.42	41.60

Figs. 3.5 and 3.6. Figure 3.5 resembles the smooth–curve d–t diagram of Fig. 2.6, which represented a uniformly accelerated linear motion, and it suggests that the centripetal component of our circular motion is of this kind. Figure 3.6 further confirms this suggestion for the first few points. It shows that the acceleration of the centripetal component motion (at least for points within 12° of starting point A) is very nearly uniform. The midpoints of the first six steps of the v–t graph fall very nearly on the solid straight line drawn, even though those of the later steps deviate more and more, as shown by the broken line. This encourages us to accept the formula for uniform acceleration for the first six positions of Fig. 3.4, as a basis for deriving a formula for the centripetal acceleration.

In order to obtain a general formula applicable to any uniform circular motion, we cannot use the particular values of the period of revolution (1.8 sec) and the radius of the circular path (100 cm) that we took in the foregoing example. We shall introduce the letter T to hold a place in the formulas for any value of the period and r to hold a place for any value of the radius. It is easy to express the time

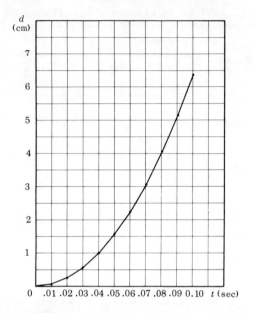

Figure 3.5 *d-t* Diagram of the Centripetal Component of Circular Motion.

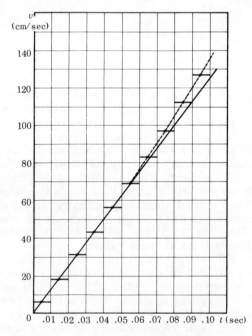

Figure 3.6 *v-t* Diagram of the Centripetal Component of Circular Motion.

required for the object to move from A to P_5 (in Fig. 3.4) as a fraction of T: the time will always be 1/36 of the period, since P_5 is 10° away from A. The time taken for the centripetal component motion $\overline{Q_5 P_5}$ is also $1/36\ T$ sec, for any value of T. We therefore write

$$t = \frac{T}{36}\ \text{sec} \tag{3.1}$$

The distance of centripetal motion represented by $\overline{Q_5 P_5}$ (which was 1.542 cm in our specific example) must also be converted into a more general expression. A simple geometric construction shows that the length of $\overline{Q_5 P_5}$, for any circle, is proportional to the radius of the circle. (The triangles $\triangle AQ_5P_5$, $\triangle OAQ_5$, and $\triangle OAP_5$ for one radius are similar respectively to those obtained for any other radius.) The proportionality constant must be such that, for $r = 100$ cm, $\overline{Q_5 P_5} = 1.542$ cm. Hence, $1.542 = k(100)$. So $k = 0.01542$, and the general expression for the distance in question is

$$d = 0.01542\,r\ \text{cm}. \tag{3.2}$$

We may now substitute the right hand members of Eqs. (3.1) and (3.2) for t and d in the formula (2.11) $[a = 2d/t^2]$ for computing the value of uniform accelerations and obtain

$$a = \frac{2(0.01542\,r)}{(T/36)^2} = \frac{(2)(0.01542)(36)^2\,r}{T^2}$$

Carrying out the indicated numerical multiplications, we find:

$$a = \frac{39.97\,r}{T^2}$$

For most practical purposes the coefficient may be rounded to 40, and we will therefore adopt

$$a = \frac{40\,r}{T^2} \tag{3.3}$$

as the equation for computing the acceleration of the centripetal component motion of an object performing a uniform circular motion at the rate of T sec per revolution along a circle of radius r cm.

Sometimes it is convenient to specify the rate of a circular motion by the *number of revolutions per second* (denoted by n) instead of the period T. Since n and T are mutually reciprocal,

$$\left(T = \frac{1}{n}\right)$$

this expression may be substituted for T in Eq. (3.3) to yield the alternative formula for centripetal acceleration,

$$a = 40 \, m^2 \qquad (3.4)$$

Although our calculations were based on the fifth position represented in Fig. 3.4, it should not be thought that this formula is restricted in any way by this choice. The student may check that choosing any one of the first six points, $P_1, P_2, \ldots, P_6$, would have led to the same result. The last column of Table 3.1 shows the numerical value, correct to two decimal places, that would actually be obtained for the constant k in Eq. (3.3) by using data from each of the ten positions. We were interested in the instantaneous value of the acceleration at points on the circle, so we picked an interval small enough to give us a close approximation to that value.

We see that the values of k steadily decrease as we read from the bottom upward in Table 3.1. It can also be seen that the successive differences between adjacent pairs of values of k themselves decrease as we proceed upward. This suggests that the sequence of numbers, if continued for angles smaller than 2°, would approach a limiting value in the neighborhood of 39.5. (By using the calculus, it can be shown that limit of k, as the angle approaches zero, is $4\pi^2$ or, rounded off to two decimal places, 39.48.)

AN EXPERIMENT ON CENTRIPETAL ACCELERATION

To obtain a more concrete understanding of the concept of centripetal acceleration before attempting a component analysis of planetary and satellite motion, it will be useful to carry out a laboratory experiment on circular motion. An interesting one utilizing readily obtainable apparatus is the following.

Laboratory exploration:

3.2 The apparatus used in this experiment consists of the front wheel of a bicycle turned upside down or any freely rotating spoked wheel on a fixed horizontal axis. A small metal ring is attached loosely around one of the spokes of the wheel. (A nail bent around the spoke will serve the purpose. See Fig. 3.7.)

Observe what happens to the metal ring when the wheel is set spinning quite rapidly. Impelled forward by the spoke on which it slides, the ring flies out to the rim where its tendency to move like a projectile (indicated by the broken lines in Fig. 3.7) is arrested. It will then remain in contact with the rim throughout each rotation of the wheel, just as a stone twirled rapidly around on a string remains at the fullest extent of the string. On the other hand, observe what

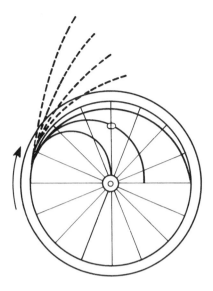

Figure 3.7   Apparatus to Determine the Value of g.

happens if the speed of rotation is very slow. The ring will slide back and forth along the spoke—outward toward the rim when the spoke points downward, and inward toward the hub when the spoke points upward. Between the two extremes of very fast and very slow rotations, there is a range of speeds at which the ring behaves as follows: the ring briefly comes away from the rim while at the top of the wheel but is thrown into contact with the rim again somewhere along the bottom. When the wheel is rotating at a speed in this medium range, we hear a click each time the ring is thrown back against the rim. ∎

Let us analyze the clicking behavior of the ring on the wheel. At some point above the horizontal plane through the center of the wheel, the ring leaves the rim toward the center. If it were under the influence of gravity alone, its path would be like one of the solid-line trajectories shown in Fig. 3.7. It might then be likened to a projectile fired upward at an angle. The shape of this free path will depend on the velocity of the ring as it leaves the rim, curving more sharply when the velocity is smaller. During the free part of its path, the ring experiences a constant downward acceleration, g, due to gravity. But when in contact with the rim, it experiences a centripetal acceleration given by Eq. (3.3). Consider the point where the spoke is attached to the rim. It has an acceleration which is *always* that given by Eq. (3.3). During the time that the ring is away from the rim, its path lies below that of the end of the spoke. From this fact we infer that its acceleration downward is greater than the centripetal acceleration of the end of the spoke (which is directed more or less downward during this portion of the journey). The tangential component motion at every point is at right angles and of uniform velocity, so it does not need to be taken into account.

From the foregoing descriptions of what we observe when the wheel is rotated at fast and medium speeds, we may draw the following inference: there must be one particular intermediate speed of rotation of the wheel at which the ring is neither firmly pressed against the rim throughout each rotation, as at rapid speeds, nor produces the periodic clicks characteristic of the medium speeds. While the wheel is rotating at precisely this speed, the ring is moving in a circular path whose radius is equal to that of the rim; moreover, at the top if its path, it is under no constraint but is in a state of free suspension—like fliers experiencing weightlessness in an airplane that is flying along an arched, trajectory-like path. These conditions make it possible to find the centripetal acceleration of the ring from Eq. (3.4).

The ring undergoes the centripetal acceleration given by Eq. (3.4) uniformly throughout each revolution. At all positions *except* at the top of the wheel, this acceleration involves both the pressure from the rim and a component of gravitational force directed toward the hub of the wheel. When the ring is at the top of the wheel, the rim exerts no pressure on it at all. (Recall that we are considering the situation when the speed of rotation is *just barely* large enough to prevent the ring from momentarily leaving the rim when at the top.) In this position the ring's centripetal acceleration must be entirely accounted for by the gravitational acceleration, since it is in a downward direction at that instant. If we can experimentally determine the critical number of revolutions per second, say n_c, at which the wheel has to be rotated in order to produce the above condition, and we substitute this n_c in Eq. (3.4), we should obtain a value of a which is equal to that of g.

Laboratory experimentation:

3.3 How might we go about determining the critical speed n_c from our experiment? Suppose we initially rotate the wheel somewhat faster than is required to produce the periodic clicks. As time goes on, the rotation gets slower and slower, because of friction with the air and the axle. Imagine that we could plot a graph showing the rate of rotation n at each instant. Actually we will have to construct a step diagram and then draw the median line. Let us suppose we did this, and obtained a downward sloping line as shown in Fig. 3.8. In this figure, the instant at which the "clicking" is first heard is labeled t_c and the rate of rotation at that instant is labeled n_c—although, strictly speaking, the required n_c is just slightly larger than this.

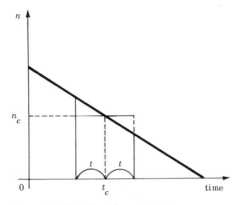

Figure 3.8 Method of Determining Instantaneous
Rotational Velocity in Bicycle Experiment.

In our experiment we count the number of revolutions starting t seconds before the "clicking" is first heard and continue counting until t seconds after that instant, so that we will have counted the total number of revolutions in an interval of $2t$ sec whose midpoint is the moment, t_c. If the n-t diagram is a straight line (which means the rotation of the wheel undergoes a constant deceleration), then the value of n at the midpoint of any time interval is equal to the average value, $\bar{n}$, taken over the interval, which may be determined by the equation

$$\bar{n} = \frac{N}{2t}$$

where N is the total number of revolutions during the $2t$-sec interval.

In most cases, a constant deceleration may safely be assumed, and hence $n_c = \bar{n}$. Therefore,

$$n_c = \frac{N}{2t} \tag{3.5}$$

We see that our experiment enables us, if rather crudely, to determine the required critical rate n_c (or a slight underestimate thereof) which, substituted in Eq. (3.4), should give us a value approximating g as the centripetal acceleration. We have

$$g = 40\,r\,n_c^{\,2} \tag{3.6}$$

where r is the radius, in cm, of the circle described by the metal ring. We can then calculate g from this experiment and compare the result with the known value.

As an example, consider the following values which were obtained in an experiment of this kind performed near sea level. The inside radius of the wheel was 19.5 cm, and 20 revolutions were counted during a 17.5-second interval, whose midpoint was the moment the click was first heard. (In practice, one starts counting revolutions at a time when one guesses the "click" will be heard shortly afterward. One then measures the time elapsed up to the click, and continues counting for *the same length of time* after the click.) Using Eq. (3.5) we find that

$$n_c = \frac{20}{17.5} = 1.14$$

From Eq. (3.6),

$$g = (40)(19.5)(1.14)^2 = 993 \ cm/sec^2$$

We see that the value obtained is very close to the generally accepted value of g for most nonmountainous locations which is 980 cm/sec^2.

As an exercise, the student may calculate the value that would be obtained for g from an experiment using the same wheel as above but in which 30 revolutions were counted in a 26-sec period, at whose midpoint the first click was heard. When performing this experiment, several trials will ordinarily be required before one acquires the necessary technique for centering the time interval on the desired point.

It is also instructive to analyze what assumptions are made in this experiment that cannot be directly checked. Perhaps the student can devise other experiments to check some of them. ■

MORE ABOUT PROPORTIONALITY CONSTANTS

In the previous chapter (pp. 54-56) a mathematical way of expressing proportionality relationships by using proportionality constants was studied. These constants are such important tools for theory construction, that it is worthwhile to reexamine some of the equations just developed from this point of view to learn more about the forms proportionality relations take.

The basic proportionality equation used in Chapter 2 was

$$y = Kx \qquad (2.6)$$

Comparing this equation with Eq. (3.4), we see that, if n is constant, the latter equation can be rewritten in the same form. Thus

$$a = (40 n^2)r = Kr$$

where K stands for $40n^2$, the proportionality constant. We conclude that a is proportional to r, *provided n is held constant*; that is, as long as the rate of circular motion is fixed, the acceleration is proportional to the radius of the circular path. If the radius is doubled the acceleration is doubled; if the radius is tripled the acceleration is tripled, and so on.

On the other hand, consider the relationship between acceleration and number of revolutions per second, when the *radius is held constant* (that is, when only circular paths of a fixed radius are involved). In this case, Eq. (3.4) assumes the form

$$a = (40\,r)\,n^2 = K'n^2$$

where K', standing for $40r$, is a constant. The acceleration is proportional to the *square* of the number of revolutions per second. When the rate is doubled, say from 3 rps to 6 rps, the acceleration is *four* times as large ($36/9 = 4$). When the rate is tripled to 9 rps, the acceleration increases ninefold; and so on.

A relationship in which one quantity is proportional, not to another quantity *itself*, but to its square, is not new. An even more complex relationship was encountered in Kepler's Third Law, where the square of one quantity is proportional to the cube of another quantity. What *is* new in Eq. (3.4) is the fact that we now have three quantities, which we may rename x, y, z, to emphasize the purely mathematical relation that when either x or y is held constant, z is proportional to the other. The prototype equation for the sort of relationship into which Eq. (3.4) fits is

$$z = Kxy \qquad\qquad (3.7)$$

In such a case we say that z is **jointly proportional** to x and y (or, simply, "proportional to x and y"). The content of Eq. (3.4) may thus be stated verbally by saying, "The centripetal acceleration of a uniform circular motion is jointly proportional to the radius of the path and the *square* of the number of revolutions per second."

Another new situation is found in Eq. (3.3). If, in this equation, r is held constant, we have the relation

$$a = \frac{K}{T^2}$$

where K stands for $40r$, a constant. This tells us that, if the period is doubled, the acceleration becomes one-fourth of the original value; if the period is tripled, the acceleration becomes one-ninth; and so on. In this case, we say that a is **inversely proportional** to the square of T.

The simple inverse proportionality relation is represented by an equation of the form

$$y = \frac{K}{x} \tag{3.8}$$

Let us study this case more closely. Let us set $K = 36$ and construct a table showing the values of $y = 36/x$ for various values of x. This is shown in Table 3.2, where we observe that, when x is doubled, y is halved; when x is tripled, y becomes one-third; and so on. Note that the product of any pair of corresponding x- and y-values in this table is 36. This is as it should be, since an alternative way of writing Eq. (3.8) is

$$xy = K \tag{3.8a}$$

and K is 36 in our present example. It is extremely useful, in the interpretation of mathematical models, to be able to recognize a relationship of inverse proportionality in the form either of Eqs. (3.8) or (3.8a).

Table 3.2 The Inverse Proportionality
Relation $y = 36/x$

x	y
1	36.0
2	18.0
3	12.0
4	9.0
5	7.2
6	6.0
7	5.1
8	4.5
9	4.0
10	3.6
11	3.3
12	3.0

To facilitate interpretation, we have plotted an approximate graph of the inverse proportionality relation $y = 36/x$ in Fig. 3.9. Note that as x increases, y becomes smaller and smaller but never quite becomes zero. In our imagination we can see that if we could extend the graph infinitely to the right, it would continue to approach the horizontal axis but would never touch it. In such a case, we say that the horizontal axis is an asymptote of the graph. Similarly, the vertical axis, too, is an asymptote of the graph for an inverse proportionality relationship. As we continue to explore scientific thought in classical physics and chemistry, we will have many occasions to write equations, either like (3.8) or (3.8a), for graphs of this type.

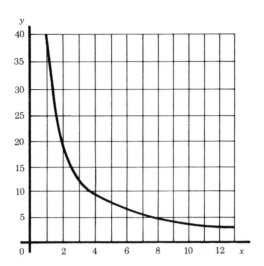

Figure 3.9 Graph for Table 3.2.

Let us now return to the slightly more complex relation exemplified by the equation $a = K/T^2$ (acceleration is inversely proportional to the square of the period). The prototype equation for **inverse square proportionality** is

$$y = \frac{K}{x^2} \tag{3.9}$$

An equation of the form (3.9) means that, if x increases twofold, then y becomes quartered; if x becomes tripled, then y becomes one-ninth of what it was; and so on. Since this relation will also be encountered frequently in the course of our study, the student should be familiar with its mathematical expression. Graphical representation of an inverse square proportionality is illustrated in Fig. 3.10, which is plotted from Table 3.3 giving the values of y, for various values of x, for the equation, $y = 36/x^2$. Note that the graph is similar to a graph of inverse proportionality (Fig. 3.9) in both its general trend and its asymptotes (both x and y axes being asymptotes again), but that the rate of descent of the graph (from left to right) is greater than that in Fig. 3.9.

Finally, recall the fact that acceleration was found to be directly proportional to the square of the number of revolutions per second

Table 3.3 The Inverse Square Proportionality
Relationship $y = 36/x^2$

x	y
1	36.0
2	9.0
3	4.0
4	2.3
5	1.4
6	1.0
7	0.7
8	0.6
9	0.4
10	0.4
11	0.3
12	0.3

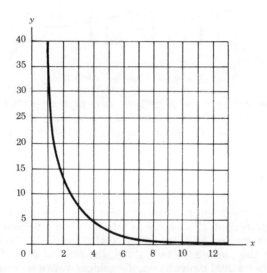

Figure 3.10 Graph for Table 3.3.

(provided radius is constant). We write the prototype equation,

$$y = Kx^2 \qquad (3.10)$$

and call this relationship *direct square proportionality*. Table 3.4 and Fig. 3.11 represent such a relationship with the particular value for K of 1/2. Although this graph suggests a graph for inverse square

Table 3.4 The Direct Square Proportionality
Relationship $y = \frac{1}{2}x^2$

x	y
1	0.5
2	2.0
3	4.5
4	8.0
5	12.5
6	18.0

proportionality (Fig. 3.10) turned the other way around, there is really little relationship. Whereas the two axes were asymptotes for the graph of Fig. 3.10, the present graph for direct square proportionality has no asymptote at all. As x gets larger and larger, so does y, and both increase without bound. Also, it has a minimum point where $x = 0$, $y = 0$. The graph goes up again when x is negative.

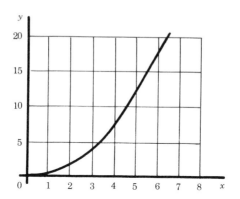

Figure 3.11 Graph for Table 3.4.

We have now covered most of the types of proportionality relations that will be encountered in our study. It may be well at this point to collect all the proportionality equations and the verbal designations of the types of relationship represented.

Direct proportionality:	$y = Kx$
Inverse proportionality:	$y = K/x$
Direct square proportionality:	$y = Kx^2$
Inverse square proportionality:	$y = K/x^2$
Joint proportionality:	$z = Kxy$

Familiarization exercise:

3.4 The student should draw a graph of each of the above types (except joint proportionality, whose "graph" would require three dimensions) in order to become thoroughly familiar with them. In each case, he should choose some suitable nonzero value for K, preferably one different from that used on the preceding pages. ∎

NEWTON'S LAW OF UNIVERSAL GRAVITATION

Having extended the concept of acceleration from the case of straight-line motion to the case of uniform circular motion, we are now ready to apply this concept to an analysis of the motion of celestial bodies. We begin by considering Newton's famous **law of universal gravitation** and then go on to see how this law, which was proposed on theoretical grounds, was tested by applying it to the motion of the moon.

A well-known anecdote has it that Newton was once sitting under an apple tree, wondering what holds the moon in its circular orbit around the earth, when an apple fell on his head. This reportedly gave Newton a flash of insight which suggested that the force responsible for the falling of the apple also explains the circular motion of the moon. We can even speak of the "falling of the moon," because it undergoes a centripetal acceleration toward the center of the earth. The moon is *falling* in the same sense in which projectiles fall throughout their flight. They are continually deviating from the linear motion they would undergo if no force were acting on them—their motion has a centripetal component.

Can we clarify the falling of the moon by considering the falling of projectiles near the surface of the earth which are given various initial horizontal velocities? What would happen, for example, if the horizontal velocity of projectiles were made larger without limit? Figure 3.12 illustrates an imaginary experiment, which Newton describes in his famous book, *Philosophiae Naturalis Principia Mathematica.* (In English, *Mathematical Principles of Natural Philosophy.* Published in 1687, it is often referred to simply as "Newton's Principia.") In the figure, seven projectiles are numbered 1, 2, 3, . . . , 7 in increasing order of their initial horizontal velocities. The experiment is imagined to be carried out on the summit of a mountain. We can see from the figure that, as the horizontal velocity becomes larger and larger, the point at which a projectile falls to earth recedes farther and farther from the mountain. According to Newton, there must be some initial velocity at which the projectile, "exceeding the limits of the earth, . . . should pass into space without touching it."

The phrase, "pass into space without touching it" can be interpreted in two ways. It might mean that the projectile flies off into outer space and never returns. But it may also mean that the projectile keeps circling around the earth indefinitely. It should be evident that before the horizontal velocity becomes so large as to send the projectile travelling farther and farther into outer space, a suitable velocity will be attained at which the projectile will circle around the earth. Object 5 is depicted as undergoing this type of motion; that is, it performs a circular motion around the earth. By means of today's powerful rockets, Newton's imaginary experiment of nearly three hundred years ago has been repeatedly carried out in actuality.

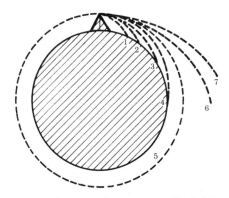

Figure 3.12 Imaginary Experiment in Which Objects Are Ejected from the Top of a High Mountain with Various Horizontal Velocities.

It is in terms of the imaginary launching of artificial satellites, to use a modern term, that Newton conceived the analogy between the motion of an apple falling to the ground and that of the moon. The moon circles the earth, according to Newton, because it was flung by some primeval force in the right direction and with the precise velocity that would put it in its present orbit. By this thought-experiment, he concluded that the same force, gravitation, was responsible for the motions of both these objects.

Newton went much further than merely speaking of gravitation as the force associated with the motions of apple and moon alike: he added to the model for circular motion a mathematical formulation of the force of gravity. What basis did Newton have for formulating a mathematical equation for gravitational force? He knew that the force exerted by the earth on any freely falling object near its surface is proportional to the mass of the object, as we saw in Eq. (2.14), $w = mg$. From this equation, we conclude that the earth pulls on such an object with a force proportional to its mass. But is the mass of the object the only thing on which the force depends? Newton introduces a strange symmetry into the argument.

Suppose an observer on the object under consideration (apple, projectile, or moon) believed himself to be stationary. From his point of view, the earth would seem to be an object being pulled toward *him*. If he could compute its acceleration, he would conclude that it is pulled toward him with a force proportional to *its* mass. If we designate the two objects as A and B, we could write the two reported forces as

$$f_A = K_A m_B$$

and

$$f_B = K_B m_A$$

What can we say about their mutual relation?

Another thought-experiment will help us here. In the case of the earth and the apple, one can measure the reported forces directly. Either observer could place a spring between the two objects so that they compress it until they stop moving with respect to each other. (For the earthbound observer, this is simply weighing the apple on a spring scale.) Naturally, the two observers would agree as to how much the spring has been compressed. It necessarily follows that the two forces reported must be equal in magnitude, although opposite in direction, so we may impartially designate the mutual magnitude of the forces of attraction of the two objects as f_{AB}. The above argument would hold, in principle, for any two objects whose distance of separation is given. We may therefore conclude that, for any two such objects X and Y, $f_X = f_Y = f_{XY}$. Since either one of any pair of objects can be taken as the point of reference, we must treat them alike and conclude that f_{XY} is jointly proportional to both masses. Following Eq. (3.7), we can write

$$f_{XY} = k m_X m_Y \qquad (3.11)$$

We call f_{XY} the **force of mutual attraction** between two objects, although it should be clear to the student that we refer to the common magnitude of two forces which act in opposite directions. (Note that the *two* forces of atraction, though equal and opposite, do not cancel each other since they do not act on the same body, but on spearate bodies.)

It seems to have been intuitively clear to Newton that the force acting between two bodies must decrease as the distance separating them becomes larger. To formulate this dependence of force of mutual attraction on the distance between the objects is the problem. Here, again, Newton drew on an analogy. Because his scientific interests led him to study light, he was familiar with the fact that the illumination of a surface by a small source of light is inversely proportional to the square of the distance between the surface and the light source. Light and gravitational attraction are both cases of action at a distance. One object (a flame in one case and the earth in the other) acts on another object (the illuminated object in one case and the attracted object in the other) without anything in between to convey the action. So it must have seemed reasonable to Newton that the relation of gravitational force to distance might be similar to the relation of illumination to distance. He tentatively assumed that the force of mutual attraction between two objects is inversely proportional to the square of the distance between them. Denoting the distance by r_{XY}, the mathematical expression is, in accordance with Eq. (3.9), as follows:

$$f_{XY} = \frac{k'}{r_{XY}^2} \tag{3.12}$$

Can we write a single equation, which combines the proportionality relationships of the two Eqs. (3.11) and (3.12)? The first equation can be interpreted as saying that the force acting between two objects is proportional to the product of the two masses, it being tacitly assumed that the distance between the two objects is given. The second says that when two *specific* objects are considered (and, therefore, the product of their masses is a constant), the force between them varies in inverse square proportion with the distance between them. Using the notion of joint proportionality again, we say that the force of gravity acting between two bodies is jointly proportional to the product of their masses and to the reciprocal of the square of the distance that separates them. The mathematical expression is:

$$f_{XY} = K \frac{m_X m_Y}{r_{XY}^2} \tag{3.13}$$

where K is a new proportionality constant. This is Newton's celebrated Law of Universal Gravitation.

One ambiguity has to be removed before we use Eq. (3.13): in the case of objects of appreciable size, it is not clear what is meant by the distance r_{XY}. Newton solved this problem by utilizing the idea of atoms. Like many of his contemporaries, he believed that matter is composed of atoms and that the gross properties of objects are manifestations of the properties of their constituent atoms. The force of mutual attraction between any two objects, he argued, can therefore be calculated from the forces between the individual atoms constituting them, which he regarded as being indefinitely small. By making this assumption, he was able to calculate the combined effect of all the *interatomic* forces and thus represent the force of mutual attraction between the *objects as wholes.*

Calculating the force of mutual attraction between large objects would be quite complicated if the summing procedure had to be followed each time in practice. Newton showed that this was not necessary: instead, one can imagine the entire mass of each object to be concentrated at a certain point and can take, as the value of r_{XY} in Eq. (3.13), the distance between this point for one object and the corresponding point for the other object. This point, known as the **center of mass** (or **center of gravity**), is easy to determine for many regularly shaped objects such as spheres and cubes in which the mass is symmetrically distributed. In such cases the center of mass is located at the geometric center.

The formula we previously wrote for the force exerted by the earth on objects near its surface, namely, $w = mg$ (see p. 71), can be derived from Eq. (3.13). Thus, this formula is a special case of the Law of Universal Gravitation. The force between the earth (designated as object A) and any other object (Y), that is, f_{AY}, is simply the weight w_Y of the other object. From Eq. (3.13), this quantity may be written as

$$w_Y = m_Y \frac{Km_A}{r_{AY}^2}$$

The quantity Km_A is a constant, when applied to earth-centered weights. With object Y near the surface of the earth, r_{AY} (the distance between the center of the earth and the center of object Y) is also constant, for all practical purposes, being very nearly equal to the radius of the earth. The entire quantity Km_A/r_{AY}^2 is a constant, which may be written as g, giving us $w_Y = m_Y g$. The fact that g is not exactly constant but varies inversely with r_{AY} has been confirmed by measurements made with precise instruments. The student will recall that it was for this reason that we rejected weight as a measure of the massiveness of an object and introduced the concept of inertial mass. (See p. 69.)

THE FALLING OF THE MOON

The first empirical test which Newton made of his equation for universal gravitation was to use it in calculating the distance of the moon's daily "falling." To set up the same calculation let m_A stand for the mass of the earth, as before; m_B for the mass of the moon; and r_{AB} for the distance between the centers of the earth and the moon. The force of gravitation acting between the earth and the moon, in accordance with Eq. (3.13), is

$$f_{AB} = K \frac{m_A m_B}{r_{AB}^2}$$

On the other hand, the relationship between a force and the acceleration it produces (Eq. 2.13a) allows us to write, for this case,

$$f_{AB} = m_B a$$

Equating right-hand members of the two equations just written and dividing both members by m_B, we have, for the acceleration of the moon,

$$a = \frac{Km_A}{r_{AB}^2} \tag{3.14}$$

We cannot yet compute a, the acceleration of the moon, because we don't know the values of K and m_A. But to find their product, the apple comes to our rescue again. Using Newton's Eq. (3.13) for the case of the falling apple, we have

$$f_{AC} = K \frac{m_A m_C}{r_{AC}^2}$$

as the force acting between the earth and the apple, where m_C is the mass of the apple and r_{AC} is the distance between the centers of the earth and the apple, which, of course, is very nearly equal to the radius of the earth. Conversely, we know that the force acting between the earth and the apple is none other than the latter's weight, which is given by

$$f_{AC} = m_C g$$

Equating the right-hand members of these two equations, just as we did before in deriving Eq. (3.14), we obtain

$$\frac{Km_A}{r_{AC}^2} = g$$

We are now in a position to determine the product of K and m_A. Multiplying both sides of this last equation by r_{AC}^2, we obtain

$$Km_A = gr_{AC}^2 \tag{3.15}$$

the desired product.

Substituting this expression for Km_A in the right-hand member of Eq. (3.14), we now have

$$a = g\left(\frac{r_{AC}}{r_{AB}}\right)^2 \tag{3.16}$$

in which we have only three values to substitute in order to compute the acceleration of the moon.

It had been determined by parallax measurements prior to Newton's work that the distance between the centers of the earth and the moon is very nearly equal to 60 times the radius of the earth. That is,

$$\frac{r_{AC}}{r_{AB}} = \frac{1}{60}$$

It was known that $g = 9.8$ m/sec^2. Substituting these values in Eq. (3.16), we get

$$a = (9.8)(1/60)^2$$

$$= 0.00272 \text{ m/sec}^2$$

for the acceleration of the moon's centripetal component motion.

We can now use Eq. (2.11), $a = 2d/t^2$, letting $t = 1$ day, or $60 \times 60 \times 24$ sec, and, employing the value just obtained for a, solve for d, which gives us the distance of the moon's daily fall. The result is

$$d = \frac{1}{2}(0.00272)(60 \times 60 \times 24)^2 \quad or \quad 10,200,000 \text{ m}$$

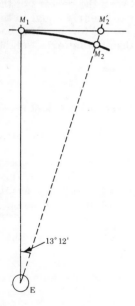

which is 10,200 km, or 6300 miles. This is the theoretically predicted distance, on the basis of Newton's gravitational equation, by which the moon "falls" in a day. We must then find the distance of the moon's daily "fall" as obtained from actual observation of the rate at which the moon circles the earth, and compare the theoretical with the empirical values.

Figure 3.13 shows that portion of the moon's orbit covered in one day, designated as $\overline{M_1M_2}$. E represents the center of the earth. If the gravitational attraction of the earth were not acting on the moon, the latter would have moved along the line segment $\overline{M_1M_2'}$ in the course of a day. As in our previous analysis of uniform circular motion, we note that the point M_2' lies on the extension of the straight line EM_2. Therefore, the distance by which the moon "falls" in the course of one day is given by

Figure 3.13 Part of Moon's Orbit Covered in One Day.

$$d = \overline{M_2'E} - \overline{M_2E} \tag{3.17}$$

and since $\overline{M_2E} = \overline{M_1E}$, then

$$d = \overline{M_2'E} - \overline{M_1E}$$

The distances $\overline{M_2'E}$ and $\overline{M_1E}$, whose difference gives the distance of the moon's daily fall, are related in the following way: the first is the hypotenuse, and the second is the base, of a right-angled triangle whose angle $(\angle M_1EM_2')$ we can evaluate. So let us first find the value of this angle. Recalling that $\overline{M_1M_2}$ is that part of the moon's orbit which is covered in one day, and knowing that it takes 27.3 days for the moon to complete one revolution around the earth, we infer that $\angle M_1EM_2'$ is equal to $360°/27.3$, or $13°12'$. By carefully constructing a right-angled triangle with $13°12'$ as one angle, or (better) by consulting a table of trigonometric functions, we can find the ratio between $\overline{M_2'E}$ and $\overline{M_1E}$. The value of this ratio is 1.027. Hence we see that $\overline{M_2'E} = 1.027\ \overline{M_1E}$. Substituting this in Eq. (3.17), we get

$$d = 0.027\ \overline{M_1E}$$

where $\overline{M_1E}$ is equal to the radius of the moon's orbit. We know this to be about 240,000 miles, so we finally have, as the empirical value for the distance by which the moon falls in a day,

$$d = (0.027)(240,000), \text{ or } 6480 \text{ miles}$$

We see that the value, 6300 miles, previously obtained as a theoretical prediction based on Newton's equation, is in fairly close agreement with the empirical value just found. (The error is about 3 percent.)

We may tentatively conclude, as Newton did, that his law of universal gravitation is confirmed by empirical evidence. When more accurate measurements were made of the distance to the moon, the agreement between the theoretical and empirical values became very much closer. A very precise agreement can be obtained taking other factors into account such as the shape of the earth (it is not exactly spherical) and the variations of the sun's attraction for the moon (it is least at full moon).

KEPLER'S THIRD LAW DERIVED FROM
NEWTON'S LAW

Although checking of Newton's Law against empirical data for the moon's motion has enhanced our confidence in it, it is desirable to confirm this law still more generally by checking it against planetary motion. Since we already have a well-established law linking the motions of all planets—Kepler's Third Law—it would be most economical to check Newton's Law directly against it. Since Newton's Law purports to be more general, applying to any pair of objects, let us see whether Kepler's Third Law, $D^3 = KT^2$, is a logical consequence of Newton's Law.

In Newton's equation,

$$f_{AB} = K \frac{m_A m_B}{r^2_{AB}}$$

we now let m_A stand for the mass of the sun, m_B for the mass of any given planet, and r_{AB} for the distance between the center of the sun and that of the planet. From this equation and $f_{AB} = m_B a$, we obtain the simpler relationship as before,

$$a = \frac{K m_A}{r^2_{AB}}$$

This expresses the centripetal acceleration of the planet's motion. On the other hand, the acceleration due to circular motion is, as given by Eq. (3.3)

$$a = \frac{40 r_{AB}}{T^2}$$

From the two equations just written, we obtain

$$\frac{40 r_{AB}}{T^2} = \frac{K m_A}{r^2_{AB}}$$

By multiplying both members by $r^2_{AB} T^2/40$, we get

$$r^3_{AB} = \left(\frac{K m_A}{40}\right) T^2$$

Since m_A, the sun's mass, is constant for any planet, the whole expression $K m_A/40$ is constant. We obtain

$$r^3_{AB} = k T^2 \tag{3.18}$$

which is equivalent to Kepler's Third Law, since r_{AB} equals D, the average distance between the sun and the planet. We see that Newton's newly postulated Law of Universal Graviation leads, as one of its mathematical consequences, to an already well-established law. We now gain even greater confidence in Newton's Law, because it has been shown to agree with a law covering the entire planetary system.

The student may have noticed that we have introduced a simplification here. In our derivation, the planet was assumed to perform a uniform circular motion around the sun, although Kepler showed that the planets follow elliptical paths and move at *nonuniform* rates. In point of fact the ellipses are (for all but one or two planets) very nearly circles, and the rates of motion of the planets are very nearly uniform. So we were not making an unreasonable simplification when we regarded planetary motion as circular and uniform.

By the use of the calculus which he invented, Newton was able to derive all three of Kepler's Laws in their precise forms involving elliptical orbits. Kepler's Laws were shown to be logical consequences of Newton's more general laws of mechanics and gravitation. Newton himself first derived the Third Law on the assumption of circular orbits, which strongly suggested that he was on the right track and undoubtedly encouraged him to pursue his inquiry. For our purpose of showing Newton's general approach, the above derivation serves well enough.

PREDICTION OF EXISTENCE OF THE PLANETS NEPTUNE AND PLUTO

We have seen two confirmations of Newton's Law of Universal Gravitation: calculation of the daily fall of the moon, and derivation of Kepler's Third Law. We have yet to mention the confirmation which marked its crowning victory. This was the use of Newton's Law in predicting the existence of an as yet undiscovered planet—a prediction which led to the subsequent actual discovery of the planet.

In 1781, the planet Uranus was discovered as the result of a fortuitous sighting through a telescope. Careful observation of Uranus' motion for several decades subsequent to its discovery, gradually revealed to astronomers that the planet was not following the particular elliptical path expected of it on the basis of Kepler's and Newton's laws. Noticeable discrepancies began to appear between the observed positions of Uranus at given times and its expected positions at those times. At first the discrepancies were small enough to be attributable to errors of measurement, but the accuracy of measurements was steadily improved, and by the 1840's it became clear that something more than observational error was to blame. Either there must be something wrong with Newton's laws, or there must be some unknown "perturbing factor" that was causing deviations in Uranus' path. But Newton's laws were highly confirmed for the other planets and the satellites, so it was difficult to imagine that they should be at fault. It was much more plausible that the perturbation was caused by some hitherto unsuspected factor; for example, an undiscovered celestial body which sometimes came so close to Uranus that the force of mutual attraction between them caused Uranus to depart from the elliptical path calculated for it.

Many astronomers and mathematicians set themselves the task of performing calculations to find the position that such a body would have to have in order to cause the observed perturbations. The first to succeed were Jean Joseph Leverrier in France and J. C. Adams in England, who independently solved the problem at about the same time. Leverrier sent his predicted data to the astronomer Johann Galle. The latter made observations that very night and, true to Leverrier's predictions, found a faint disc of light within one degree of the theoretically predicted position. (The light was so faint that it would inevitably have escaped notice unless someone was specifically looking for a celestial body in that particular position in the sky.) This newly discovered body was subsequently followed with careful measurements of its position by which it became established beyond any reasonable doubt that it was a planet with an orbit outside that of Uranus. It was eventually given the name Neptune.

The discovery of Neptune then was the climax of the remarkable story of "Universal Gravitation"—a theoretical law used to make a prediction of a previously unobserved phenomenon, subsequently borne out in actual observation. So great is the "surprise value" of such a result that one can easily imagine what a tremendous impression it made upon scientists of the last century, and what an enormous triumph it meant for Newton's theory of forces and motions. The whole system of Newtonian mechanics came to be regarded as absolute, infallible truth. Indeed it seemed as though the words of Leibnitz (a contemporary of Newton's) uttered much earlier, had turned out to be an accurate prophesy: he had said that Newton was a genius, and a fortunate genius, for the true system could be established but once; and Newton established it.

At the risk of being anticlimactic, we mention in passing that circumstances essentially similar to those surrounding the discovery of Neptune led also to the discovery of another planet, Pluto, in 1930. Erratic behavior of Neptune led astronomers to postulate still another planet. Theoretical predictions of the existence of Pluto and of its schedule of motion were made by Percival Lowell in 1914. But it was not until 1930 that the planet was actually observed by staff members of the Lowell Observatory. Long before this time, of course, the validity of Newton's Law of Universal Gravitation was so fully accepted by the scientific world as to require no further support. The prediction and discovery of Pluto, therefore, did not create nearly as great an impact as did the prediction and discovery of Neptune. This more recent event, while of considerable importance to students of the solar system, was, as far as theoretical physics was concerned, only a routine application of a well-established law whose scope of applicability was quite fully understood.

NEWTON AND DETERMINISM

To gain a full appreciation of the impact which Newton's work had on the intellectual world of his day, we must look back at the

Aristotelian synthesis of mechanics and astronomy, for this outlook was the prevalent view until Newton's day. Underlying Aristotle's concentric-sphere conception of the universe was his theory that every basic quality of matter was associated with a natural position. Earthy things belonged at the center of the universe, watery things on top of the earthy, airy things on top of the watery, and fiery things above the airy. Then there was a fifth, or celestial, quality whose natural position lay above the sphere of the moon. In this view, nature left alone would stabilize in layers. But through the interference of human beings and other living things (not to mention spirits), the world never achieved this stable state. According to the Aristotelian view, the apple is made of earthy and watery substances carried up from the ground by intervention of the tree, but when the tree lets go, the apple falls down, returning again to its natural position.

In the Newtonian synthesis we have a picture of the universe in which every atom attracts every other atom with a force (a very small one to be sure (which is jointly proportional to their masses and inversely proportional to the square of the distance between them. The apple falls because every atom in the earth attracts every atom of the apple; the combination of these attractions produces the weight of the apple. The tree sustains the weight of the apple until it becomes too heavy (and the stem gets too brittle), whereupon the apple falls.

Why have not all things fallen together into one huge aggregate of matter under the influence of this universal attraction? How can one account, on Newton's view, for the fact that the great massive bodies making up the solar system (the sun, planets, and satellites) stay apart despite the force of mutual attraction between them. According to Newton's theory, this is because they have the right velocities to keep them going around in their orbits. Moving faster, the moon would fly away from the earth and never return. Moving more slowly, it would fall to the earth. The only question then is: how did all the moons and planets acquire the right velocities to keep them going? Newton's answer to this question was derived from the then nearly universal belief that the universe had been created in a brief space of time. The Creator had evidently set the planets and satellites in motion at the moment of their creation, giving them just the right velocities to keep them going forever. It would appear that Newton did not regard such a conclusion as a proper part of science. He was a very religious man and a very sound student of scientific method. He refused to add untestable hypotheses to his theory simply to provide a more mechanistic basis for his postulated gravitational force. There is a natural desire in most men to push beyond the limits of the minimum theoretical model needed to account for observed phenomena, and it requires a disciplined mind to refuse to add more hypotheses to a theory than are needed to sustain it.

The distinction between hypotheses needed to account for experimental data and speculation as to causes that are unrelated to such data was often ignored by Newton's enthusiastic followers. This fact was reflected in the impact the theory of celestial mechanics had on the intellectual world. It was frequently understood to imply the deterministic conception of the universe as a gigantic machine. If the planets are held in their orbits by the mutual attraction between their constituent atoms, then generalizing this idea, one might suppose that the gross effects of all matter should be entirely due to the motions of their atoms. Should we conclude, then, that all forms of life, humanity included, simply behave as determined by the mechanical properties of the atoms of which they are made? Deterministic philosophy, building on this idea, has often gone to the extreme of concluding that man can do nothing to alter his predetermined future. The rise of non-Newtonian physics during the present century has done much to suppress such a generalization and, at the same time, to give recognition to alternative modes of explanation. In a rather pragmatic vein most scientists prefer some form of determinism applied to the objects they study, but think of themselves as free individuals in conducting such study, deserving praise or blame as they have used their freedom wisely or not.

METHODOLOGICAL REVIEW

The discussions in this chapter illustrate several important points about scientific method. The first is that *analogy* is a powerful and frequently used tool for the development of new scientific laws or theories. The role played by analogy in the scientific endeavor deserves careful examination. There are at least two distinct aspects to analogy, both well exemplified in Newton's development of his Law of Universal Gravitation. In the first place, before an analogy can serve to extend a theory into a broader and more general one, it must be *recognized*. Someone examining two phenomena that are superficially quite different—one of them already well accounted for by a theory, and the other yet to be explained—must see the connection. Newton's recognition of the analogy between the falling of an apple and the "falling" of the moon was clearly a feat of creative imagination. To a greater or lesser degree, such imaginativeness characterizes all scientific thinking worthy of the name.

Once an analogy has been recognized, scientists have to discover exactly how the laws applicable to the familiar phenomenon can be generalized or reinterpreted to make them apply to the novel phenomenon. This is not a feat that can be accomplished by a routine process of examining and analyzing a mass of data. It calls for a creative leap such as exemplified in Newton's leap from the idea that weight is proportional to the inertial mass of one object to the idea of attraction which is jointly proportional to the masses of two objects.

On the other hand, an argument based on analogy alone—no matter how appealing and convincing it may sound—does not confirm the validity of a hypothesis. Newton's Law of Universal Gravitation had only the status of an *hypothesis*, until it was confirmed in its own right on the basis of observational evidence. He was not satisfied even after he had shown that his hypothesized law permitted correct calculations for the daily fall of the moon; he undertook, further, to demonstrate that Kepler's Third Law (itself well confirmed by observations of all the planets) could be derived from the newly hypothesized law. Analogy plays an important role in guiding the scientist to formulate potentially fruitful hypotheses; but finding an analogy that generates hypotheses does not establish these hypotheses as laws of nature.

A second point is that the concepts of a well-knit scientific theory form a hierarchy ranging from directly measurable concepts to highly abstract concepts that have no direct observational interpretation. We can visualize this sort of structure of a theory by examining Fig. 3.14, which depicts the principal concepts of Newtonian mechanics as we have studied it and the way in which those concepts are interconnected by definitions and laws. The three primitive terms—distance, time, and mass—are located at the bottom to represent their status as

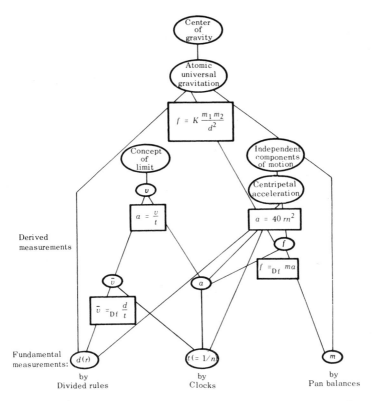

Figure 3.14 Interrelationships of Concepts of a More Advanced System of Mechanics Including Newton's Law of Universal Gravitation.

fundamental quantities measured in the direct ways listed in the diagram. The terms representing more abstract concepts are located at higher levels. Although these may not be directly measurable, they can be interpreted through their connections (specified by definitions and laws) with terms which are directly measurable. In this way, the more abstract concepts can be measured indirectly.

Two other concepts are used in the theory as a means of defining the more abstract terms. They are the mathematical concepts of limits and proportionality constants. In the theory of mechanics, these are used as primitive terms, as are the equal sign, the fraction bar, and other mathematical symbols. The special concepts of components-of-motion and center-of-mass were introduced into the vocabulary of the theory in order to solve particular problems.

In Newton's time, and until the twentieth century, acceleration was the key concept which linked gravitational force to motions recorded in terms of distance and time. Gravitational attraction is the key concept that unifies the whole theory, connecting laws of diverse origin, such as Kepler's laws and Galileo's laws of mechanics. Such unifying concepts, not directly tied to the world of experience, can often be found in well-developed scientific theories.

The general structure of a scientific theory, just described, has been neatly portrayed by the philosopher of science, Carl G. Hempel:

> A scientific theory might therefore be likened to a complex spatial network: Its terms are represented by the knots, while the threads connecting the latter correspond, in part, to the definitions and, in part, to the fundamental and derivative hypotheses included in the theory. The whole system floats, as it were, above the plane of observation and is anchored to it by rules of interpretation. These might be viewed as strings which are not part of the network but link certain points of the latter with specific places in the plane of observation. By virtue of those interpretive connections, the network can function as a scientific theory. From certain observational data, we may ascend, via an interpretive string, to some point in the theoretical network, thence proceed, via definitions and hypotheses, to other points, from which another interpretive string permits a descent to the plane of observation.[1]

We have seen how successful Newtonian mechanics was in its astronomic applications. We will later see how successfully it was applied in several other fields of physical science. So great was its success that at the end of the 19th century most scientists believed that Newtonian physics provided a definitive and final picture of the physical world. They were soon to be jolted out of their comfortable certainty.

In 1905 Einstein published his special theory of relativity, in which he changed certain fundamental (even unexpressed) assumptions of

---

[1]Carl G. Hempel, *Fundamentals of Concept Formation in Empirical Science*, International Encyclopedia of Unified Science (Chicago: University of Chicago Press, 1952), II, 36. Quoted by permission.

Newtonian mechanics, including the assumption that the mass of an object was constant. In his theory, mass increased with velocity. In 1925, Heisenberg published a theory of quantum mechanics in which a definite limit was set to the accuracy with which it was meaningful to speak simultaneously of the position and velocity of a particle. These new developments forced scientists to recognize the limitations of Newtonian mechanics. In particular, Newtonian mechanics was found to break down for motions with velocities approaching the velocity of light, and for particles smaller than atoms.

So forceful was the impact of this revolution in modern physics that most scientists of the present century are convinced of the futility of seeking absolute finality in any scientific theory. This by no means implies that the scientific enterprise itself is futile. We can still say that Newtonian mechanics is a true theory, in the sense that it enables us to make calculations from observational data which are found to yield correct descriptions and predictions of other observations—provided we consider only *objects of "medium" and "large" size undergoing motions at "ordinary" velocities*.

When we have come to accept a theory as true because it has been found in agreement with a substantial variety of observations, but later we find that it disagrees with some new observations, the theory still does not have to be rejected. If the data the theory fits and those that it does not fit can be neatly delineated, we may say that the theory is true for a restricted but specifiable range. In such a case, it can justly be claimed that an advance in knowledge has been made. For at least part of our previous ignorance concerning the range of phenomena to which the theory applies has been removed. A new range of phenomena has been revealed which calls forth efforts to develop a more general theory.

PROBLEMS

1. A thin slab of ice supports a massive block of lead on a smooth metal table. It is pulled by the force of small weights on a string, as shown in Fig. 3.15. The time taken by the block in traveling 2.5 meters, starting from rest, is given in the figure for each force applied.

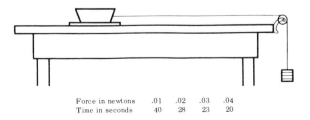

Force in newtons	.01	.02	.03	.04
Time in seconds	40	28	23	20

Figure 3.15 Diagram for Problem 1 with Data.

a. Plot a graph from which you can read off the force when the time taken is known, and vice versa.

b. From the graph, determine the time taken when the force applied is .025 newtons and when it is .035 newtons, respectively. Also determine the force when the time taken is 33 seconds and mark the corresponding points on the graph.

c. Using the largest force given and the corresponding time, calculate the mass of the block and slab together. (Specify the unit.)

d. Five types of proportionality are represented by the formulas on p. 95. Select the one which best represents the data of this problem.

2. a. On a high cliff facing the sea, a cannon fires. The horizontal velocity of the cannon shell is 400 m/sec. Taking the origin at the upper left-hand corner of your diagram, plot the shell's position after 1, 2, and 3 sec, assuming for computational convenience that the gravitational acceleration is 10 m/sec^2.

b. A rocket is fired at the same time as the cannon, aimed in the same horizontal direction. If the mass of this rocket is 5 kg, and the thrust of its motor is 1000 newtons, calculate the acceleration of the rocket in the horizontal direction.

c. On the same diagram plot the positions of the rocket after 1, 2, and 3 sec. From the graphs of the cannon shell and the rocket, estimate the horizontal distance from the cliff to the point where the rocket may be expected to hit the shell.

3. A boy swings a bucket of water vertically in a circle. If the radius of the circle described by the surface of the water is one meter, what is the longest time (in seconds) he can take for one revolution without spilling the water?

4. A space platform revolves around the earth once in 30 *hours*, and its average distance from the center of the earth is 30,000 miles. Astronomers on this platform observed a boulder-sized natural satellite and discovered that it takes 10 *days* to make one revolution around the earth.

Assuming that Kepler's Third Law applies, at least approximately, to satellites revolving around the earth as well as to planets revolving around the sun, calculate the average distance of the newly discovered satellite from the center of the earth.

5. A 20-kg satellite is being launched by means of a three-stage rocket. The first two stages have taken the satellite up to a height of several thousand km.

a. The third stage of the rocket then fires and accelerates the satellite horizontally from a speed of 500 m/sec to 3500 m/sec in 10 sec. Calculate the acceleration and the force on the satellite.

b. If the satellite were mounted on top of the third stage by means of a heavy spring which requires 1000 newtons to compress it by 1 cm, by how many centimeters would the spring be compressed when the third stage is firing?

c. The satellite is at a height of 2,500,000 m above the surface of the earth, or 5,000,000 m from the center of the earth. Traveling at the final speed indicated in (a), how many seconds will the satellite take to make one revolution? Also calculate the centripetal acceleration, $a = 40\,r/T^2$.

d. The acceleration due to gravity, like the gravitational force, varies inversely as the square of the distance. Recalling that the distance of the satellite from the center of the earth is twice the radius of the earth, and that g at the surface of the earth is 9.8 m/sec^2, calculate g at the orbit of the satellite.

Which, if any, of the previous answers should agree with this last result?

6. A multi-stage rocket is to be used for launching a 100-kg lunar probe in an orbit around the moon. Calculations have shown that the next-to-last stage of the rocket will bring the probe to position A in Fig. 3.16 (2,000,000 m from the surface of the moon), and that, at this point, the probe will have a velocity of 250 m/sec. The last stage of the rocket must then give the probe a thrust lasting 2 sec so that, at the end of this time, its velocity will be just right to maintain it in a circular orbit.

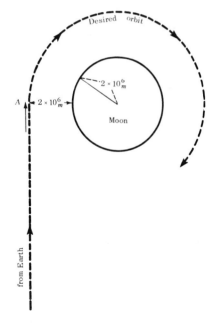

Figure 3.16 Diagram for Problem 6.

Following the steps indicated below, calculate the force with which the last stage of the rocket must propel the probe during the rocket's 2-sec thrust.

a. Given that the acceleration of gravity at the surface of the moon is 1.6 m/sec^2, and that the radius of the moon is 2,000,000 m, calculate the acceleration of gravity at point A (4,000,000 m from the center of the moon).

b. For the probe to go into orbit, the centripetal acceleration must be equal to the acceleration of gravity found in (a). Calculate the number of seconds the probe should take to make one revolution around the moon at the height of point A.

c. Take π to be 3.125, so that the circumference of a circle is 6.25 times its radius; find the circumference of the desired orbit, and thence calculate the velocity with which the probe must travel in order to make one revolution in the length of time found in (b).

d. Recalling that the final stage of the rocket must, in 2 sec, boost the probe's velocity from 250 m/sec to the value just calculated, find the acceleration that must be given the probe, and thence the force with which it must be propelled during these two seconds.

SUPPLEMENTARY READINGS

Anthony, H. D. *Sir Isaac Newton.* New York: Collier Books, 1961.
A biography.

Bronowski, J. *The Common Sense of Science.* Cambridge, Mass.: Harvard University Press, 1955.
A very illuminating analysis of the relationships between types of scientific models and the intellectual climate in which they developed. Bronowski's first three chapters add considerable perspective to our first three chapters.

Gamow, G. *Mr. Tompkins in Wonderland; or Stories of c, G, and h.* New York: Macmillan, 1945.
A very unusual and very readable presentation of the basic ideas of the relativistic and quantum mechanical models.

Holton, Gerald and Roller, Duane H. D. *Foundations of Modern Physical Science.* Reading, Mass.: Addison-Wesley, 1958.
Chapters 11 and 12 are valuable sources of additional historical and technical detail on Newtonian gravitation.

Hoyle, Fred. *The Nature of the Universe.* New York: Harper, 1950.
A very readable account of a recent, highly controversial model of the universe by its originator.

Jammer, Max. *Concepts of Force; a Study in the Foundations of Dynamics.* Cambridge, Mass.: Harvard University Press, 1957.
A penetrating, historical and philosophical analysis of the development of ideas relating to force, from ancient times to the present.

Kline, Morris. *Mathematics and the Physical World.* New York: Crowell, 1959.

Chapters 14-16 treat the subject of trajectories and gravitation in somewhat more detail but in a very readable fashion.

Munitz, Milton K. *Space, Time and Creation; Philosophical Aspects of Scientific Cosmology.* Glencoe, Ill.: The Free Press, 1957.
Models of the universe examined in the light of philosophical analysis.

_____ *Theories of the Universe from Babylonian Myth to Modern Science.* Glencoe, Ill.: The Free Press, 1957.
Contains an interesting selection from Newton's *Principia* and his correspondence.

Schwartz, George and Bishop, Philip W. (eds.). *Moments of Discovery, Vol. I, The Origins of Science.* New York: Basic Books, 1958.
Selections on "The Nature of Science and Discovery" by Roger Bacon, Francis Bacon, Descartes, Newton, Poincare, and Einstein are especially recommended. Also highly recommended are selections on mechanics by Newton and Galileo.

Shapley, Harlow and Howarth, Helen E. *A Source Book in Astronomy.* New York: McGraw-Hill, 1929.
Contains another selection from Newton's *Principia.*

Struve, O., Lynds, B. and Pillans, H. *Elementary Astronomy.* New York: Oxford University Press, 1959.
A well-illustrated and clearly written survey of modern astronomical knowledge, emphasizing basic physical principles.

* * * * *

Excellent and highly readable books on Einstein's theory of relativity include: George Gamow's *Gravity* (Garden City, N. Y.: Doubleday, 1962); Martin Gardner's *Relativity for the Million* (New York: Macmillan, 1962); T. M. Helliwell's *Introduction to Special Relativity* (Boston: Allyn and Bacon, 1966); and Jacob T. Schwartz' *Relativity in Illustrations* (New York: New York University Press, 1962).

4

SOLVING THE PUZZLE
OF ATOMIC WEIGHTS

Today, chemistry and atomic physics dominate the scientific scene. The outward thrust of the earth sciences and the exploration of space receive much of the publicity, but natural scientists as a body, from biologists to astronomers, seem to be more interested in molecular, atomic, and nuclear aspects of their sciences than anything else. Chemistry and atomic physics utilize theoretical models of considerable complexity and great explanatory power. They have grown together so that it is now impossible to tell at precisely what point chemistry stops and physics begins. Ninety elementary substances are found in nature and, in addition, some dozen artificial elements have been created by means of the ponderous but precisely controlled tools called particle accelerators and nuclear reactors. It is assumed today that the atoms of each element have distinctive structures and that the properties of all substances, including elements, compounds, and mixtures, are the gross manifestations of the properties and arrangements of their constituent atoms. The concept of atom and the related concept of molecule are now among the most significant and pervasive concepts ever developed in science. But how was it possible for man to learn about atoms? How could he penetrate gross matter to determine the properties and arrangement of the extremely small particles of which it is made? How could he learn that atoms exist—that is, that matter is actually composed of small particles identical in most of their properties?

These questions are answered primarily by the methods exhibited in this chapter. But the investigations reconstructed here represent only the beginnings of scientific atomic theory. The studies reconstructed in the remainder of this book also contribute to the growth of knowledge about atoms that took place during the middle of the nineteenth century. As classical physics came to its climax at the end of the nineteenth century, most physicists were very much concerned with questions about atoms. As we shall later see, they succeeded in applying the great theory of Newtonian mechanics as well as the newer sciences of thermodynamics, optics, and electromagnetism to the growing atomic theory. That their efforts eventually encountered certain limitations is no discredit to their monumental work.

The atomic conception of matter, in a general form, is very old indeed. Democritus and Leucippus formulated the idea of atoms as ultimate particles in the fifth century B. C., an idea summarized five centuries later by Lucretius in his poem, *On the Nature of Things*. This prophetic affirmation of the reality of atoms was accompanied by rather convincing evidence and impressive reasoning. Despite this early start, the sciences of chemistry and atomic physics, as compared with mechanics and astronomy, were very late in developing into rigorous experimental and theoretical disciplines—disciplines capable of linking the gross properties of matter with properties ascribable to the atoms. This was not for lack of trying. Newton and some of his contemporaries were atomists. They made explicit use of the idea of atoms during the latter part of the seventeenth century; but it was not until nearly two hundred years later that scientists had acquired *any* quantitative knowledge of the different kinds of atoms.

There are probably many reasons the science of the structure of matter was so singularly slow in development in comparison with the science of motion. So that the student may appreciate the extent of the conceptual difficulties which had to be overcome in developing a *scientific* atomic theory, the next section is devoted to considering one of the chief competing approaches to explaining the gross properties of matter.

A new theory may not make much headway against the accepted one until the old approach is in serious difficulties. (This we saw in the case of Copernicus and Kepler.) The approach that competed with atomism may be traced back to Aristotle and beyond, and, in one form or another, it permeated chemical thought until the work of Lavoisier in the late eighteenth century. The transition that occurred in chemical thought at that time was comparable in depth to the Copernican revolution in astronomy two centuries earlier in that a new model replaced an old one as the old one became too complex to manage and the new one came to be worked out in convincing detail.

Aristotle's theory, which classified matter in terms of the four ancient elements, earth, water, air, and fire, is so different from modern views that it is not easy to understand its exact character. It may be quite rewarding to examine this ancient theory as a point of departure for one of the most influential intellectual revolutions of our time. Aristotle's four **elementary principles,** as they were sometimes called, were abstractions which could only be given concrete expression as they were used to describe the actual observed qualities of objects, such as colors, hardness, odors, and weight. We have already seen this model applied to a mechanical problem, the falling apple. (See p. 107.) How was it applied to chemical problems?

ARISTOTLE'S MODEL OF THE QUALITIES OF SUBSTANCES

Aristotle argued that it was not important to study the basic structure of matter since all matter was similar in structure and presumably composed of small particles called atoms. What was important, he said, was rather the study of the qualities by which objects differed from each other. This was the purpose of the system of elementary principles. With each of the four principles, earth, water, air, and fire, was associated a set of qualities, and it was with these *qualities*, rather than the *substances* usually known by these names, that the elementary principles were identified. For example, the air in which we live has properties which the Aristotelians attributed to the air-principle, but it also has (in varying degrees, depending on the weather) the qualities of dampness, associated with the water-principle, and warmth, associated with the fire-principle. The different kinds of gases (as we now know them) were said to involve, besides the predominant air-principle, various proportions of the other three. Similarly there is a great diversity of liquids, the sea, rain water, milk, urine, etc., all partaking primarily of the properties of the water-principle, but differing in the proportions of other principles associated with them. A piece of limestone is primarily earthy but also has some of the air-principle, as shown by the bubbles of gas that arise from it when it is placed in vinegar. These bubbles were thought to contain the same basic kinds of atoms that were left in the limestone, but to have been transformed in appearance by the air-principle.

Perhaps a more striking example may be found by considering some commonly known facts about wood. By heating wood appropriately, gases, including water vapor, are driven out and charcoal remains. Since both wood and charcoal are combustible, the fire-principle associated with wood and all combustible things is said to remain with the charcoal while the air- and water-principles escape with these gases. It would have to be recognized by any careful observer of wood fires that the gases driven off by heating wood also contain some fire-principle, since, under proper conditions these gases will burst into flame. However, the air- and water-principles have been largely removed transforming some of the atoms into gases. The quality of lightness that causes the gases to rise is attributed to the air-principle. After charcoal is burned, ash remains, evidence that charcoal also contains the earth-principle. The transformation of the wood to charcoal was not thought of as a removal of one kind of atom, leaving other kinds behind. For Aristotle, all atoms were alike. Some of the atoms had been removed, transformed by the now separated qualities of air and water, but those atoms that remained were transformed, taking on a new appearance because of the now greater abundance of the earth- and fire- principles. Charcoal came to be regarded, in this model, as containing essentially pure fire-principle with just enough of the earth-principle to give it solidity.

That wood contains all four elementary principles is also evident to an Aristotelian from the conditions necessary for its formation. Trees grow only where there is sufficient soil, water, and sunlight, and growth always takes place in the atmosphere. The atoms of each of the substances (soil, water, and the atmosphere) and the sunlight are always accompanied by the corresponding principle (earth, water, air or fire), which is to say that each of these objects has certain characteristic qualities associated with it. In a similar manner the Aristotelian would have approached any chemical analysis or synthesis.

This theory sounds very strange to us today as an explanation of chemical phenomena, because we are so imbued with a very different one. However, the idea of elementary qualities has a long and respectable history and continues to be a useful mode of analysis in some limited aspects of sensory experience. For example, the artist's system for describing pigments is also based on elementary qualities. The color of a pigment sample can be partially but usefully described by specifying its hue. In theory, by mixtures of the primaries, yellow, red, and blue, any other hue can be produced. The idea of hue gives us a general basis for comparison of colors. We may say of two greens, "this one has a little more blue in it than that one." But specification of hue does not provide a sufficient description of every color. By the addition of white or black paint we change a paint of pure hue to one of reduced intensity. We may describe pigments more accurately by taking notice of the amount of black or white in them as well as the amount of each primary color. In pastel colors, white is in evidence, while navy blue and dark red show the presence of black.

We are not to suppose that every pigment at hand was actually *manufactured* by combining two or more pigments of the five basic sorts we have mentioned. Pigments may be extracted from many natural sources in a great variety of hues and intensities. In addition, innumerable combinations of the many natural pigments are possible. But all pigments and their combinations can be *described* as combinations of the three primary colors and black and white. It is only for the purpose of having a simple basis for describing and comparing colors that we adopt the system of primary hues and black and white as "elementary qualities." Pigments probably do not exist that will always function as pure primary hues in this theory, but this is no difficulty. The artist finds this system of elementary color qualities serves as a useful language for analyzing a given color or comparing two colors, and if it also has some practical value as a rough guide for mixing pigments in order to obtain a desired result, so much the better.

In a very similar way, the early metallurgist or alchemist used the Aristotelian system of elementary principles to predict and to explain the effect of adding this or that substance to the mixtures in his crucibles. When charcoal was added to ores in the process of refining them, the increase in quality and quantity of metal produced was attributed to the fire-principle concentrated in the charcoal. The relation of the fire-principle to the production of metal was a matter of great interest, not only because of the practical importance of metallurgy, but also because of the obvious connection between the degree of heat and the refining, tempering, and annealing of metals. Qualitative connections between the shine of metals and the light of fire were also attributed to the fire-principle.

The Aristotelian system was a considerably richer and more flexible system than the artist's system for describing colors in terms of hue and intensity. The latter only serves to classify or order pigment specimens by reference to a small number of "elementary colors." If each Aristotelian principle had been associated with just one property, then that system too could only have served for naming and ordering objects systematically. The Aristotelian system was intended to explain as many properties of objects as possible, and each principle held together in theory a number of qualities that could usually be found together in experience. With the water-principle were associated such qualities as dampness, coldness, nonflammability, fluidity, tendency to fall to the earth, etc.

The system of color description may be somewhat extended analogously by considering still other qualities of pigments besides hue and intensity. Another familiar aspect of pigments is that of warmth or coolness. We can notice that warm colors tend to have a lot of red or yellow in them, and cool colors have blue in them. We have an association of the quality of warmth with the hues of the red and yellow primaries and of coolness with the hue of the blue primary. These associations are preserved in mixing pigments so that one can generally make a pigment warmer in color by mixing in another pigment whose color is warmer than the first. Another quality of pigments, the amount of light reflected by a sample, is called its value. Thus white has the highest value and various pastel tints are also of reasonably high value. But value is not the same as the proportion of white, because the *value* of primary yellow is higher than that of primary red, which in turn is higher than that of primary blue. So value, as a quality of colors, is also associated in a particular way with the system of primary colors and black and white.

To be sure, the analogy cannot be pressed too far between the Aristotelian elements, earth, water, air, and fire, and the system presented for describing pigment samples. Aristotle's system applied to all natural objects and had no definite limits, but color analysis cannot be as readily applied to natural objects as to pigment samples because of the complexities of texture, reflection, background, and many other qualities that affect perceived color.

The Aristotelian system naturally underwent considerable development during the two thousand years it was in use. A great deal of attention was paid to the idea of a transformation of one principle into another, bringing about new qualities in a substance. In this way it was hoped to change base metals into gold. Some later chemists tried other sets of elementary principles, e.g., mercury and sulfur came to play this role. In the century before it was abandoned, **phlogiston,** a modification of the fire-principle, dominated chemical theory. These later developments showed an increasing tendency for a closer identification of the elementary principles with physical substances and for the recognition of different kinds of atoms. But there was no ready replacement for the old theory until Joseph Priestley discovered oxygen and A. L. Lavoisier identified it as an elementary substance. In retrospect, we may assume that the growing interest in finding elementary substances may have been motivated by the growing difficulty of determining exactly what sets of qualities belonged together with each elementary principle. It is interesting to note that the new concept of elementary substances had been clearly enunciated by Robert Boyle in 1772, but neither he nor anyone else could compile such a list of elements until a great deal of experimental work had been done.

When it was discovered that heating an ore produced an amount of metal that weighed less than the ore that was consumed, it was explained that phlogiston had gone *into* the ore, adding the qualities of lightness of weight and metallic lustre—lightness and brilliance were two of the general properties still associated with the fire-principle. Since many metals were known to have a similar relationship with their ores, the pattern appeared to be a very general one. Many scientists regarded phlogiston as a very subtle fluid whose atoms had very different properties from the atoms of more "basic" matter. If phlogiston, in this transition period, was thought of as having its own kind of atoms, then the quality of tending to rise or of having "negative weight," which was associated with phlogiston, stood in contrast with the view Newton had advocated, that every atom attracted every other atom in the universe with a definite force—which is to say that all atoms have a positive weight.

THE DISCOVERY OF THE LAWS OF
CHEMICAL COMBINATION

The transition from the Aristotelian model of matter, based on qualities or principles, to the concept of elementary chemical substances was essentially completed by 1790 when Lavoisier experimentally established the law of conservation of weight. The evidence for this law was obtained by weighing all of the substances involved in a chemical reaction both before and after the change in properties occurred. His law is often stated in this way: matter is neither created nor destroyed in undergoing changes. So stated, it is called the law of conservation of matter. Implicit in this formulation is the assumption that all matter has a positive mass—and, when in the neighborhood of the earth, a positive weight. Once this assumption was adopted, and the negative-weight phlogiston had been banished, then quantitative experiments could lead to the discovery of many of the modern chemical elements.

The key element was oxygen, because, as soon as it was recognized that many metallic ores, when heated, yield oxygen and their metal, the different metals themselves became recognized as elements. Because of the convincing evidence of weight measurements, this new approach was readily adopted by chemists—that is, after Lavoisier's clear exposition of it.

When chemists working with these newly discovered elements weighed them and their compounds, they established a basis for the later discovery of an orderly system in their data. Whenever a compound substance was synthesized by combining two or more elements, and utmost care was taken against contamination by other substances, then the proportions of the different elements actually used by were found to be very nearly constant. This is known as the **principle of constant composition** and was eventually recognized as a general law. It applied as well in the analysis (or taking apart) as it did in the synthesis of compounds. This law, together with the law of conservation of matter, permitted the chemist to predict quantitatively the results of combining different amounts of substances and made possible the discovery of still other laws.

The chemist's interest in prediction of results was not just a means of verifying the laws, but more important perhaps, a means of investigating new reactions and seeking new elements and compounds. This was the challenge of the new approach—quantitative prediction. It is interesting to note that the old challenge, the prediction of qualitative transformations in color, odor, and fluidity, still remained, but the new approach could do nothing to meet it. The old approach was failing, even in achieving qualitative predictions. For new reactions were being discovered rapidly and the Aristotelian model could not be adjusted to fit them rapidly enought. All one could do was to list the qualities (as well as the quantitative properties) of each element and compound. One learned how to synthesize compounds and analyze compounds for the presence of particular elements, but gone was the old confidence that one knew how to bring out this quality or that—like a cook adding seasoning to bring out a particular flavor. Instead, chemistry became a fascinating mathematical puzzle; one had to determine how much of each would be used up as two or more elements were combined.

A third law of chemical combination was discovered by Dalton through the study of different compounds of the same elements and the proportions of the elements required. In the next exercise, the student can discover this relationship for himself by examining the proportions by weight of nitrogen and oxygen contained in the compounds listed in Table 4.1. (The names listed are those of Dalton's

Table 4.1 The Composition of Five Nitrogen-Oxygen Compounds

	H (%)	N (%)	O (%)	Parts of O for 1 part of N	Parts of N for 1 part of O
"Nitrous air"	0	40	60	1.14	0.89
"Nitrogen oxide"	0	30	70	2.28	0.44
Nitrous oxide	0	64	36	0.57	1.75
Nitrogen trioxide	0	36	64	1.71	0.58
Nitric acid	1.6	22	76	3.43	0.29

time, because the modern names would reveal the relationship he discovered.) It is most instructive to note that a clear relationship does not appear unless the combining proportions are calculated in certain ways.

Theoretical exploration:

4.1 In Table 4.1 the proportions have been calculated in three of the many possible ways. Before reading the next paragraph, the student should study each of the three columns of data to see if he can detect a regular relationship among the proportions given for the five compounds. While no general pattern appears in the percentages, most students will readily detect a relationship between the numbers of parts of oxygen for one part of nitrogen, and in the numbers of parts of nitrogen for one part of oxygen. ■

The student may have noticed that the number of parts of oxygen for "nitrogen oxide" is twice that for "nitrous air." The third entry in the same column is half of the first entry, and the fourth is three times the third. In fact, we could rewrite all the values for parts of oxygen as multiples of the third and smallest figure, 0.57, with very little error. In the last column of Table 4.1, the multiple relationship is almost as clear: All but one of the figures may, with little error, be written as multiples of the smallest, and the exceptional value is very nearly equal to 3/2 of the smallest value. By taking one half of the smallest quantity as the base, all of the values for parts of nitrogen turn out to be multiples of the same base to a very reasonable degree of accuracy. Table 4.2 demonstrates this relationship explicitly. The first column provides the most interesting representation of the relationship between these compounds because the multipliers are small. The relationship exhibited is called the **law of multiple proportions** since the proportion of one element to the other, in any of these compounds, is a whole number multiple of a fixed quantity.

Consider how unlikely it is that a scientist studying these chemical compounds for the first time would discover this law. No simple relationship stands out in the percentage values of Table 4.1, yet the calculation of percentages or proportions of the total is a reasonable

Table 4.2 Multiple Proportions in Five N-O Compounds

Compounds of N and O	Parts of O for 1 part of N	Parts of nitrogen for 1 part of oxygen	
"Nitrous air"	$.57 \times 2 = 1.14$	$.29 \times 3 = .87$	$.145 \times 6 = .87$
"Nitrogen oxide"	$.57 \times 4 = 2.28$	$.29 \times 3/2 = .44$	$.145 \times 3 = .44$
Nitrous oxide	$.57 \times 1 = 0.57$	$.29 \times 6 = 1.74$	$.145 \times 12 = 1.74$
Nitrogen trioxide	$.57 \times 3 = 1.71$	$.29 \times 2 = .58$	$.145 \times 4 = .58$
Nitric acid	$.57 \times 6 = 3.42$	$.29 \times 1 = .29$	$.145 \times 2 = .29$

way (and was the customary way for the early chemists) to prepare data for comparison. To discover a law by compiling data in a table and looking for relationships is therefore not a simple process. If one searches only for certain obvious relationships, it is quite possible that one will not have prepared the data in the right form to permit discovery of whatever relationship does exist. Conversely, there is no point in simply trying to find just any pattern in a given collection of data, for some pattern can *always* be found or created which fits a particular collection. What is desired is a pattern which will fit many more data in the same way. The scientist's best guide in this effort is a theoretical model. But whatever pattern he discovers, he must always attempt to find out whether it is a matter of chance or a lawful pattern.

The law of multiple proportions has a broad scope since the same relationship is found in any group of compounds containing at least two elements in common. The law is also quite suggestive of an atomic constitution of matter. For the relationship is expressed in ratios of small whole numbers, and the masses of individual atoms may represent some kind of lowest common denominator of the combining proportions. Yet this law and the law of definite proportions, although they are empirical generalizations of considerable value, do not explicitly connect atomic properties with gross properties of matter. They do not constitute a general scientific theory of matter. In scope, they correspond closely to Kepler's laws in astronomy, but they fall short of Newton's theory of gravitation. Although these empirical laws serve to organize a great deal of chemical research, they still lack explanatory value. How can a more explanatory theory be developed—in particular, a theory which has something quantitative to say about atoms?

DALTON'S ATOMIC THEORY

John Dalton did not excel as an experimental chemist and was not even primarily devoted to chemical research; he was a schoolteacher. Yet he undoubtedly contributed more to the science of chemistry than any other man working in the first half of the nineteenth century. He was inspired by Newton's great work and set out in a very imaginative way to formulate an explanation of chemical reactions in terms of the well-known concept of atoms. This concept had never been regarded as amenable to quantitative measurement, even in Newton's theory, but Dalton took the bold step. He made some definite assumptions of quantitative properties of atoms which enabled him to explain chemical reactions; he then tried to find evidence to justify them.

The atomic concept is best represented by the idea that any object, if broken down into sufficiently minute parts, must finally be reduced to particles which cannot be further divided. Atoms are the bricks out of which the objects of our everyday experience are made. Since the idea of elementary substances had, by Dalton's time, been generally adopted in chemistry, it was natural for him to think of an atom of nitrogen as different from an atom of oxygen, or of phosphorus, or of any other element. Furthermore, it was natural to think of every atom of one element as an identical twin of every other atom of that element. A piece of phosphorus was like a building made of just one kind of brick, while the oxide of phosphorus formed by burning it was made of two kinds of atoms, like a building made of bricks of two colors.

Dalton did not think of a compound as just a *mixture* of elements. It was *not* as though a brick mason had used two kinds of bricks at random, or that he had alternated them in some definite pattern, but rather, it was as though the brick mason had first put the two kinds of bricks together to make larger compound bricks and then constructed the building from these compound bricks. Imagine that one red brick was joined to each brown brick to make a compound brick, and a building was then constructed out of many such compound bricks. Similarly, Dalton spoke of the "atoms of nitrous oxide" as each being composed of one atom of nitrogen and one atom of oxygen. Modern chemists use the word **molecule** in speaking of the smallest unit of a compound—one of the "compound bricks"—and reserve the word **atom** for the smallest unit of an element. A unit of two or more atoms joined together is a molecule. The modern terminology will be used in discussing Dalton's work for the sake of greater clarity.

Dalton began, simply and imaginatively, to draw pictures of molecules. He used a special symbolic figure to represent each of the different kinds of atoms known to him. Dalton assigned to each kind of atom a certain relative size, mass, and quantity of heat. These quantities were necessarily quite hypothetical, for he had no direct way of measuring them. Although he had no way of knowing in advance which of these three quantities was the most accessible, it turned out that it *was* possible in his time to work out relative atomic masses. We can see now that his attempts in this direction were most successful. It should not be forgotten that he was unable to tell which of his ideas would be most successful, and this is one reason his theory was rather slow in its development. He simply introduced quantities which he had good reason to believe were important. Modern science has confirmed that all three are important, but it is also clear that only the relative masses of atoms were anywhere within Dalton's reach.

Dalton knew from the published data of various experimenters that the proportion of oxygen to hydrogen in water was approximately 7:1 by weight. (Modern measurements put it almost exactly at 8:1, but gaseous elements were very difficult to weigh in Dalton's time.) He reasoned, therefore, that if a molecule of water consists of one oxygen atom joined to one hydrogen atom, then the oxygen atom must be 7 times as heavy as the hydrogen atom. If, however, a water molecule consists of one oxygen atom joined to two hydrogen atoms (according to the formula H_2O, which we have learned is correct), then an oxygen atom, Dalton argued, would be 14 times as heavy as a single hydrogen atom. The relative mass to be assigned to each kind of atom depends on the number of each kind that is supposed to make up the molecule. Putting it in modern terms, the **formula** for the molecule must be known before one can infer the **relative atomic weights** (i.e., the relative masses of the atoms) from the combining proportions (i.e., the proportion by weight of the elements in the compound). Without knowing the formula for a compound, it was impossible to calculate the relative atomic weights for the elements making it up.

Faced with such a difficulty, most chemists may have given up hope of any solution. Dalton, confident of the general correctness of his theory that density, hardness, and other quantitative properties of matter were attributable to corresponding properties of their atoms, plugged the gaps in his knowledge as best he could. Assuming that each kind of atom had a characteristic mass, he concluded that equal numbers of two different kinds of atoms would have different gross weights proportional to their characteristic atomic weights.

To supplant his lack of any knowledge of numbers of atoms or of formulas for molecules, Dalton simply assumed that the Creator would not have made a molecule any more complex than necessary. Dalton knew of only one compound which contained only hydrogen and oxygen, water; so he assumed on this principle of parsimony, that its formula was HO, that is, that the water molecule consisted of just one atom of each element.

When he knew of more than one compound composed of the same elements, as in the case of the nitrogen and oxygen compounds, he initially assigned the simplest formula to the most abundant compound and the more complex formulas to the less abundant ones. We might say that he proceeded to build a model of matter, as though he were creating matter for the first time and wished to do it in the most economical manner. The significant contribution of Dalton's imaginative model to chemistry was that it provided, for the first time, a way to connect quantitatively some gross property of matter with a property ascribed to atoms. The concept of atomic weight proved to be of great assistance to chemists in suggesting new experiments, even though there was initially little empirical basis for the formulas and relative atomic weights Dalton had assigned.

Most of Dalton's initial formulas and atomic weights proved wrong, but the interesting point is that the errors were gradually uncovered and corrected, many of them by Dalton himself, because they led to inconsistent conclusions about combining proportions. We shall see in the next section how such inconsistencies can be detected.

FINDING A CONSISTENT SET OF ATOMIC WEIGHTS
AND MOLECULAR FORMULAS

If we are to make a series of calculations, similar to those which Dalton made, it will be convenient to set up an algebraic formula for the calculations. Let us assume that there is a definite number of molecules, N, in a certain sample of a given compound of the elements Q and R. Let x be the number of Q atoms and y the number of R atoms in a single molecule of this compound. A molecule of the compound will be represented by the chemical formula $Q_x R_y$. Let A_Q be the mass in grams of one atom of Q, and A_R be the mass in grams of one atom of R. Let W_Q and W_R be the total mass in grams of the two elements, respectively, in the sample. Then

$$W_Q = N \cdot x \cdot A_Q \qquad \text{and}$$

$$W_R = N \cdot y \cdot A_R$$

From these formulas, we can write an equation for the combining proportion of Q to R in the sample of the compound $Q_x R_y$ as follows:

$$\frac{W_Q}{W_R} = \frac{N \cdot x \cdot A_Q}{N \cdot y \cdot A_R}$$

which, since $N/N = 1$, reduces to

$$\frac{W_Q}{W_R} = \frac{x}{y} \cdot \frac{A_Q}{A_R} \tag{4.1}$$

If we regard each fraction in Eq. (4.1) as a single quantity (a ratio), we have a formula with three variables much like the formulas used in mechanics. There is one significant difference which is worthy of special attention. In Eq. (4.1) only one of the three quantities can be measured—the combining proportion W_Q/W_R. The formula ratio x/y and the atomic weight ratio A_Q/A_R are both unknown quantities. By contrast, in the formulas of mechanics that contained three variables, two of them were always measurable quantities. This difference effectively blocks the method of model building used in mechanics. Some new procedure is required to move ahead.

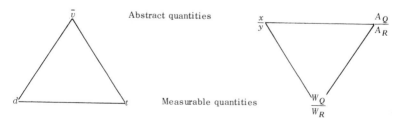

Figure 4.1 Comparison of Atomic Molecular Theory with Average Velocity.

We may represent the relationship of the three ratios in Eq. (4.1) by means of a diagram like that used at the end of Chapter 3. Such a diagram is the right-hand triangle in Fig. 4.1. Compare it with the triangle representing the concepts of average velocity, distance, and time on the left. In either case, if we know any two quantities we can calculate the third. But in the velocity formula, two of the three quantities are measurable, and once we measure these, the velocity is determined by the formula. We may regard this situation as represented by the fact that the left-hand triangle has a stable base to rest on. In Eq. (4.1), on the other hand, since only the quantity W_Q/W_R is measurable, its measurement still leaves the other two quantities indeterminate; for there is an indeterminate number of pairs of numbers whose product is equal to any given number. That the right-hand triangle is anchored by observations at only one of its vertices, so that the other two are free to move like a seesaw, represents the indeterminacy of this situation. How can one ever hope to arrive at definite conclusions on the basis of Eq. (4.1)?

The basis for Dalton's approach to this apparent methodological impasse may be clarified by noting that when a number of triangles (compounds) are connected, by relating their atomic weight ratios, certain combinations of formulas and atomic weights turn out to be inconsistent. The same elements occur in many different compounds and, by trying all combinations of formulas for these compounds, one may eliminate some sets of formulas which yield atomic-weight ratios that are not consistent for all compounds. The tremendous task of determining whether or not consistent atomic-weight ratios are obtained is greatly facilitated by taking some fixed value as the atomic weight of one element and expressing the atomic weights of other elements in terms of this fixed value. This is just what Dalton did.

He picked the lightest known element, hydrogen, and assigned it an atomic weight of 1. If the formula for water is taken to be HO, so that $x = y = 1$, then (using the modern value for the combining proportion) an oxygen atom must be eight times as heavy as a hydrogen atom, so it would then be assigned an atomic weight of 8. (See the left-hand triangle of Fig. 4.2.) If another formula were picked for water, of course, oxygen would have another atomic weight. Dalton also adopted several parsimonious rules that reduced his task: for example, he assumed that the most abundant compounds of two given elements will have the simplest formulas and that each element had a different atomic weight. To see how inconsistencies were detected and how Dalton's rules helped, we shall examine a group of three compounds having just three elements among them.

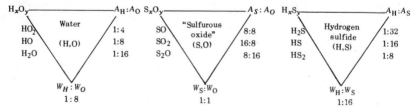

Figure 4.2 Calculating Relative Atomic Weights Simultaneously from Three Compounds.

The combining proportion of sulfur and oxygen in a certain compound, which we will call sulfurous oxide (avoiding modern names which already presuppose knowledge of the correct formula), is very nearly 1:1. (See the center triangle in Fig. 4.2.) If we should adopt the formula SO for this compound, then sulfur must have the same atomic weight as oxygen—an unlikely circumstance according to Dalton's idea that atomic weight was a distinguishing characteristic of each element. Furthermore this compound is not as common in nature as certain minerals containing sulfur and oxygen so, following Dalton's second economy rule, let us pick another formula, say SO_2. The sulfur atoms would then have twice the weight of oxygen atoms in order to yield the combining proportion 1:1. Taking the atomic weight of oxygen as 8, based on Dalton's first rule of parsimony, the atomic weight of sulfur would then be 16.

If we now go on to consider the analysis of the familiar "rotten egg" gas, hydrogen sulfide, we find the combining proportion of hydrogen to sulfur is 1:16. But these numbers are the atomic weights we have tentatively adopted for H and S, so we adopt the simplest formula, HS, for hydrogen sulfide. We have, so far, rejected the formulas and atomic weights of the first row in Fig. 4.2 and accepted the second row as consistent. The third set of formulas given in Fig. 4.2 for the three compounds also yields a consistent, but different, set of atomic weights.

By continuing this sort of analysis over a large number of compounds it is possible to eliminate, as mutually incompatible, many sets of formulas and atomic weights. As the list of compounds is extended, each new compound restricts the consistent possibilities still more, provided that the number of elements involved in the table does not increase.

It actually took chemists of the nineteenth century more than fifty years to put enough information together to arrive at a completely consistent set of atomic weights and molecular formulas. Their difficulties were very largely due to apparently conflicting results based on volume measurements. By concentrating on weight measurements (as did Berzelius, who published an essentially correct list of atomic weights in 1828, twenty years after Dalton's book), we can avoid this trouble and get a much clearer picture than most chemists of the early nineteenth century had. From the analysis in the exercise below, it can be seen that the best determination of a set of formulas and atomic weights can be expected when the number of compounds is increased without increasing the number of elements. This condition is reminiscent of the situation encountered previously when we studied evidence for the law of multiple proportions.

Theoretical exploration:

4.2 In order to show the nature of the inconsistencies that arise when atomic weights are assigned on the basis of the combining proportions of several compounds, the student should examine systematically all possible combinations of the three simplest formulas for the three compounds depicted in Fig. 4.2. To do this, first consider all combinations of formulas for two of the three compounds. For each of these combinations, atomic weights can be determined. No inconsistencies arise thus far, except with Dalton's economy rule against assigning two elements the same atomic weight. Next, determine whether the sets of atomic weights assigned for each of these combinations of formulas for two compounds are consistent with any of the simplest formulas for the third compound.

In Table 4.3, the columns to the right of the double line are provided for the nine combinations of three formulas for the first two compounds, water and sulfurous oxide. In each column, atomic weights have been entered opposite formulas with which they are consistent. In the first three of these columns, the test of consistency with the third compound has already been applied and the results indicated. If a consistent set of atomic weights was found, the weights have been entered opposite the formula with which they are consistent. If none was found, as is the case in the second column, the lower part of the column is crossed out. The student should continue this exercise by applying the same test to the remaining six columns. ■

The explanation of the law of multiple proportions was one of the most convincing accomplishments of Dalton's theory. Dalton's explanation is quite simple. Each different compound of the same two elements has a different formula. Since these formulas contain only small whole numbers, the combining proportion of the several compounds, obtained from Eq. (4.1), must stand in small whole-number ratios to each other. But the explanation of the law of multiple proportions does not determine what the atomic weights and molecular formulas in Table 4.2 actually are. We can again apply Eq. (4.1) to the data in this table and try to find a consistent set of atomic weights and formulas for the compounds of nitrogen and oxygen.

Not yet having selected an atomic weight for either oxygen or nitrogen, but recalling from the preceding calculations that it is convenient to use whole numbers for combining ratios, let us convert the ratios of Table 4.2 to the simplest common fractions that approximate them. For example, 7:4 is the best small-number approximation to 1:0.57, the ratio of N to O in "nitrous oxide." Keeping the 7 as a constant value for the number of parts of nitrogen, we can, from the multipliers in Table 4.2, write appropriate multiples of 4 for the parts of oxygen in the other compounds. The student should compare the combining proportions in Table 4.4 with those in the first column of Table 4.2 to see that they are correct.

Can we assign a different formula to each compound while maintaining the same ratio of atomic weights throughout? There are just five possible formulas with no more than four atoms each. We omit formulas like N_2O_2 which would give the same atomic-weight ratio as a simpler formula, in this case, NO. This actually constitutes another

Table 4.3 Compatible Combinations of Atomic Weights and Formulas for Three Compounds, Each Containing Two of Three Elements

Name of compound	Combining proportions	Molecular formulas	Atomic weights H:O:S	The nine possible combinations of atomic weights								
				H:O:S	H:O:S	H:O:S	H:O:S	H:O:S	H:O:S	H:O:S	H:O:S	H:O:S
Water	H:O	HO	1 8	1 8	1 8	1 8						
	1:8	H₂O	1 16				1 16	1 16	1 16			
		HO₂	1 4							1 4	1 4	1 4
Sulfurous oxide	S:O	SO	1 1	8 8			8 8			8 8		
	1:1	S₂O	2 1		8 4			2 1			2 1	
		SO₂	1 2			8 16			1 2			1 2
Hydrogen sulfide	H:S	HS	1 16			1 16						
	1:16	H₂S	1 32									
		HS₂	8	1 8	✕							

principle of parsimony and another appeal to the aesthetics of simplicity. Using Eq. (4.1), we have calculated the atomic-weight ratio for each compound using each of the five formulas in turn and entered them in Table 4.4. Can we assign these formulas to the five compounds in a way which gives us the same atomic-weight ratio throughout? Inspection shows that we cannot, for among the 25 entries in the table, no single ratio occurs five times, although the ratio, 7:8, occurs four times. We cannot restrict our selection to the five simplest formulas.

Theoretical exploration:

4.3 The student should extend Table 4.4 in the space provided by determining the atomic-weight ratios for the next two formulas, those containing five atoms each. If he cannot find an assignment of five formulas to the five compounds which give the same atomic-weight ratios, he should then proceed to add more and more complex formulas to the table until he reaches a solution. ∎

Even when we arrive at a consistent set of formulas, we will not have proved that these formulas are the correct ones for the compounds in question. But we will have shown that they are the simplest ones that will fit the given combining proportions. We will have achieved the most parsimonious solution to the problem of finding formulas for these compounds. By a similar but necessarily more complex procedure, all the compounds known to chemistry may be compared, and the simplest set of formulas and atomic weights determined for this set.

From the data we have already studied, we can take one further step in finding formulas for these compounds. The student will recall that in Table 4.1 it was indicated that "oxynitric acid" contains a little hydrogen as well as nitrogen and oxygen. This element was temporarily ignored since no other compound in the table contained it. This means we must add one or more H's to the formula that we chose for "oxynitric acid," NO_3. To determine how many hydrogen atoms to assign to the molecule, we need to determine the number of parts of hydrogen that combine with 7 parts of nitrogen and 24 parts of oxygen. Table 4.1 shows that this compound contains 1.6% H and 22% N. Dividing by 3, we find that approximately 1/2 part of hydrogen to 7 parts of nitrogen to 25 parts of oxygen are required. The weight of nitrogen is thus about 14 times the weight of hydrogen, and the weight of oxygen is about 50 times that of hydrogen.

If H = 1 and if "oxynitric acid" has the formula HNO_3, then, to the nearest integer, $A_N = 14$ and $A_O = 16$. But if the formula were H_2NO_3, then $A_N = 28$ and $A_O = 33$. It turns out that data on other compounds containing one or more of the elements H, N, and O rules out the latter but not the former possibility. The student who knows some

Table 4.4 Ratios of Atomic Weights for Nitrogen and Oxygen for Hypothetical Formulas of Different Compounds

Compounds containing both nitrogen and oxygen	Combining proportions N : O	Ratios of atomic weights for N and O					Possible formulas containing more than 4 atoms		
		Possible formulas containing no more than 4 atoms					N_2O_3	N_3O_2	N_3O_4 - - -
		NO	NO_2	N_2O	NO_3	N_3O			
Nitrous air	7 : 8	7:8	7:4	7:16	21:8	7:24			
Nitrogen dioxide	7 : 16	7:16	7:8	7:32	21:16	7:48			
Nitric acid	7 : 24	7:24	7:12	7:48	7:8	7:72			
Nitrous oxide	7 : 4	7:4	7:2	7:8	21:4	7:12			
Nitrogen trioxide	7 : 12	7:12	7:6	7:24	7:4	7:36			

The number of different formulas for which each ratio is found is as follows:

7:8   4
7:4   3
7:12 3
7:24 3
7:48 2

formulas of modern chemistry will recognize that we have finally arrived at atomic weights which are the same as those accepted today. The formulas selected in Table 4.4 are also correct according to modern information, and the interested student can determine the modern names of the compounds listed by referring to a modern chemistry text. We have seen how the problem of atomic weights and formulas, which seemed impossible to solve when thought of in terms of its separate aspects, can be resolved by a systematic, unified approach. Let us now consider a different approach to the problem—one based on the volumes of gaseous elements.

AVOGADRO'S PRINCIPLE

It was earlier mentioned that Dalton had tried to assign relative sizes as well as relative weights to various atoms. His consideration of atomic sizes did not lead to fruitful results. It remained for another scientist, the Italian physicist Avogadro, to show how the space occupied by an atom could be meaningfully interpreted in terms of the gross properties of matter. Specifically, Avogadro (in 1811) advanced the hypothesis that equal volumes of any gas, under the same conditions of pressure and temperature, contain equal numbers of molecules. He postulated that the volume of a given bulk of gas was proportional to the number of molecules it contained, no matter what the gaseous substance was. Notice how this simple assumption nevertheless is out of keeping with Dalton's conception of simplicity.

Avogadro's hypothesis was formulated as a means of explaining certain relationships between the volumes of gaseous elements which combine to make different compounds. When two volumes of hydrogen are mixed with one of oxygen and ignited, an explosion occurs, and the product formed is water, with no hydrogen or oxygen left over. According to Dalton's theory, there must be a simple whole-number ratio between the numbers of H and O atoms in these gases.

The proportions by volume of gases which combine to form compounds are so frequently expressible as ratios of small whole numbers, that there is a strong suggestion of some simple relationship between the numbers of atoms and the volume of these different gases. When the resulting compound is also gaseous, as is often the case, there is the further interesting fact that the gaseous product also shows simple volumetric proportionality to the gases which enter into the reaction. From this, it was concluded that the numbers of both gaseous molecules and atoms stand in simple relation to the volumes of the gases they form.

There are a few cases in which Avogadro's hypothesis is readily seen to be compatible with the experimentally determined volume ratios, such as the four shown in Fig. 4.3. There are others, where certain difficulties are encountered. (See Fig. 4.4.) Dalton, in particular, was sure that these cases contradicted Avogadro's hypothesis.

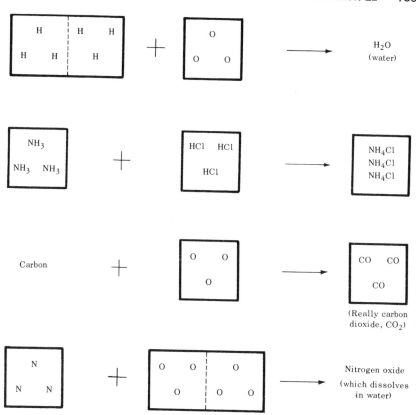

Figure 4.3 Volume Ratios in Gaseous Reactions Explainable by Avogadro's Principle and the Monatomic Element Assumption.

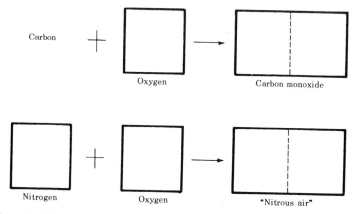

Figure 4.4 Volume Ratios in Gaseous Reactions *not* Explainable by Avogadro's Principle and the Monatomic Element Assumption.

His argument was as follows: If the volume of a gaseous compound is twice the volume of one of the elements that enters into the reaction then, according to Avogadro's hypothesis, there must be twice as many molecules in the compound produced as there were atoms in the element used. Either only half the compound molecules have atoms of the element (which would mean it is a mixture and not a single compound—but this conflicts with the fact that no separation of the compound can be performed) or the "atoms" of the element are split in two, so that half an "atom" of the element would enter into each molecule of the compound. This is unthinkable since an atom is, by definition, the smallest part of an element. (Recall that "atom," for Dalton, was used to describe both atoms and molecules in the modern sense.)

Students familiar with the formulas O_2, H_2, and N_2 for these common gases may wonder why Dalton found it unthinkable that half an "atom" of these elements could enter into a molecule of a compound. The answer lies in the fact that a tacit assumption in Dalton's argument was, in modern terminology, that the *molecules of an element are monatomic*, that they consist of one atom each. It is interesting to note that this formulation of Dalton's assumption, while clear enough to be examined, would be reduced to nonsense if the term *molecules* were replaced by the corresponding Daltonian term *compound atoms*. Dalton was possibly prevented by his terminology from realizing his assumption that there could be no such thing as a compound atom of an element and therefore from examining it. In any case, Dalton never admitted, even on Avogadro's urging, that the atoms of an element might be stuck together in pairs. It is difficult to determine the reasons for Dalton's resistance although such resistance is a recognized phenomenon in science as in other fields of thought. We may speculate that linguistic habits are very hard to shake, but also that Dalton found it hard to give up the economy principles which had served him so well.

It was forty years after the original controversy between Dalton and Avogadro, that someone finally put his finger on the difficulty. In a paper circulated at a scientific meeting, Stanislao Cannizzaro showed how all the controversial cases could be explained on the assumption that N, O, H, Cl, and F had *diatomic molecules*, molecules consisting of two atoms each: N_2, O_2, H_2, Cl_2, and F_2. The formulas for compounds derived from these assumptions and data on combining volumes were identical with the formulas obtained by the atomic-weight method and the data on combining weights. The paper was enthusiastically received, and Avogadro's hypothesis was accepted as an established principle.

Theoretical exercise:

4.4 To test his understanding of Avogadro's principle, the student should complete Fig. 4.4 by representing a fixed number of molecules (say 3) in each unit volume. Also, Fig. 4.3 should be redrawn to illustrate the new explanation which assumes diatomic molecules for these gaseous elements. ■

Once the principle was established that equal volumes of different gases contain equal numbers of molecules, it became possible to solve a particular kind of problem concerning molecular formulas which Dalton's atomic weight approach by itself had not been able to solve.

The student will recall that formulas which are multiples of simpler ones cannot be distinguished by the method of combining proportions. (See p. 130.) If water molecules were really H_4O_2 or H_6O_3 or some other multiple of H_2O, the fact could not be discovered by analysis of combining proportions. Avogadro's principle helps out here, for from it the relationship between the weight and volume of a gas and its molecular weight can be derived. Let us see how this can be done.

Avogadro's principle tells us that

$$V = KN$$

at a given temperature and pressure. The weight of a gas, W, is the sum of the weights of all its molecules, namely, Nw. The gram weight of one molecule, w, although unknown, must be directly proportional to the sum of the atomic weights of its atoms, a quantity known as its molecular weight (e.g., the molecular weight of water is 18, since the atomic weights of its constituent atoms are 1,1, and 16). Thus $w = kM$, where M is the molecular weight. This gives us

$$W = NkM$$

Now we have two equations with one quantity in common, N. Since we have no way of determining N, it would be convenient to get rid of it by substitution. From Avogadro's principle, $N = V/K$ so

$$W = \frac{V}{K} kM$$

Our problem is to find the molecular formulas of gaseous molecules, which we could do if we could calculate their molecular weights. So let us solve for M in terms of W and V, which are measurable. We get a new proportionality,

$$M = \frac{K}{k} \cdot \frac{W}{V} \qquad \text{or} \qquad M = K_1 \frac{W}{V} \tag{4.2}$$

If we know the molecular weight of one gas, we can determine it for all others. Let us pick oxygen, in whose formula O_2 and molecular weight of 32 we have the greatest confidence from the Dalton-type analysis because of the large number of oxygen compounds known. If we weigh a 1000 cubic centimeter sample of oxygen, at some standard temperature and pressure, and find its weight to be 1.43 grams, we can calculate K_1 as follows:

$$32 = K_1 \frac{1.43}{1000}$$

$$K_1 = \frac{32,000}{1.43} = 22,400$$

Now, when we measure the weight and volume of any other gas under the same standard conditions of temperature and pressure, we can calculate its molecular weight by formula (4.2):

$$M = 22,400 \frac{W \text{ (grams)}}{V \text{ (cubic centimeters)}}$$

In this way we can discover that water vapor has a molecular weight of 18, and hence its formula is H_2O and not H_4O_2 or something else.

This is really a remarkable conclusion considering the very tentative assignments of atomic weights and formulas with which we began this development. It is this combination of Dalton's and Avogadro's solutions of the seemingly impossible task of determining the relative weights and the formulas of invisible molecules that has led Anthony Standen, a professor of chemistry at St. John's College, Maryland, to remark that, in the nineteenth century, chemistry "lifted itself by its own bootstraps." What it did next, according to Professor Standen, was to "kick a table underneath and stand on it." The table, of course, was the famous periodic table of Mendelyeev. This development we shall examine in the next chapter.

METHODOLOGICAL REVIEW

The chemical revolution of the nineteenth century provides an excellent example of the way in which a new, more fruitful approach "sneaks in the back door" while everyone is still absorbed in the old, accepted approach. The concern with the qualities of different substances seemed a fundamental one. How could one deny that chemists should be studying the colors, odors, densities, and the tendencies to change, of substances and studying the ways in which these properties changed? For any chemist to have concentrated on combining proportions alone would have seemed insane. Yet this was the very approach that led to the atomic sciences.

The significance of the chemical revolution must have been lost on many who participated in it. Even Dalton must have regarded his work with atomic weights as merely one small aspect of the science of chemistry. Yet it was, for him, clearly a beckoning passageway, along which he groped with determination. We find in Dalton a man of conviction rather than the passive, objective observer of nature. His religious faith seems to have come to his aid when logic failed to show him the way. He overcame the apparent impossibility of solving an equation with two unknowns (Eq. (4.1)) by diligent work and an assumption about the Creator—that He would not have been wasteful of His atoms.

We have seen that Dalton's conclusions were not always borne out. Many of the formulas he assigned to compounds turned out to be inconsistent. But such inconsistencies led to success by the elimination of error. Some of the atomic weights which Dalton calculated proved unacceptable, but he succeeded in introducing the concepts of atomic weight and molecular formulas and in showing how these concepts may be related to observational data. Thus he paved the way for the eventual determination of weights and formulas by a massive attack.

In scientific thought, a whole system of related problems can sometimes be solved when any one of the problems, taken singly, cannot be. If chemists had confined their attention to determining the atomic-weight ratio for hydrogen and oxygen, there would have been an unlimited number of possibilities, and no solution could have been obtained. Only by simultaneously considering the related problems of determining the atomic-weight ratios for sulfur and oxygen, for hydrogen and sulfur, oxygen and nitrogen, etc., could one eliminate some of the many possibilities; and the more of these problems one considered simultaneously, the more possibilities could be eliminated, until one finally arrived at a single set of atomic weights that were mutually consistent and consistent with the evidence.

In this connection, it will also be instructive to compare the structure of Dalton's atomic theory more closely with that of elementary mechanics. In Fig. 3.14 (p. 109), we depicted the net-like structure of a theory that the philosopher of science, Carl Hempel, has described, whereby it is possible to ascend from the plane of observation to a point in the theoretical network, and "to proceed, via definitions and hypotheses, to other points" from which it is possible to descend again to the plane of observation.

Such a movement is not so simple in Dalton's theory, since the observational data for one substance will not support any theoretical inference. Using Professor Hempel's analogy, we may say that, in Dalton's model, the theoretical concepts cannot be "anchored firmly" to the plane of observation until a very large number of separate observations have been made. In mechanics, a law (say, $f = ma$) which is confirmed for an object made of iron works equally well for a piece of copper; this is not the case for atomic weights and formulas. Separate data and formulas are necessary for every new substance.

Dalton's contribution may be described as building the theoretical "net" before it could be anchored—that is, as showing the interrelationships of atomic weights of all the elements through the formulas of many compounds. Figuratively speaking, we might say that he held the net steady, in order to show its structure, by means of a kind of "sky hook," namely, the rule of always assuming the simplest admissible formula. This made it possible for others to understand the model and to make the many particular observations needed to adjust and fasten the "net" securely.

We saw on page 130, however, that it was not possible, by Dalton's approach alone, to decide whether a molecule should have the formula $A_x B_y$ or $A_{2x} B_{2y}$ or $A_{3x} B_{3y}$, etc. It took an entirely different approach, initiated by Avogadro, to settle questions of this sort. We see here an excellent example of the way in which two or more quite different theories sometimes converge, to clear up problems in a field of scientific research. The convergence in this case is so striking that some authors speak of the "Dalton-Avogadro theory" in referring to the system of atomic-molecular theory and gas-volumetric theory taken together.

What are the methodological lessons to be learned from the developments discussed in this chapter? First, that a major change in point of view in a science is often necessary to further advancement but that there is no method for producing such a change. Second, that the scientist must often postulate some features of a model for which he has no evidence, perhaps appealing to an essential simplicity in nature, in order to make any start at all. Third, that the scientist must be willing to abandon such a postulate based on simplicity (or any postulate, for that matter) if it should turn out to lead to inconsistencies—either internally, or with empirical data, or with the predictions from a better-confirmed theory. Fourth, that several different approaches are often required in order to obtain a complete solution to a given set of problems. What appears to be a complete solution by one approach may really be only a partial solution that has run into a blind alley.

Methodological exericse:

4.5 The above conclusions apply almost as well to theories of the universe and of mechanics developed in earlier chapters, as well as to those theories to be developed in later ones. The student should make a detailed comparison of the development of atomic theory with the history of astronomy, Chapters 1 to 3. ∎

PROBLEMS

1. A chemical equation represents a rearrangement of the same set of atoms, starting with atoms or molecules of one or more sub-

stances and ending with atoms or molecules of other substances. An equation is said to be balanced when the number of atoms represented by symbols is the same before and after the rearrangement. In front of each of the formulas in the equations below, write the smallest number of atoms or molecules needed to bring the equation into balance.

$$S + O_2 \longrightarrow SO_3$$

$$N_2 + O_2 \longrightarrow NO$$

$$Na_2O_2 + H_2O \longrightarrow NaOH + O_2$$

$$SO_2 + H_2O \longrightarrow H_2SO_3$$

$$NO + O_2 \longrightarrow NO_2$$

$$CH_4 + O_2 \longrightarrow CO_2 + H_2O$$

2. One laboratory animal was fed only carbohydrates, $C_{12}H_{22}O_{11}$, and another only fats, $C_{11}H_{23}COOH$. How many oxygen molecules does each require to change one molecule of fuel completely into molecules of H_2O and CO_2?

3. By means of a respirometer, it was determined that a man consumed 8 grams of oxygen in fifteen minutes. If the "fuel" he was respiring had as its simplest chemical formula, CH_2O, how many grams of "fuel" were consumed?

4. Imagine yourself a chemist studying compounds of four elements, A, B, C, D, whose properties had never before been determined. You want to determine the formulas of the known compounds and the relative atomic weights of the elements. Tables 4.5 to 4.7 summarize the data available to you concerning the proportion of each element in each compound.

   a. Table 4.5 gives the combining proportions by weight of four of these compounds, all of which are composed of just two of these

Table 4.5 Table for Problem 4 (a)

Compound	Combining proportion by weight	Ratios of B and D atomic weights necessitated by different possible formulas for each compound					Simplest set of formulas
	B : D	BD	B_2D	BD_2	B_3D	BD_3	
belladine	1 : 1						
beady salt	1 : 6						
budane	1 : 3						
salabatica	2 : 3						

elements, B and D. Complete this table, filling in for each compound the relative atomic weights for B and D by assuming, for each formula in turn, that that formula is the correct one for each compound. From the table, so completed, select the simplest set of formulas for the four compounds.

b. Table 4.6 gives the combining proportions of three compounds, each composed of two of the elements A, B, and C. Test the consistency of each combination of the possible formulas that are listed. The following procedure is suggested: one formula may be eliminated because it necessitates equal atomic weights for two elements. For each combination of the remaining formulas, determine the most consistent set of atomic weights, letting the smallest atomic weight be 1. Select that set of the smallest atomic weights which agrees with the combining proportions.

Table 4.6   Table for Problem 4 (b)

Compound and proportions by weight	Possible formulas	Atomic weight ratios A:B:C	Atomic weights for A, B, and C					
			A:B:C	A:B:C	A:B:C	A:B:C	A:B:C	A:B:C
arobatica 1:3	AB	—						
	$A_2 B$	—						
acidone 1:12	AC	—						
	$A_2 C$	—						
	AC_2	—						
bittercein 1:1	$B_2 C$	—						
	$B_2 C_2$	—						

c. Table 4.7 gives the results of volume measurements of the elements used in forming three gaseous compounds. One of them was examined in part (a). The elements A, B, and D are gaseous, but C is a solid. In the spaces provided, write the two simplest sets of formulas that are consistent with Avogadro's principle and the data given. Cross out any formulas which are not consistent for all three compounds.

d. Finally, putting together all of the results from parts (a), (b), and (c), determine the formulas and atomic weights, for the compounds listed below, which are most consistent with the data in all three tables.

Table 4.7 Table for Problem 4 (c)

Compound	Combining proportions by volume	Consistent sets of *formulas* for each element and compound			
		A_n	B_m	D_k	Compounds
arobatica	2 vols. A_n + 1 vol. B_m = 2 vols. A_xB_y		—		
			—		
bittercein	1 vol. B_m + C (solid) = 1 vol. B_xC_y	—	—		
		—	—		
budane	1 vol. B_m + 1 vol. D_k = 1 vol. B_xD_y	—			
		—			

Formulas: arobatica _____ belladine _____   Atomic weights: A _____
          bittercein _____ beady salt _____   B _____
          budane _____ salabatica _____   C _____
          acidone _____   D _____

5. In a few sentences, criticize the following argument:
   Dalton, in developing his atomic theory, made many false assumptions such as that the simplest formulas were the correct ones, and that atoms could not be split. Therefore, we may say that he was not careful enough in testing his assumptions before making them.

6. An industrial chemist had a large quantity of a gaseous compound of nitrogen and oxygen for which he wished to determine the formula. He had instruments for measuring its volume in cubic feet and its weight in pounds. To standarize his measurements, he first weighed a large quantitiy of carbon dioxide (CO_2); this had a volume of 45 cubic feet and weighed 5.5 pounds.

   a. Using Eq. (4.2), $M = K_1(W/V)$, calculate the value of the proportionality constant K_1, based on the above measurements for CO_2. Its molecular weight is 44.

   b. Given that the unknown gaseous compound of nitrogen and oxygen weighed 3.8 pounds for a volume of 18 cubic feet at the same temperature and pressure as the CO_2, calculate the molecular weight of the gas.

   c. On the basis of the molecular weight calculated above, determine the molecular formula of the gas. Do this by making a table of the molecular weights for various formulas until you discover a formula which gives exactly the same molecular weight as that calculated in (b).

SUPPLEMENTARY READINGS

Boorse, Henry A. and Motz, Lloyd. *The World of the Atom*, Vol. I. New York: Basic Books, Inc., 1966.
    Selections 1 (Lucretius), 3 (Boyle, from the *Sceptical Chymist*), 9 (Higgins), 19 (Cannizzaro), and Part II, "The Foundations of Atomic Chemistry," are recommended original scientific writings appropriate for this chapter.

Conant, James Bryant and Nash, Leonard K. (eds.). *Harvard Case Histories in Experimental Science*. Cambridge, Mass.: Harvard University Press, 1957.
    Case 2, "The Overthrow of the Phlogiston Theory"; Case 4, "The Atomic-Molecular Theory"; and Case 5, "Plants and the Atmosphere" provide historical details of the theoretical developments analyzed in this chapter.

Faraday, Michael. *The Chemical History of a Candle*. New York: Harper, 1861 (reprinted by Crowell and in paperback by Collier and Viking).
    Faraday's lectures unfold the process of combustion in a series of simple experiments, many of which can be usefully repeated by the student.

Farrington, Benjamin. *Greek Science: Its Meaning for Us*. Baltimore Penguin Books, 1944.
    Volume I, "Thales to Aristotle," summarizes Greek atomism (Chapter 4) and Aristotle's theory of matter (Chapter 8).

Garrett, Alfred B. *The Flash of Genius*. Princeton, N. J.: D. Van Nostrand Co., 1963.
    Dedicated to revealing, through examples, the processes of thought leading to scientific discovery, this interesting collection of vignettes from many fields of science is worthwhile reading. Passages related to this chapter include, from Part I, selections 17 (Dalton), 18 (Priestley), 19 (Lavoisier) and 20 (Kekule).

Jaffe, Bernard. *Crucibles: The Story of Chemistry*. New York: Fawcett (A Premier Book), 1957.
    Chapters 1 through 8 contain short biographical sketches of the men who contributed most to the development of chemical theory during approximately the same period as that covered in the present chapter.

Munitz, Milton K. *Theories of the Universe from Babylonian Myth to Modern Science*. Glencoe, Ill.: The Free Press, 1957.
    The selections from Lucretius (*The Nature of the Universe*) and Plato (*Timaeus*) will considerably illuminate Greek atomism and the Aristotelian theory of the four elementary principles.

Pachter, Henry M. *Magic into Science; The Story of Paracelsus*. New York: Schuman, 1951.
    An account of the fabulous physician and alchemist who put medicine on a practical, chemical basis in the sixteenth century. Graphically portrays the primitive stage of an experimental science.

Schwartz, George and Bishop, Philip W. (eds.). *Moments of Discovery, Vol. I, The Origins of Science*. New York: Basic Books, 1958.

Short selections by Lucretius, Van Helmont, Stahl, Black, Priestley, Scheek, Cavendish, and Lavoisier will help illuminate the present chapter.

Toulmin, Stephen and Goodfield, June. *The Architecture of Matter; The Physics, Chemistry, and Physiology of Matter, both Animate and Inanimate, as It Has Evolved Since the Beginnings of Science*. New York: Harper & Row, 1962.

A detailed analysis of the growth of scientific ideas about matter, synthesizing a wealth of historical material.

Woolf, Harry (ed.). *Quantification; A History of the Meaning of Measurement in the Natural and Social Sciences*. Indianapolis: Bobbs-Merrill Co., 1961.

The chapter by Henry Guerlac entitled, "Quantification in Chemistry," is valuable additional reading for the student interested in the role of measurement in the chemical revolution.

5

THE PERIODIC TABLE:
A CONFIRMATION OF ATOMIC WEIGHTS

In the preceding chapter we saw how Dalton's atomic theory introduced a great deal of order into the field of chemistry by ignoring
qualitative properties and concentrating on weight relations. In this
chapter we will see how the concept of atomic weight increased the
scope and precision of previous classifications of the elements and
reintroduced the theoretical value of qualities in the discovery of a
relationship between atomic weights and the general qualitative properties of the elements. Man's understanding of this relationship has
developed steadily in the last one hundred years and now embodies a
number of models of atomic structure which successfully explain a
great many of the gross properties of matter. Classification of the
elements led, therefore, to a fundamental development in modern
science, but we shall confine our attention to the question of how such
a powerful system of classification got started.

Long before Dalton's day, chemists identified certain categories
of substances, eventually recognized as elements, which possessed
remarkably similar physical and chemical properties. Let us consider briefly some of these groups or "families" of elements that
had early been recognized as belonging together. In discussing
familial similarities, however, we will make free use of post-
Daltonian concepts.

PRE-DALTONIAN GROUPINGS OF ELEMENTS

Copper, silver, and gold are three moderately soft metals that are
not corroded by either dilute hydrochloric or sulfuric acid. These
metals have been recognized as members of a family since the early
days of alchemy. This group held special significance for alchemists
who were preoccupied with attempting to transmute "base" metals into
the "noble" metal, gold. Of all the baser metals, copper most nearly

resembled gold and played an important role in the alchemists' attempts to produce gold. It was natural for them to associate this common metal with the precious metals, silver and gold, on the basis of its physical properties.

Lithium, sodium, and potassium were also quite early recognized as a family. These are soft metals which exhibit a metallic lustre when freshly purified but tarnish rapidly when exposed to air. They react violently with water, giving off a flammable gas (hydrogen) and turning the water into an alkaline solution. For this reason they are known as alkali metals.

If one investigates these similarities further, other similarities turn up. When the alkaline compounds that they produce by reacting with water are analyzed, they turn out to be very similar kinds of alkalis. These compounds (known as *hydroxides*) not only share the properties of those alkaline substances known as strong bases, but they also possess very similar chemical formulas: $Li(OH)$, $Na(OH)$, and $K(OH)$. This situation clearly suggests a connection between the general qualities of elements and the quantitative properties bestowed upon them by atomic theory. In each case, as the formulas indicate, *one* atom of the metal combines with *one* OH combination, known as the **hydroxyl group**. When this property is possessed by an element, the element is said to have a **valence** of 1, or to be **univalent**. (The hydroxyl group itself is also said to have a valence of 1 because it combines with H, the reference standard for determining valence, on a one-to-one basis. The result of this combination is $H(OH)$, more commonly written as H_2O.)

The valence of an element can be determined from chemical formulas and has proven to be quite useful in classification. If an element X has a hydroxide whose formula is $X(OH)_2$, or a hydride XH_2, X is said to be **bivalent** or to have a valence of 2; if $Y(OH)_3$ is the formula for the hydroxide of Y, or YH_3 its hydride, Y is said to be **tervalent** or to have a valence of 3; and so forth. The next example of a family of elements also illustrates the usefulness of the concept of valence in the classification of elements.

Chlorine, bromine, and iodine are elements having a strong acrid smell, and they are also very active chemically. They combine readily with hydrogen to produce gaseous hydrides (HCl, HBr, HI) whose water solutions are strong acids. The formulas for these hydrides show that these elements have a valence of 1. They also form white crystalline salts with the alkali metals, Li, Na, and K. The elements of this family (Cl, Br, I) are therefore known as **halogens**, which means "salt-producing." The formulas for the alkali-halogen salts show that one atom of an alkali metal combines with one atom of a halogen: LiCl, LiBr, LiI, NaCl, etc. The one-to-one combination in these formulas is consistent with the univalence of both the halogens and the alkali metals.

The foregoing examples will serve to illustrate the idea of families of elements. Two of the above examples also illustrate how molecular formulas, and the related concept of valence, add some theoretical significance to the observational evidence showing that the elements of a family do belong in the same category. The relevance of chemical formulas in classification leads to the natural question whether the elements in a family might not also be related by their atomic weights.

One might, as a first approach to this question, determine whether elements with similar properties have similar atomic weights. But this turns out not to be the case. For instance, the alkali metals have widely different atomic weights (Li = 6.9, Na = 23.0, K = 39.1). But there could be other relationships between atomic weights and properties of elements besides the simple one just suggested. The search for such relationships, which many chemists (especially the younger ones) by the middle of the nineteenth century intuitively felt must exist, eventually became fairly widespread. It should be pointed out, however, that belief in the existence of such orderly relationships was not universal. Some of the older chemists of those days, having received their training in pre-Daltonian times, apparently did not see the full significance of atomic theory and scoffed at the attempts of their younger colleagues to seek a relationship between atomic weights and properties of elements. An English chemist named John Newlands, for example, who reported his efforts to classify elements by atomic weight in 1864, was asked by fellow chemists if he had tried an alphabetical arrangement.

THE CONTRIBUTIONS OF DÖBEREINER AND NEWLANDS

One of the earliest discoveries of a relationship among the atomic weights of families of elements was made by Johann Wolfgang Döbereiner in about 1830. Groups of similar elements, such as those described above, usually contained three elements each, so far as was then known, and were known as "triads." What Döbereiner discovered was that the atomic weight of the middle of the three elements in a triad was very nearly equal to the average of the atomic weights of the other two. Let us consider a few examples of this rule, known as Döbereiner's rule of triads.

In the triad of alkali metals, Li = 6.9, Na = 23.0, and K = 39.1. The average of the atomic weights of Li and K is 23.0 which is exactly equal (to the first decimal place) to the atomic weight of Na.

The atomic weights of the triad [Cl, Br, I] are 35.5, 79.9, and 126.9, respectively. Taking the average of the smallest and largest of these three numbers, we have 81.2, which is fairly close to 79.9, the atomic weight of Br.

Another triad, known in the early 19th century, consisted of the elements calcium (Ca), strontium (Sr), and barium (Ba), whose atomic weights are 40.1, 87.6, and 137.4, respectively. The average of the extreme numbers is 88.75, which is not far from 87.6, the atomic weight of Sr.

We see that, elementary as Döbereiner's rule of triads was, it did provide some evidence of a connection between the atomic weights and the properties by which elements had been placed in families. However, this rule does not work for the family consisting of copper (Cu = 63), silver (Ag = 108), and gold (Au = 199).

A more elaborate rule was found by Newlands who showed that, when the elements are arranged in order of increasing atomic weight, a similar element occurs, by and large, in every eight position. He called this the "octave rule." This rule was far from perfect, especially for the heavier elements. To make things fit, Newlands had to put many of the elements out of order in terms of their atomic weights. Examine his arrangement (shown in Table 5.1) and note that he placed chromium (Cr) right after calcium (Ca), to make it come under aluminum (Al), despite the fact that, among the then–known elements, titanium (Ti) was next to Ca in order of atomic weight.

Table 5.1 Newland's Arrangement of Elements

H	Li	Be	B	C	N	O
F	Na	Mg	Al	Si	P	S
Cl	K	Ca	Cr	Ti	Mn	Fe
Co, Ni	Cu	Zn	Yt	In	As	Se
Br	Rb	Sr	Ce, La	Zr	Di, Mo	Rh, Ru
Pd	Ag	Cd	U	Sn	Sb	Te
I	Cs	Ba, V	Ta	W	Nb	Au
Pt, Ir	Ti	Pb	Th	Hg	Bi	Os

Newlands' system was actually a compromise between an arrangement of elements in the order of atomic weights and an arrangement in terms of their chemical properties. We can see some validity in his octave rule. At least up to Ca, the elements are strictly in atomic-weight order, and we see some families in columns. There are four halogens in the first column: fluorine (F), chlorine (Cl), bromine (Br), and iodine (I). In the second column, we find the by now familiar triad of alkali metals [Li, Na, K]. The presence of H in the same column with the halogens may seem odd; but H does resemble them in valence. Despite its limitations, it is clear that Newlands' system was a significant step toward a comprehensive classification of the elements.

THE GRAPHICAL METHOD OF LOTHAR MEYER

Several years after Newlands had proposed his octave rule two scientists, a Russian, Dmitri Mendelyeev, and a German, Julius Lothar Meyer, each independently developed a more refined system

for classifying the elements. The name of Mendelyeev is associated
with the periodic classification of the elements, although just as much
credit would seem to be due to Meyer.

The search for a systematic classification of the elements is an
effort to find relationships between different properties of the elements. Searching for relationships is basic to all scientific inquiry,
and it is often useful to borrow a technique from another field of science that has proved particularly rewarding. In our study of motion,
we have seen that plotting a graph of two quantities may be helpful in
revealing the existence of a relationship between them. Meyer employed this same technique in investigating relationships between
quantitative properties of the elements with very notable success.
Because the graphical method is more familiar than the method used
by Mendelyeev, we will consider Meyer's approach before going on to
Mendelyeev's table.

Only two of the properties of the elements mentioned so far could
be represented by numerical measures at the time of Meyer's work:
atomic weight and valence. Plotting these two quantities against each
other yields a graph which shows a more or less regular pattern.
The unique contribution of Meyer was that he systematically sought
and found other properties of the elements related to their atomic
properties, which had been or could be measured, and plotted graphs
to show their relationships to atomic weight.

Numerical measures for such chemical properties of the elements
as the tendency to form acids or bases and the tendency to undergo
violent reactions have only been developed in the twentieth century,
and some chemical properties, such as odor, cannot be measured
quantitatively even today. But Meyer utilized properties that could be
measured, such as the melting points of solids, the boiling points of
liquids, and the densities of solids and liquids. From density and
atomic weight, he computed the relative volume occupied by the atoms
of each element.

Taxonomic exploration:

5.1 A portion of one of Meyer's most interesting graphs, that relating
atomic volume to atomic weight, is shown in Fig. 5.1. Plot one or
more graphs of other properties in a similar manner. (Tables of
physical and chemical properties of the elements may be found in
the chemical handbook listed at the end of this chapter.) Compare students' graphs with Fig. 5.1 in order to discover how different properties of the elements are related. ∎

All of Meyer's graphs showed a general wavelike form somewhat
like that of Fig. 5.1. A relationship whose graph takes such a form is
said to be **periodic**, by analogy with relationships between certain re-
curring phenomena and time—such as the waxing and waning of the
moon or the oscillation of a pendulum. In Meyer's graphs the length

of the "period" between successive peaks is not measured in time units but in units of atomic weight.

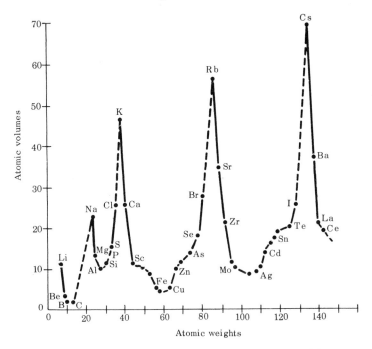

Figure 5.1 The Periodic Relationship Between Atomic Volume and Atomic Weight of the Elements. (After Alexander Findlay, *A Hundred Years of Chemistry*, p. 58.)

Although the "periods" in Fig. 5.1 are *not* all equal, we notice that the sharp peaks are occupied by the alkali metals, Li, Na, K, and two more elements, Rb (rubidium) and Cs (cesium), which are clearly recognizable by their properties as members of the same family. This graph is evidence that atomic volume has a fundamental relationship with the properties by which the elements are classified into families. The elements belonging to any given family all occupy similar positions with respect to the major peaks and valleys of the graph. The halogens (Cl, Br, I) occupy similar positions on the slopes; Cu and Ag occupy similar positions in the valleys.

One might have supposed that the volume of atoms would increase steadily with atomic weight—that the heavier an atom the bigger it would be. Surprisingly, the graph shows that volume increases and decreases regularly in a pattern that corresponds with variations in chemical properties. Similar surprises turn up in other graphs, so that one is forced to admit the periodic properties of the elements must reflect a very basic pattern in the nature of matter. Any theory that can explain this periodicity will be highly prized. To a very considerable extent the main thrust of physics and chemistry in the twentieth century has been an effort to do just this.

COMPUTING ATOMIC VOLUMES

From the numerical values of the atomic volumes plotted in Fig. 5.1 one can see that they are obviously not measured in cubic centimeters. These are *relative* atomic volumes, derived from relative atomic weights. Since it is impossible to measure directly the volumes of single atoms, what is here called "atomic volume" is actually a measure of *the average amount of space occupied by each atom in a sample of a given substance*. This may be determined in the manner shown below.

In a sample of volume V cm³, containing N atoms of an elementary substance, the average space occupied by each atom, which we may call the "volume per atom," may be defined as (V/N) cm³. Whatever empty space there may be between the atoms is thereby apportioned equally to each atom.

Using much the same treatment that we used in connection with Avogadro's principle (p. 137), we may replace N by an expression involving atomic weight, A, and the mass m of the sample (in grams). Since

$$m = kNA$$

$$N = \frac{m}{kA}$$

Then the volume per atom in cm³ is

$$\frac{V}{N} = \frac{V}{m/kA}$$

which may be rewritten as

$$\frac{V}{N} = k \frac{A}{m} V \tag{5.1}$$

Since volume per atom in cm³ would be an extremely small quantity, and since we only need to know the *relative* volume occupied by atoms, we may choose some more convenient unit and call the volume per atom measured in this unit, *atomic volume*, V_A. Thus:

$$V_A = K \frac{V}{N} \tag{5.2}$$

where K is the conversion factor for the new unit.

Substituting from Eq. (5.1) into Eq. (5.2), we get

$$V_A = (Kk) \frac{A}{m} V$$

Noting that the expression outside the parentheses involves only measurable quantities and also that the unit for V_A is still unspecified, it would be most convenient if we chose this unit so that $Kk = 1$. Then the definition of atomic volume becomes,

$$V_A =_{Df} \frac{A}{m} V \tag{5.3}$$

where A is atomic weight, m is the mass of the sample in grams and V its volume in cm^3. In arbitrarily setting the product of the constants, Kk, equal to 1, we have given up any concern for the actual size of atoms. This is an interesting side issue not really necessary to the question at hand.

From Eq. (5.3) we can see that, if we were to prepare a sample of each element containing A g (e.g., a 27.3 g sample of Al, a 40 g sample of Ca, or a 65 g sample of Zn), we would have $m = A$, and hence, *for such a sample*, $V_A = V$. The atomic volume has the same numerical value as the volume, in cm^3, of a sample of A g of the element.

Theoretical exercises:

To gain familiarity with the use of Eq. (5.3) and Fig. 5.1, the student should perform the following calculations.

5.2 A 126 g piece of copper was found to have a volume of 14 cm^3. Calculate its V_A. ∎

5.3 A 100 g piece of potassium was found to have a volume of 87 cm^3. Calculate its V_A. ∎

5.4 Using the data plotted in Fig. 5.1, calculate the volume of a 140 g piece of aluminum. ∎

5.5 The density of mercury is 13.6 g/cm^3. Determine the mass of mercury in a tube whose inside cross-sectional area is 1 cm^2 and whose height is 76 cm, and find its atomic volume. ∎

Having seen from Meyer's graphs, such as the one shown in Fig. 5.1, that the periods separating similar elements are not all equal—the first two being much shorter than the others—let us now reexamine Newlands' octave rule. We have already seen that this rule worked well only up through Ca. After Ca many adjustments were necessary to preserve it. From Meyer's graphs we find 14 then-known elements between Ca and Sr, the next element with properties similar to those of Ca. Between Sr and Ba, which is the next element of this family, 15 known elements intervened. While these two periods are nearly the same length, they are just over twice as long as the first two periods. We see that the basic flaw in Newlands' scheme was his assumption that similar elements were separated by equal periods all the way through. A closer approximation would be an assumption that

2 periods of 7 elements are followed by 3 periods of 15 elements.

Can we construct a table similar to Newlands' except that the rows are allowed to be unequal in length? A convenient set of elements with which to start the rows of such a table is the family of alkali metals, since they occupy the peaks of Meyer's graphs. In forming a table with rows of unequal length, we face the further problem of determining which elements in the shorter rows go in which columns. In Table 5.2, five columns have been formed (two on the left and three on the right) in which the elements are unquestionably similar. There remain several elements (H, B, C, Al, Si) whose positions cannot be so easily determined. The fact that there is one more element in the fourth row than in the third prevents a definitive vertical alignment of the elements in these rows except for the five columns already mentioned.

Table 5.2 A "Long Form" of Periodic Table

Valences:	1	2												3	2	1
							H									
	Li	Be					B		C					N	O	F
	Na	Mg			Al					Si				P	S	Cl
	K	Ca	Sc	Ti	V	Cr	Mn	Fe	Co	Ni	Cu	Zn		As	Se	Br
	Rb	Sr	Yt	Zr	Nb	Mo	Ru	Rh	Pd	Ag	Cd	In	Sn	Sb	Te	I
	Cs	Ba														

Despite the ambiguities we have mentioned, Table 5.2 has one advantage which should be noted. Excluding the five ambiguous elements, Table 5.2 can be divided into three distinct parts in each of which the several families of elements bear a strong resemblance to one another. All elements in the first two columns, and no others, are light metals which form strong bases. The elements in the last three columns, except oxygen, all form acids in combination with oxygen and hydrogen or with hydrogen alone. The remaining elements, located in the middle of the table, are dense metals which form weak bases. These three major groups roughly correspond to categories chemists refer to respectively as light metals, nonmetals, and transition metals. Note the positions occupied by the elements of these three categories on the periodic graph in Fig. 5.1.

MENDELYEEV'S PERIODIC TABLE

Both Meyer and Mendelyeev, independently, pursued their studies of periodic properties in great detail, having produced similar tables that facilitated their studies. It was Mendelyeev who made the more effective use of detailed comparisons between neighboring elements in his table. For this purpose he needed to assign every element to a definite position in relation to the others. After trying various arrangements of tables, he hit upon a pattern of maximum regularity and minimum distortion. It had alternating periods of 7 and 10 elements each, but it began with 2 periods of 7 preceded by H in a period all by itself. (See Table 5.3.)

This arrangement only worked by leaving numerous blank spaces. It was Mendelyeev's chief contribution, distinguishing his efforts from those of all his predecessors, that he proposed that there might exist as yet undiscovered elements. But how could he determine where such elements belonged?

Having placed the known elements in his new table in order of their atomic weights, he studied the relationships of neighboring elements. Whenever an element, so placed, more closely resembled the elements in a column one or more places farther to the right, Mendelyeev moved it over and left the appropriate number of *blank spaces*. He thereby preserved the order of atomic weights by moving such elements ahead, instead of exchanging their positions with those of heavier elements, as Newlands had done.

Note that Mendelyeev left period 9 entirely blank. There were two reasons for this. First, there was the very large jump in atomic weight from Ce (cerium) to Er (erbium). If Er had been placed in period 9, but still in Group III, there would have been only 8 blank spaces separating it from Ce. The difference between their atomic weights, 38, is too large for this small separation. Second, by assuming that period 9 was missing, he was able to preserve the pattern of alternating periods of 7 and 10 elements.

The blank spaces which Mendelyeev left would, he predicted, eventually be filled as chemists discovered new elements. He boldly predicted that such discoveries would meet the specifications for those positions with respect to atomic weight and other chemical and physical properties. (Compare the positions of elements in Table 5.2 with the arrangement in Newlands' table, page 149.)

The first blank space in Mendelyeev's table occurs after Ca in the fourth row. Although among the elements known in Mendelyeev's day Ti (titanium) followed Ca as the next heavier element, the physical and chemical properties of Ti more closely resembled those of C and Si (silicon) than they resembled those of B (boron) and Al (aluminum). Accordingly, Mendelyeev left a blank space after Ca, moving the position of Ti one place to the right, placing it in Group IV with C and Si. Mendelyeev predicted that an element whose atomic weight would lie between those of Ca and Ti would eventually be discovered, and whose chemical and physical properties would resemble those of the Group III elements, B and Al.

The two blank spaces following Zn (zinc) in the fifth row indicate that the next heavier element, As (arsenic), was moved two places to

Table 5.3 Mendelyeev's Periodic Classification of the Elements

	Group I R_2O	Group II RO	Group III R_2O_3	Group IV RH_4 RO_2	Group V RH_3 R_2O_5	Group VI RH_2 RO_3	Group VII RH R_2O_7	Group VIII RO_4 (Hydrides) (Oxides)	No. of Elements
1	H=1								1
2	Li=7	Be=9.4	B=11	C=12	N=14	O=16	F=19		7
3	Na=23	Mg=24	Al=27.3	Si=28	P=31	S=32	Cl=35.5		7
4	K=39	Ca=40	—	Ti=48	V=51	Cr=52	Mn=55	Fe=56, Co=59, Ni=59	10
5	Cu=63	Zn=65	—	—	As=75	Se=78	Br=80		7
6	Rb=85	Sr=87	?Yt=88	Zr=90	Nb=94	Mo=96	—	Ru=104, Rh=104, Pd=106	10
7	Ag=108	Cd=112	In=115	Sn=118	Sb=122	Te=125	I=127		7
8	Cs=133	Ba=137	?Di=138	?Ce=140	—	—	—	— — —	10
9	—	—	—	—	—	—	—		7
10	—	—	?Er=178	?La=180	Ta=182	W=184	—	Os=195, Ir=197, Pt=198	10
11	Au=199	Hg=200	Tl=204	Pb=207	Bi=208	—	—	— — —	7
12	—	—	—	Th=231	—	U=240	—	— — —	10

the right into Group V because of its properties. Mendelyeev predicted
the eventual discovery of two new elements with atomic weights intermediate between Zn and As and with properties resembling those of
the Group III and Group IV elements, respectively.

The boldness of Mendelyeev's approach can be readily appreciated
from the plan of his table just described. Mendelyeev went even further than this: wherever possible, he made numerical predictions of
measurable physical properties, such as the density and boiling point
of the hypothesized missing elements and the properties of some of
their compounds. One remarkable example is offered by his predictions pertaining to the missing element under Ti in Group IV. He
called this hypothetical element "Eka-silicon," and predicted the following properties for it.

> Atomic weight: 72
> Density: 5.5 g/cm^3
> Oxide: white solid, density 4.7 g/cm^3
> Chloride: liquid, boiling point < 100°C, density 1.9 g/cm^3

Fifteen years later, a new element with the properties as listed
below was discovered in 1886 by Clemens Winkler, a german chemist,
who named it germanium (Ge).

> Atomic weight: 72.5
> Density: 5.46 g/cm^3
> Oxide: white solid, density 4.7 g/cm^3
> Chloride: liquid, boiling point 86°C, density 1.887 g/cm^3

The agreement with the properties predicted by Mendelyeev for "Eka-
silicon" is little short of amazing.

Most of the blank spaces left by Mendelyeev in his periodic table
were eventually filled by newly discovered elements, each one having
properties quite close to those predicted for the corresponding missing element. The surprise value of these fulfilled predictions con-
vincingly confirms that Mendelyeev's scheme of leaving blank spaces
was not a makeshift device but an expression of his insight into the
detailed relationships between elements.

In the light of Mendelyeev's table, let us review some of the relationships between atomic weight and properties of the elements discussed in previous sections of this chapter. First, consider Döbereiner's rule of triads in relation to Mendelyeev's classification. We
noted earlier that this rule (that the atomic weight of one member of
a triad is approximately equal to the average of the atomic weights of
the other two) applies to many, but not all, triads of elements known
in Döbereiner's day. In particular, we saw that it works for the following triads: [Li, Na, K], [Cl, Br, I], [Ca, Sr, Ba]. But it does not
work for another well-known triad, [Cu, Ag, Au]. Is there a difference, on the basis of Mendelyeev's table, between triads for which
Döbereiner's rule holds and those for which it does not?

Referring to Table 5.3, we see that Li, Na, and K are the second,
third, and fourth elements, respectively, of Group I, and that exactly

the same number of elements (i.e., 6) lie between Li and Na as between Na and K, when we read the table serially. Ca, Sr, Ba are the third, fifth, and seventh elements of Group II, and again, the number of elements (including blank spaces) which lie between Ca and Sr is the same as that lying between Sr and Ba—the number being 16 this time. Similarly, Cl, Br, and I are the second, fourth, and sixth elements of Group VII, and 16 elements lie between Cl and Br as well as between Br and I. We see that Cu, Ag, and Au are the fifth, seventh and eleventh elements of Group I, and there are 16 elements lying between Cu and Ag and 36 elements between Ag and Au.

The observations just described suggest the following generalization: Döbereiner's rule holds for those triads in which the number of elements intervening between the first and second members, according to Mendelyeev's table, is equal to the number of elements intervening between the second and third members. This generalization requires that the atomic weight increase fairly regularly from one element to the next. The student should examine the table to see how closely this condition is met.

Now compare Mendelyeev's table with Table 5.2, which we constructed on the basis of Meyer's graphs. In contrast with Mendelyeev's table, having only eight groups, Table 5.2 resembles a periodic table of what is called the long form. If we filled in the missing elements in Table 5.2, the long-form table would have periods containing 1, 7, 7, 17, 17, ... elements. The correspondence is clear between this pattern and that of Mendelyeev's table, in which the numbers of elements in the successive periods are 1, 7, 7, 10, 7, 10, 7, ... Now look into the pattern of Mendelyeev's table in somewhat greater detail.

In going through Mendelyeev's table, after we reach Al, the successive elements in a given family, for instance, K and Rb (both alkali metals) or Ca and Sr, are separated by a long period of 16 intervening elements. This shift from short to long periods had been clearly shown by Meyer's graphs. Mendelyeev broke the long periods (K through B being the first) into two subperiods of 7 elements each, with 3 elements (Fe, Co, and Ni in this case) set aside as a bridge between the two subperiods. The corresponding elements of the two subperiods of a long period resemble each other only in valence. The bridging elements differ but slightly from one another in atomic weight and are all hard metals. They were put aside into group VIII, a new group created for them. Similarly, the next long period of 17 elements, from Rb through I, was divided into two subperiods, with Ru, Rh, and Pd as bridging elements placed in group VIII. The result of this procedure was that the families of elements were somewhat interwoven. Starting from the fourth period, elements of a given group which belonged to the fourth, sixth, and eighth periods are members of one family, and those in the fifth, seventh, and ninth are members of another family. Each column, as a whole, included elements from two families which resembled each other chiefly in that they formed compounds having similar formulas.

Mendelyeev placed a somewhat greater emphasis on the chemical property of valence in forming his periodic table than on the physical properties such as density and melting point. Today, the concept of valence as used by Mendelyeev has been superseded by more modern ideas on the structure of atoms and compounds. One difficulty with the classical concept of valence is that many elements have not one, but several different valence values, with the result that elements in different groups may turn out to have a common valence value. The concept of valence is sufficiently important to warrant a little further study—if only for the historical reason that it was this idea which mainly guided Mendelyeev in constructing his table.

Earlier in this chapter, we indicated how valence was determined for elements which combine either with H or OH: the number of H atoms (or OH groups, as the case may be) which combine with one atom of a given element indicates the valence of that element. But some elements were not known to combine with either H or OH, and others were known to combine with these only to yield rather unstable hydrides and hydroxides. Oxygen combines with nearly all elements to form stable oxides, so it is more convenient to use this as a standard. Since one atom of O combines with two atoms of H to form H_2O, the valence of O is 2. Some elements do not always have the same valence. O sometimes has a valence of 1. But this occurs only in compounds known as peroxides, e.g., H_2O_2, Na_2O_2, which are unstable and fairly easy to recognize. Any element which, in forming oxides other than peroxides, combines atom-for-atom with oxygen has a valence of 2: for example, MgO, CaO. If two atoms of a given element combine with one of O, the element is univalent: for example, Na_2O, Cl_2O. In general, if an element X has an oxide (other than the peroxide) whose formula is $X_m O_n$, X has the valence of $2n/m$.

Returning to Mendelyeev's periodic classification, we list in Table 5.4 the oxides of a few typical elements of each group, in which the valences of these elements are characteristic of the group.

Table 5.4 Formulas of Selected Oxides Showing
Characteristic Valence of Each Group

Group	Oxides	Valence
I	Na_2O, K_2O, Cu_2O, Ag_2O	1
II	MgO, CaO, ZnO	2
III	B_2O_3, Al_2O_3	3
IV	CO_2, SiO_2	4
V	P_4O_{10}	5
VI	SO_3, CrO_3	6
VII	F_2O, Cl_2O	1
VIII	RuO_4, OsO_4	8

It was Mendelyeev's intention, in numbering the groups, I, II, III, etc., that these numbers should indicate the valence of the elements in each group. As mentioned earlier, this simple regularity does not always hold. In the first four groups it holds fairly well; in the other four groups many of the elements do not have a unique valence but several different valence values. Usually the valence values of an element include the number of the group it is in, but sometimes an element has a valence equal to *8 minus its group number*: for example, nitrogen (group V) has two valences, 5 and 3, and each of the halogens (group VII) has a single valence of 1.

Theoretical exploration:

In order to sharpen his understanding of Mendelyeev's approach, the student should work out the following problem as an exercise.

5.6 In Table 5.3, designate the missing element between Ca and Ti in the fourth period by X. Also designate the missing element just below X (next to Zn) by Y. Given the information in Table 5.5 about the elements neighboring X and Y, make "predictions" of the corresponding properties of the "undiscovered" elements. Check these "predictions" by reference to a chemical handbook. ∎

Table 5.5 Chart for Exercise 5.6

	Atomic weight	Oxide	Density	Melting pt. °C
Al	27.3	Al_2O_3	2.71	658.6
Ca	40	CaO	1.55	851
Ti	48	TiO_2	4.5	1812
Zn	65	ZnO	7.14	419.5
As	75	As_2O_5	5.7	817 (36 atm)
Yt	88	Yt_2O_3	5.57	1475
Zr	90	ZrO_2	6.4	1852
X	–	–	–	–
Y	–	–	–	–

SOME LATER DEVELOPMENTS IN PERIODIC CLASSIFICATION

We have traced the course of historical developments which brought increasingly greater order and system into the field of chemistry during the mid-nineteenth century. The essential feature of these developments was classification, or the grouping of elements in accordance with certain similarities. We saw, in forming these groupings, the emphasis shifted from such qualitative properties as color, smell, texture, type of reaction with water, and alkalinity or acidity of the product, to more quantitative properties such as density, melting point, valence, and atomic volume. We also saw the great impact of atomic theory, and its fundamental concept of atomic weight, in enabling the definition of such quantitative properties as the last two just mentioned, and, ordering the elements to reveal the relations between all of these properties. Using mathematical terminology, we may summarize this relationship in the following law: *The properties of elements are periodic functions of their atomic weight*—because graphs of quantitative measures of many properties of elements plotted against their atomic weights look something like Fig. 5.1 showing regular, wavelike ups and downs. But once the quantitative relations had been worked out, it became clear that qualitative properties of elements were ordered in the same way.

We have just seen that the simple, periodic relation between valence and atomic weight which Mendelyeev envisaged does not always hold. For example, valence is not a periodic function of atomic weight, because a function can have only one value for each argument and most elements have more than one valence. Also, if the student examines the atomic weights listed in a modern periodic table, he will find one exception to the rule that the elements were arranged in order of increasing atomic weight. This exception occurs in the case of Te and I: The atomic weight of Te is 127.6, but the atomic weight of I, which comes after Te, is only 126.9. The similarity between Te and Se is so close that Te unmistakably belongs in Group VI, and I, just as unmistakably, belongs in Group VII with the other halogens, F, Cl, and Br. In his understandable enthusiasm for his periodic law, Mendelyeev convinced himself that the then–accepted atomic weight of Te (128) was incorrect, and estimated it as 125, thus putting Te before I in order of atomic weight. Subsequent and more accurate determinations of the atomic weights of Te and I yielded the values cited above, showing Mendelyeev to have been wrong in believing that the ordering by atomic weight held with absolute regularity. There is this single exception to his rule. Let us now briefly consider other more recent developments in the periodic law to see how fruitful the work of Mendelyeev and Meyer was.

The recognition that there was a definite pattern in the periodic groupings of the elements naturally led to speculations as to why the elements should group themselves so neatly. Such speculations and questions prompted chemists and physicists of the late-nineteenth and early-twentieth centuries to delve deeper into the nature of matter. Inquiry into the structure of the atoms of the diverse elements was begun. The key to the answer lay in the recognition that the atoms of all the different elements were composed of but a few kinds of *elementary particles*.

Current theory accepts the view that some of the constituent particles of which atoms are composed are electrically charged. For a given atom, exactly one half of the charged particles bear positive charges and the other half, negative charges of equal magnitude. The number of positively charged particles (known as protons) or, equivalently, of negatively charged particles (known as electrons) in an atom of a given element is called the **atomic number** of that element.

The study of the structure of atoms was very greatly aided near the beginning of the twentieth century by the study of spectra. Elements can be made to give off light in several ways—for example, by passing an electric current through their vapors. When such light from an element is suitably passed through a prism or, better yet, a finely ruled grating, a characteristic pattern of colored lines is produced. When metallic elements are used as the "target" in high-power X-ray machines, spectra of the X-rays can be formed by using the surface of a crystal instead of a ruled grating. From the X-ray spectra of metals, a British physicist named Henry Gwyn-Jeffreys Moseley was able to determine many atomic numbers experimentally, thus confirming the positions assigned by Mendelyeev. Atomic number, it turns out, is a more fundamental quantity than atomic weight. Mendelyeev's arrangement of the elements is found to agree exactly (without a single exception) with the order of increasing atomic number. Te and I, which are out of order in terms of atomic weight, are no longer so in terms of their atomic numbers—52 and 53, respectively.

In 1904 Lord Rayleigh and Sir William Ramsay were given the Nobel Prize in chemistry for their contributions to the discovery of an entirely new family of elements, the *rare gases*: helium, neon, argon, krypton, and xenon. Until quite recently these gases were thought not to form compounds, so the principal means of identifying them was by the characteristic spectra of the light they omit. Interestingly the spectrum of helium had been detected in the atmosphere of the sun nearly thirty years before Ramsay studied the spectrum of a sample of this gas isolated from certain minerals. This evidence that the sun contained helium led to its being named after *helios*—the sun. These new elements had not been missed from the periodic table and their discovery was a great surprise. The reason for this is that they form an entire new column in the periodic table, falling immediately before the alkali metals or after hydrogen and the halogens. (See Table 5.6.) Adding this new column did nothing to disturb the rest of the periodic system. It was as easily added as its absence had been easily overlooked. When all of the atomic numbers had been determined, they confirmed the placement of these elements and revealed no further gaps.

Not only have recent developments fully confirmed the general conclusion that the chemical elements form a system which relates chemical behavior and observable qualities to quantitative properties of elements, but this system has also been thoroughly explained in terms of atomic structure. It is scarcely conceivable that modern theories of the structure of atoms could have developed without prior

Table 5.6 A Modern Periodic Table of the Elements

Period	Subperiod	Group O	Group I		Group II		Group III		Group IV		Group V		Group VI		Group VII		Group VIII		
			A	B	A	B	A	B	A	B	A	B	A	B	A	B			
1	1			1 Hydrogen H																
2	2	2 Helium He	3 Lithium Li		4 Beryllium Be			5 Boron B		6 Carbon C		7 Nitrogen N		8 Oxygen O		9 Fluorine F			
3	3	10 Neon Ne	11 Sodium Na		12 Magnesium Mg			13 Aluminum Al		14 Silicon Si		15 Phosphorus P		16 Sulfur S		17 Chlorine Cl			
4	4	18 Argon A	19 Potassium K		20 Calcium Ca		21 Scandium Sc		22 Titanium Ti		23 Vanadium V		24 Chromium Cr		25 Manganese Mn		26 Iron Fe	27 Cobalt Co	28 Nickel Ni
4	5			29 Copper Cu		30 Zinc Zn		31 Gallium Ga		32 Germanium Ge		33 Arsenic As		34 Selenium Se		35 Bromine Br			
5	6	36 Krypton Kr	37 Rubidium Rb		38 Strontium Sr		39 Yttrium Y		40 Zirconium Zr		41 Niobium Nb		42 Molybdenum Mo		43 Technetium Tc		44 Ruthenium Ru	45 Rhodium Rh	46 Palladium Pd
5	7			47 Silver Ag		48 Cadmium Cd		49 Indium In		50 Tin Sn		51 Antimony Sb		52 Tellurium Te		53 Iodine I			
6	8	54 Xenon Xe	55 Cesium Cs		56 Barium Ba		71 Lutetium Lu		72 Hafnium Hf		73 Tantalum Ta		74 Wolfram W		75 Rhenium Re		76 Osmium Os	77 Iridium Ir	78 Platinum Pt
6	Lanthanides (Rare earths)	57 Lanthanum La		58 Cerium Ce	59 Prageodymium Pr	60 Neodymium Nd		61 Promethium Pm	62 Samarium Sm	63 Europium Eu		64 Gadolinium Gd		65 Terbium Tb	66 Dysprosium Dy	67 Holmium Ho		68 Erbium Er	69 Thulium Tm	70 Ytterbium Yb
6	9			79 Gold Au		80 Mercury Hg		81 Thallium Tl		82 Lead Pb		83 Bismuth Bi		84 Polonium Po		85 Astatine At			
7	8	86 Radon Rn	87 Francium Fr		88 Radium Ra															
7	Actinides (Rare earths)	89 Actinium Ac		90 Thorium Th	91 Protactinium Pa	92 Uranium U		93 Neptunium Np	94 Plutonium Pu	95 Americium Am		96 Curium Cm		97 Berkelium Bk	98 Californium Cf	99 Einsteinium Es		100 Fermium Fm	101 Mendelevium Md	102 Kobelium Nb

establishment of the order and system in the field of chemistry that were brought about by the periodic classification of elements according to atomic weight. Theories of science are always subject to modification, though the successive modifications required by further evidence usually seem to grow smaller. We should not make the mistake of believing that the final truth has been determined, though we can be proud that great progess has been made.

METHODOLOGICAL REVIEW

In our evaluation of Mendelyeev's periodic law we have brought to bear a new criterion for judging the merits of a scientific theory or system: to what extent does it point out directions in which further inquiries and investigations can fruitfully be made? Such new investigations may change and even result in the overthrow of the theory which suggested them; but this does not detract from the scientific contribution made by the older theory. It is as a means to further advances in understanding nature that we must judge the products of the creative imagination and patient investigations of such scientists as Mendelyeev and Lothar Meyer.

Our conception of a scientific theory as consisting of a model together with an interpretation (see p. 72), carries with it the suggestion that absolute finality should not be expected. For the term *model* suggests the idea of an incomplete imitation (of nature) and not an exact replica. Scientists understandably become quite emotionally involved in their work, and a word which reminds them continually that their work may be improved upon by later workers may be beneficial. If a scientist claims that he has discovered the precise nature of matter, he may find difficulty in accepting negative criticism. But if he says merely that he has constructed an improved model of matter, then while he can be justly proud of his contribution, he can also more readily admit that it has limitations. How can the contributions discussed in this chapter be interpreted on the view of chemical theory as providing some sort of model of the structure of matter?

At the end of Chapter 4, it was pointed out that Dalton's atomic theory had a logical structure like a "network" of links which was anchored at so few points to the data of chemical experiments that no isolated portion of it could be stable. Only by obtaining data on a great many compounds interrelated by common elements could numerical values be found for atomic weights and for chemical formulas that made all such links fit into a stable structure. Avogadro's principle made possible independent determinations of the molecular weights of the gaseous compounds. It thereby confirmed many of the values determined by Dalton's method, so that we might say that a new type of link had been invented which fitted well the structure already built.

In Meyer's graphs and Mendelyeev's table, qualitative and quantitative connections between elements were established by virtue of the similar properties of adjacent elements in the groups and periods. These were mostly new connections. The Daltonian links connected elements in a compound, and most of these links occur between non-adjacent elements in the periodic table. (The student may be interested in seeing how many exceptions to this rule he can find.) The conviction carried by these new relations between elements is quite significant, because of the great "surprise value" of the confirmed predictions Mendelyeev's table led to. By the addition of such strong new links, considerable rigidity was added to the model of chemical theory.

At this point in the development of chemistry, atomic theory had become extremely well stabilized—and, as one would expect, very well accepted. How could there be anything wrong with the system of atomic weights when three different approaches (based respectively on atomic weight-formula relations, weight-volume relations in gases, and periodic classification of elements) all fitted together so beautifully?

Each approach, taken in isolation, must be recognized as model-building of a very limited, empirical sort—just finding a model to fit the given data. Such an approach is not to be trusted too highly, because there are always many ways of fitting a model to a finite collection of data. We gain more confidence if, upon putting together several sets of links, we can construct a broadly consistent and unified structure. Even then there is no guarantee that the unified structure is *complete*—even if, as in this case, the three sets of links are found to fit together almost perfectly. But even when many thousands of individual facts fit precisely with a given model, it is still true that other models could fit these data as well and yet yield different predictions of unobserved phenomena. At any given time, it is only man's limited capacity to generate more elegant theories to fit his knowledge that leads him to accept existing theories as believable accounts of nature.

When it turned out that a piece had been missing from the period table which had not been noticed in the same way that other gaps were, there was no feeling of failure or defeat—quite the contrary. Usually a theoretical model gains strength by the discovery that it is incomplete, for it is often the case that it does not have to be torn down to fill the gap. The subsequent development of models postulating the construction of atoms from more fundamental particles have provided the means of making the relationships between different kinds of elements even more precise than in Mendelyeev's table. Such refinement of a theory is always to be expected, and even hoped for, as science develops.

PROBLEMS

1. A chemist of the latter half of the nineteenth century has just discovered what appears to be a new element. After prolonged research, he has been able to find only one oxide of this element. In

Table 5.7 Chart for Problem 1

	I	II	III	IV	V	VI	VII	VIII
1	$H=1$ H_2O H_2O_2							
2	$Li=7$ Li_2O	$Be=9.4$ BeO	$B=11$ B_2O_3	$C=12$ CO CO_2	$N=14$ NO NO_2 N_2O N_2O_3	$O=16$ O_2	$F=19$ F_2O	
3	$Na=23$ Na_2O	$Mg=24$ MgO	$Al=27.3$ Al_2O_3	$Si=28$ SiO_2	$P=31$ P_2O_3 P_2O_4	$S=32$ SO_2 SO_3	$Cl=35.5$ Cl_2O ClO_2	
4	$K=39$ K_2O	$Ca=40$ CaO		$Ti=49$ TiO Ti_2O_3 TiO_2	$V=51$ VO VO_2 V_2O_3	$Cr=52$ CrO_3 Cr_2O_3	$Mn=55$ MnO Mn_2O_3 MnO_2	$Fe=56$ FeO Fe_2O_3 Fe_3O_4 $Co=59$ CoO Co_2O_3 Co_3O_4 $Ni=59$ NiO Ni_3O_4 NiO_2
5	$Cu=63$ Cu_2O CuO	$Zn=65$ ZnO			$As=75$ As_2O_3 As_2O_5	$Se=78$ SeO_2	$Br=80$ $HBrO_3$	
6			$Y=88$ Y_2O_3	$Zr=90$ ZrO_2	$Nb=94$ Nb_2O_3	$Mo=96$ Mo_2O_3 MoO_3		$Ru=104$ Ru_2O_3 RuO_2 RuO_4 $Rh=104$ RhO Rh_2O_3 Rh_2O $Pd=106$ PdO PdO_2
7	$Ag=108$ Ag_2O Ag_2O_2	$Cd=112$ CdO	$In=113$ In_2O_3	$Sn=118$ SnO SnO_2	$Sb=122$ Sb_2O_3 Sb_2O_4	$Te=125$ TeO_2 TeO_3	$I=127$ I_2O I_2O_5	

this oxide, 15 parts (by weight) of the new element combine with 8 parts of oxygen.

Table 5.7 shows the elements known to him as well as their known oxides. In which of the six blank spaces in the table does his new element probably belong? Present the necessary calculations and arguments to support his best choice, including reasons why the other blank spaces are inferior choices.

Elements having atomic weights greater than that of I (127) are not shown in the table and need not be considered. The student should attempt to determine the maximum atomic weight the new element could have, based on the fact that it has a combining-weight proprtion of 15:8 with oxygen.

2. In Table 5.8 the atomic volumes of a number of elements are given. These values of the classical concept of atomic volume are determined by mass and volume measurements on samples of elements in the solid state, as described on pages 152-153. This concept is

Table 5.8 Two Measures of the Volume of Atoms (and Their Difference) for Selected Elements

Element		Volume of atoms in bulk ($\mathring{A}^3$)	Volume of atoms as individuals ($\mathring{A}^3$)	Difference between bulk and individual volumes
Aluminum	(Al)	16.6	11.8	4.8
Argon	(A)	39.6	29.2	10.4
Arsenic	(As)	21.8	8.2	13.6
Berylium	(Be)	8.2	6.0	2.2
Bromine	(Br)	42.5	6.1	36.4
Calcium	(Ca)	43.0	31.8	11.2
Carbon	(C)	9.0	1.9	7.1
Chlorine	(Cl)	28.1	3.8	24.3
Chromium	(Cr)	12.0	8.9	3.1
Germanium	(Ge)	22.4	11.4	11.0
Hydrogen	(H)	18.8	14.2	4.6
Iodine	(I)	42.7	10.3	32.4
Iron	(Fe)	11.8	8.4	3.4
Krypton	(Kr)	46.2	33.5	12.7
Lithium	(Li)	21.6	16.1	5.5
Magnesium	(Mg)	23.2	17.2	6.0
Neon	(Ne)	23.2	17.1	6.0
Potassium	(K)	74.7	56.5	18.2
Phosphorus	(P)	28.2	5.3	22.9
Ruthenium	(Ru)	13.8	10.0	3.8
Selenium	(Se)	27.2	6.5	20.7
Silicon	(Si)	19.9	6.7	13.2
Sodium	(Na)	39.8	29.4	10.4
Sulfur	(S)	25.7	5.0	20.7

referred to as the atomic volume in bulk. The unit chosen here is $\overset{\circ}{A}^3$ (1 angstrom, written 1 Å, is equal to one ten-billionth of a meter), instead of the unit chosen on page 153.

Atomic diameter is defined on a different basis in the modern theory of atomic structure. From the atomic diameter can be derived a measure of the volume of atoms based only on the theoretical structure of atoms. This measure is unaffected by possible variations in size that might occur when atoms are packed together to form a solid and may be called the individual atomic volume. These values, also in $\overset{\circ}{A}^3$, are shown in the third column of Table 5.8.

a. For each element listed, plot a point having individual atomic volume and atomic volume in bulk as its coordinates.

b. Draw straight lines connecting points so plotted for members of each family of elements. Table 5.6 identifies the families as the subgroups, IA, IB, IIA, etc.

c. Determine which families of elements show evidence, in the diagram so obtained, that their atoms are the most highly compressed in bulk form? Which are the least compressed?

d. Plot the difference between atomic volume in bulk and individual atomic volume for each element listed in Table 5.8 (fourth column) against atomic number.

e. State any conclusions you can draw from these data by means of your graphs.

SUPPLEMENTARY READINGS

Benfey, O. Theodor. *Classics in the Theory of Chemical Combination.* Volume I of Classics of Science (Gerald Holton, ed.). New York: Dover, 1963.
Original papers of chemists who elaborated the atomic theory of Dalton, Berzelius, and Mendelyeev into substantial contact with the vast diversity of substances. Difficult but rewarding reading in scientific "detective work."

Boorse, Henry A. and Motz, Lloyd. *The World of the Atom*, Vols. I and II. New York: Basic Books, Inc., 1966.
Selections 20 (Mendelyeev), 53 (van der Brock), and 54 (Moseley) are recommended readings for this chapter.

Bronowski, J. *The Common Sense of Science*. Cambridge, Mass.: Harvard University Press, 1955.
Chapter IV, on "The Eighteenth Century and the Idea of Order," provides an interesting discussion of the thesis that classification, such as classification of the elements, was a style of science that came into full sway in many fields in the 18th century.

Findlay, Alexander. *A Hundred Years of Chemistry*. London: Duckworth, 1937.

Chapters III, X, and XI summarize the history of the development of periodic classification of the elements, the discovery of new elements and the beginnings of the modern theory of atomic structure.

Garrett, Alfred B. *The Flash of Genius*. Princeton, N. J.: D. Van Nostrand Co., 1963.
Readings related to this chapter include selection 23 (Helium) from Part 1; and from Part 2, selections 4 (Moseley), 5 (The Curies), 7 and 8 (Transmutation), 15 (Mendelyeev), and 21 (Argon).

Handbook of Chemistry and Physics (11th edition). Cleveland, Ohio: Chemical Rubber Co., 1959.
Contains tables of the elements giving their properties, including special tables of the density, specific heat, melting and boiling points of the elements.

Hecht, Selig. *Explaining the Atom*. New York: Viking, 1950.
A very clearly written account of the development of modern conceptions of the atom, starting from the periodic law.

Jaffe, Bernard. *Crucibles: The Story of Chemistry*. New York: Fawcett (A Premier Book), 1957.
Chapter 9 contains interesting biographical material on Mendelyeev.

Jones, G. O., Rotblat, J. and Whitrow, G. J. *Atoms and the Universe*. New York: Scribner's, 1956.
"An account of modern views on the structure of matter and the universe." Authoritative and readable.

Seaborg, Glenn T. and Valens, Evans G. *Elements of the Universe*. New York: E. P. Dutton & Company, Inc., 1958.
A readable and well-illustrated account of elements 1-102 and their discovery. The senior author was codiscoverer of nine elements.

Singer, Charles. *A Short History of Scientific Ideas to 1900*. New York: Oxford University Press, 1959.
Pages 454-458 summarize the work of chemists such as those whose work is represented in the Benfey collection.

Weisskopf, Victor F. *Knowledge and Wonder; the Natural World as Man Knows It*. Garden City, N. Y.: Doubleday (Anchor Books), 1962.
An interesting extension of scientific thought, from the classical science this book portrays into modern physics and biology.

6

HEAT EXCHANGES AND
THE CONSERVATION OF HEAT

Heat exchanges, gas phenomena, optics, and electricity are the principal subjects of scientific investigation not yet discussed which contributed to the development of the atomic physics and chemistry of the late nineteenth century. Some understanding of these topics is required to demonstrate the interlocking structure of physics and chemistry as they emerged at the turn of the century. These topics not only constitute key parts of the foundation on which modern physical science is built, but they also serve extremely well our second purpose—that of developing an understanding of the procedures of scientific thought. One finds in them new applications of procedures already studied as well as some very important new ones. We shall examine aspects of these four subjects in the remaining chapters of this book.

The study of heat provides an excellent subject for further understanding of the interplay of experimental and theoretical procedures, because in it a few simple experiments suffice for setting up a theory. In this it resembles the science of mechanics; but it differs from mechanics in the greater subtlety of the problems of measurement encountered. In studying heat the student may emulate the methodology of Chapter 2, conducting experiments himself and constructing equations to represent the relationships between physical quantities—procedures he could only follow vicariously in Chapter 4 because of the more complex laboratory techniques of quantitative chemistry.

We depart from our previous practice in that we shall not attempt to place this chapter in an historical setting. The reason is that the historical development of the first mathematical theory of heat exchanges is complicated throughout by the conception, later discarded, of a subtle fluid known as the caloric fluid. For our present purposes, a more direct development of a mathematical model representing heat phenomena seems desirable. Like the concept of phlogiston in eighteenth century chemistry and the concept of celestial spheres in pre-Newtonian astronomy, the caloric fluid provided the substantive type of conceptual model that was demanded in an age in which purely mathematical models were still regarded with great suspicion. Even

Kepler's and Newton's elegant and accurate equations of celestial motion, for most pre-twentieth century scientists (Kepler and Newton included), needed to be supplemented by the conception of a medium which could transmit force from one celestial body to another.

Interaction of two bodies separated by empty space was inconceivable to scientists of a mechanistically oriented age. But ours is an age in which most physical scientists readily accept mathematical models without requiring a mechanical model to go with them. Since we have already had adequate opportunity to see the useful role that imaginary substances can play in temporarily organizing observational data until a mathematical model can be developed, we shall pay less attention to mechanical models than we did in the case of the celestial spheres and that of the transition from the Aristotelian four-principle theory of the theory of elementary substances. We shall proceed to construct mathematical models as directly as possible to represent the available data in order to study more closely the nature and power of this method.

A basic necessity in most mathematical model building is some means of associating numbers with observations. One naturally thinks of measurements as playing this role. (Mathematical models are possible which do not depend on numbers and such models are useful in the biological and social sciences, but we will not encounter any in this book.) Any systematic procedure for producing a number for each observation of a physical property may be called measurement. In previous chapters we have employed measurements of distance, angle, time, force, mass, and other quantities, without giving a great deal of attention to the procedures themselves because they are quite familiar to most people. It frequently happens, in the development of a new theory, that new quantities are proposed. When this happens, the quantities must either be given explicit theoretical definitions or suitable procedures for measuring them must be found. For example, in our reconstruction of Newtonian mechanics (Chapter 2) *force* was first introduced into the theory by means of a measurement procedure and later by a theoretical definition. The quantities—*combining proportions*, *valence*, and *atomic volume*—had to be measured or defined in terms of quantities that had already been introduced, such as *distance*, *mass*, and *weight*.

In our present investigation, we shall eventually find it possible to define the quantity of heat lost or gained by an object, but such a definition can only be the result of the study of heat exchanges and thus cannot be a prerequisite to such study. We necessarily begin with our vague, everyday notion of heat. There is one quantity sufficiently familiar that it can contribute significantly to the development of a mathematical model of heat exchanges—the concept of temperature. Although we assume that the measurement of temperatures by a thermometer is a familiar procedure, there are several presuppositions about such measurements which the student should consider at the outset.

PRESUPPOSITIONS IN THE MEASUREMENT
OF TEMPERATURE

All measurement presupposes certain regularities which make standard procedures meaningful, and in some forms of measurement such regularities may be easily confirmed. In measuring force by the compression of a spring, it is easy to corroborate the basic assumption that force and amount of compression are proportional within suitable limits, since weights may be matched independently and ratios of force established as a check on the validity of the spring balance. (See p. 61.) In most cases the assumed regularities in measurements cannot be so easily checked. The measurement of temperature is dependent upon the expansion of a thermometric substance, for example. But without any standard temperature ratios, it is not easy to tell whether the expansion is proportional to temperature or not.

Methodological exploration:

6.1 The student should consider the following hypothetical case. Assume that two thermometers have been constructed using mercury for the expansion liquid and that each has been marked in two places to show the mercury levels at the freezing and boiling points of water. Suppose that the distances between the marks for boiling and freezing are not the same on the two thermometers. What would this indicate about the construction of the two thermometers? ■

6.2 Suppose that, on each thermometer, we placed a third mark half the distance between the other two. When the two thermometers are both immersed in the same water bath to the same extent, and the mercury level of one stands at the halfway mark, will the mercury level of the other also stand at the halfway mark? If we so predict, what assumptions are we making? ■

6.3 If the distance between the first two marks on each thermometer were divided into 100 equal parts, would you expect that readings made on the two thermometers would always agree when both are immersed in the same water bath? If not, what explanation could you give? ■

6.4 Suppose that two thermometers are constructed so that, with mercury in the bulbs, both agree precisely at every temperature between the 0-mark and the 100-mark. Further suppose that the mercury in one is replaced by an equal volume of another liquid so that they both agree at the 0-mark but do not agree at any other temperature including the 100-mark. Suppose that, on the thermometer containing the new thermometric substance, all the marks except the 0 mark are removed and a new top mark is made at the level of the new liquid in boiling water, so that it agrees with the other both when it reads 0 and 100. If the distance between the 0- and the new 100-mark is divided into 100 equal parts, is it possible that the two thermometers would not agree at the 50-mark? At all intermediate marks? Why? ∎

The above exercise in analysis of measurement procedures should have made it clear that the presupposition that thermal expansion is proportional to temperature cannot be checked directly. One might be faced with a variety of thermometers, containing different liquids which, though constructed so as to agree with each other at two points, do not agree on any intermediate points. One would need to find some reason for choosing one liquid rather than another as the standard thermometric substance. Such a reason can only rest on a theory that has something to say about temperature.

We shall see how a criterion of choice was finally obtained, but it was most fortunate for the early development of the science of heat that such useful liquids as mercury and alcohol did not differ markedly in their thermal expansion properties. The situation is clearly not as simple as that which prevailed in establishing a measure of force. While it was possible to produce forces in exact multiples of a given force, and do so independently of the measuring instrument, nothing of the sort could be done for temperatures. There are two points of contrast: (1) The elasticity (ratio of force to displacement) of most springs turns out to be constant, within appropriate limits, but the thermal expansion of most liquids is not. (2) There is a method for calibrating springs by multiple application of equal weights, but the thermal-expansion rates of different substances can only be compared with each other, not with an absolute standard. The measurement of temperature can only be precisely settled after the development of a theory. Typically, defining a means of measurement is a very uncertain proposition when starting an investigation into a new field of research. The presuppositions of measurement often turn out to be far less justified even than those made in connection with the use of thermometers.

MIXING HOT AND COLD WATER

Perhaps the simplest example of heat exchange we could study is the heating of an object by some means. We could use a fire, an electric hot plate, the sunlight, or some other hot object, as a means of heating the particular object we have in mind. We should choose a method that can be used quite generally and repeated precisely without difficulty. In order to draw any general conclusions from our study, it is necessary to be able to compare the conditions under which different experiments on the heating of objects were conducted. Fire and sunlight are quite variable sources of heat; the heat from a hot plate depends partly on the electrical energy consumed (which could be measured with appropriate instruments), but partly also on the construction of the hot plate and the extent of contact between plate and object.

In order to maintain uniform contact between a heat source and an object being heated, it is most convenient either to immerse the object to be heated in a hot liquid completely or to heat a liquid by immersing a hot object in it. Quantitative experimentation is also facilitated by using a liquid since it is also quite easy to measure the temperature, volume, and weight of a liquid. Let us agree to use hot water as a means of heating objects, since, if we have a reliable thermometer, it is easy to determine quite precisely how hot the water is and to repeat the experiment as often as desired with a large number of different objects.

We also need to standardize the instrument for measuring temperature. The instrument most commonly used in this kind of work is a mercury-in-glass thermometer, calibrated in **Celsius degrees** (°C). In the Celsius scale of temperature, the freezing point of water is taken as 0°C and the boiling point (under standard atmospheric pressure) as 100°C, and the distance between these two points on the mercury-in-glass thermometer is divided into 100 equal parts, each being 1°C.

What object shall we heat? The reasons for choosing a liquid as the source of heat also make it desirable to use a liquid as the object to be heated. We must be able to standardize the contact between the object being heated and the source of heat and also its contact with the instrument of measurement. By a similar argument we arrive at the conclusion that, in order to heat one liquid, we should add to it a hotter liquid—much as we do in warming up a bath by adding hot water to the water already present. The simplest possible case is to take a certain amount of cold water whose temperature and volume have been measured and add to it an *equal* volume of hot water whose temperature has also been measured. What relation will the temperature of the mixture have to the temperatures of the hot and cold water? Most people can guess the result intuitively.

Upon trying this experiment, if we are careful and we work quickly, the temperature of the mixture is about halfway between the temperatures of the cold and hot water before mixing. As usual we find some variation in the results when we repeat the experiment. On the average, our final temperature will differ by only a few degrees from the average of the two initial temperatures. There may be both random and systematic errors but they become smaller (percentagewise), the more carefully we work and the larger the quantities of water we use. After trying a variety of initial conditions, we arrive at our first empirical conclusion: *When equal quantities of water are mixed, the temperature of the mixture is (approximately) equal to the average of the initial temperatures.*

We might ask ourselves what the temperature of the mixture would be if we mixed *unequal* amounts of hot and cold water. Intuitively, we expect that if we use more hot water than cold, the temperature of the mixture will be higher than the average of the two temperatures; and, if there is more cold water than hot water, the final temperature will be lower than the average. A simple experiment shows our intuition to be correct. Using twice as much hot water as cold water, we find the mixture has a temperature higher than the average of the two original temperatures. Conversely, using twice as much cold water as hot, the result is again about what we would expect it to be: a mixture that is cooler than the average of the two temperatures.

Let us now be more quantitative and determine just how much higher, or how much lower, than the average temperature is the temperature of the mixture. Just how do the unequal amounts of hot and cold water affect the result of mixing? Could it be that, if we use twice as much hot water as cold, the final temperature will be, so to speak, "twice as close to" (that is, half as far from) the initial hot temperature as to the initial cold temperature? Take 40 cc of hot water at 99°C, and mix it with 20 cc of cold water at 21°C. Carrying out this experiment, we get a mixture whose temperature is something like 71° or 72°. Is this consistent with our hunch?

What is the temperature which is "twice as close" to 99°C as it is to 21°C? That is, can we find a number between 21 and 99 such that its difference from 21 is twice as large as its difference from 99? If we divide the difference between 21 and 99 into three equal parts, the required temperature is one part away from 99°, hence two parts away from 21°. $(99 - 21)/3 = 78/3 = 26$. The desired temperature is $99 - 26 = 73°$. (As an arithmetic check, $73 - 21 = 52 = 26 \times 2$.) If on actually performing the above experiment we find the temperature to be 71° or 72°, we may conclude that the result is consistent within a degree or two with our hypothesis: when using twice as much hot water as cold, the temperature of the mixture will be "twice as close" to the hot temperature as it is to the cold. Analogous results are obtained if we use three times, four times, etc., as much water at one temperature as water at the other temperature. If the amounts of water at the two temperatures stand in some ratio, say 3:2, the differences between the final temperature and the two initial temperatures, respectively, will be in the same ratio, i.e., 3:2, in this case. Figuring it differently, the final temperature will be located *three fifths* of the way from the initial temperature of the *smaller* amount of water to the initial temperature of the *larger* amount of water.

The empirical conclusion stated verbally above can be expressed more compactly in the form of an equation. To make the expression perfectly general, we shall use variables for the hot and cold temperatures (instead of particular temperatures like 99° and 21°). We shall also use variables for the amounts of water. With water, it makes no practical difference whether we use volume in cubic centimeters or mass in grams as the measure of amount. Prior to any theoretical development, we are not in a position to do more than follow a hunch. Faced with such a choice, we may wish to measure the quantity of water in a way that is as generally applicable as possible. For most objects, some volume expansion or contraction occurs with change in temperature, and for some substances the change is quite appreciable. But mass is constant over changes in temperature, so it would seem to be the better measure to use.

We shall let m_H and m_C be the masses in grams of the hot and cold water, and let t_H and t_C stand for the respective temperatures in degrees Celsius. The temperature of the mixture, or the final temperature, t_F is, according to our empirical conclusion, given equivalently by either

$$t_F = t_H - (t_H - t_C)\,\frac{m_C}{m_H + m_C} \quad \text{or}$$

$$t_F = t_C + (t_H - t_C)\,\frac{m_H}{m_H + m_C}$$

The student should verify that these two expressions do indeed give the same result for t_F. One way to do this is to express the entire right-hand member of each equation in terms of a common denominator, $(m_H + m_C)$. The first equation then becomes

$$t_F = \frac{t_H(m_H + m_C) - (t_H - t_C)m_C}{m_H + m_C} \quad \text{or}$$

$$t_F = \frac{t_H m_H + t_C m_C}{m_H + m_C}$$

It can be shown that the second equation reduces to exactly the same form when the right-hand side is written with the same common denominator. The relation just expressed can also be written in slightly modified form as follows:

$$t_F = t_H\left(\frac{m_H}{m_H + m_C}\right) + t_C\left(\frac{m_C}{m_H + m_C}\right) \tag{6.1}$$

Verbally, this can be stated as follows: *The temperature of the mixture is equal to the temperature of the hot water multiplied by the proportion (in mass) of hot water in the mixture, plus the temperature of the cold water multiplied by the proportion (in mass) of cold water in the mixture.* The expression to the right of the equal sign is called a **weighted average** of the two temperatures.

In ordinary averages each quantity is multiplied by a fraction which indicates that it is "one-out-of-so-many" quantities. For example, the average of two temperatures can be expressed as half of one temperature plus half of the other (which is the same as half of the sum of the two temperatures). In a weighted average each quantity is multiplied by a fraction, called its "weight," but the "weights" need not all be equal. In the present case each "weight" is the ratio of the mass of the water at that temperature to the total mass of the mixture.

The weighted average includes the ordinary average as a special case, that is, when the "weights" are all equal. So, in Eq. (6.1), we have arrived at a general conclusion which embraces the first conclusion as a special case.

A transformation of Eq. (6.1) produces a much-simplified but equivalent equation which makes it possible to describe the process of heat transfer. If we clear the denominators in Eq. (6.1) by multiplying through by $(m_H + m_C)$, and then collect the terms involving m_H and those involving m_C on opposite sides of the equation, the result is:

$$m_H(t_H - t_F) = m_C(t_F - t_C) \tag{6.2}$$

Note that the two members of this equation are expressions for the changes in temperature undergone by the hot and cold water, respectively, *each multiplied by* the appropriate mass.

That two such products are equal, whereas the two temperature changes themselves are not (unless the two masses happen to be equal), suggests that the quantity, "temperature change *times* mass," may prove to be a more convenient measure of the capacity of one thing to warm up another than is the temperature itself. This suggests that we may define *the amount of heat transferred* as the product, *temperature change times mass*. From this interpretation, we conclude that Eq. (6.1) means that HEAT LOST (by hot water) equals HEAT GAINED (by cold water). This statement suggests, as a general hypothesis, that the total quantity of heat is conserved in heat exchanges—a generalization which is analogous to the Law of Conservation of Matter in chemical reactions. (See p. 121.) Equation (6.2) does indeed express the conservation of heat for the case when both hot and cold substances are water. It implicitly defines a unit for measuring heat change, namely, the amount of heat lost or gained when the initial mass of water and the temperature change are both unity. In order to arrive at more general conclusions, we must investigate cases in which other substances besides water are used in a heat-exchange experiment.

HEAT EXCHANGES BETWEEN OBJECTS OF
DIFFERENT MATERIALS

Let us now examine the situation in which we use water as one of the substances, but the other is of a different material, say copper. What would happen if we filled a flask with copper shot, weighed the flask and shot, heated them to 100°C by bathing the flask for a long time in a beaker of boiling water (kept boiling by a burner), and then mixed the shots with an equal mass of water at 20°C? Would the mixture have a temperature higher than, lower than, or equal to 60°C? (Since 60°C is the average of the two initial temperatures, it would be the final temperature when equal amounts of water are mixed at the given temperatures.) Here the intuition of most people fails; there is no basis for guessing the outcome. Upon carrying out the experiment, it turns out that the temperature of the mixture is considerably lower than 60°C.

The simple relationship of Eq. (6.1) between final and initial temperatures no longer holds when we use different materials in the mixing experiment. Could it be that *mass* is not an appropriate measure of the amount of matter in heat experiments involving different substances? Would it be possible to find some other means of measuring the amount of matter, such that the temperature of a mixture of two different substances would again be the weighted average of the two initial temperatures, each weight being the ratio of the amount of material at that temperature to the total amount of mixture?

We could reconsider our choice of the measure of amount of the substances involved. Would it be appropriate to measure amounts of interacting substances in terms of *volume*? To mix equal *volumes* of water and copper-shot, we would use less water (or more shot) than in our previous experiment, in which we mixed equal *masses* of these substances. This would raise the final temperature, so it is a step in the right direction. But the experiment, when carried out, shows that this step does not go far enough; the temperature of the "mixture" is still far below the new weighted average temperature. Surface area does not appear very hopeful as a measure of amount of interacting substance, since it is an ambiguous concept when applied to liquids, whose surface area depends on the shape and size of the container. But these do not exhaust all the possibilities for measuring the amount of substance. We may still, if we search hard enough, find some way of measuring equal amounts of different substances to that the law of "average temperature" will hold. We cannot hope to solve this problem all at once, but we will keep it in mind as we try to generalize our theory to cover broader and broader ranges of heat phenomena.

As our next approach to the problem of finding a mathematical representation of thermal mixtures of different substances, let us study the following related problem: can we find a way to use the formula for mixtures of hot and cold water in representing mixtures involving another substance? We found that mixing equal masses of hot metal and cold water yields a mixture whose temperature is lower than the average of the two initial temperatures. We can measure the actual temperature of the mixture, and then turn around and ask: how much hot *water*, at the same temperature as the hot metal, would have yielded a mixture of the temperature we actually got by mixing hot metal with the cold water? Taking a given amount of hot metal, how much hot water would have been *equally effective* if the water replaced the metal as the heating agent? This amounts to translating the actual mass of hot metal into an **equivalent mass** of hot water. If we do this, we need not restrict ourselves to mixing *equal* masses of hot metal and cold water in the first place, since we already know the general law for mixing unequal masses of hot and cold water, that is, Eq. (6.2).

Let us suppose that we mixed 50 g of aluminum at 100°C with 63 g of water at 20°C and found the mixture to have a temperature of 31°. How many grams of boiling water (100°C) would have produced the same effect, yielding a 31° mixture when added to 63 g of 20° water? We can find the answer directly by calculation from the general law for mixing hot and cold water. We can use either Eq. (6.1) or (6.2), the two being algebraically equivalent. The first is the more convenient form when we want to calculate the temperature of the mixture. When we already know that temperature, 31°C, the second equation is more convenient. We have the three temperatures, $t_H = 100°$, $t_C = 20°$, $t_F = 31°$, and also the mass of the cold water, $m_C = 63$ g. What we want to find is the *equivalent mass of hot water*. Denote this by $(em)_H$, and substitute in Eq. (6.2), getting

$$(em)_H (100 - 31) = (63)(31 - 20)$$

or $69 \cdot (em)_H = 693$; whence, $(em)_H = 693/69 = 10.05$ g. We see that 10 g of water at 100° could have produced about the same effect as 50 g of aluminum actually did. On the basis of this experiment, we conclude that 10 g of water is equivalent, as far as heating power is concerned, to 50 g of aluminum. Using other initial temperatures, it turns out, gives the same conclusion.

If we carry out the above experiment using 100 g of aluminum instead of 50 g, leaving all other conditions unchanged, we find the equivalent mass of hot water to be approximately 20 g, or twice the value obtained above. If 25 g of aluminum is used, the equivalent mass of hot water is found to be about 5 g. So the equivalent mass of hot water seems to be *proportional* to the actual mass of hot aluminum used. It turns out that this proportionality holds within about 5% even if the initial temperatures of aluminum and water used in the experiment vary from 0°C to 100°C. In each case, calculation shows that it takes only about 1/5 as much water (in mass) as aluminum to produce the same heating effect. Aluminum is only about 1/5 as effective as water in heating power. If such experiments are performed with great care to avoid loss of water and the loss of heat is carefully controlled, the "heating-power" constant of proportionality of aluminum to water is closer to 0.22. We therefore say that *each* gram of aluminum has a **water equivalent** of 0.22 g.

In the same manner, the water equivalent of 1 g of various other substances can be found. Table 6.1 shows the values of water equivalents, arranged in order of magnitude, for some of the common metals.

Table 6.1 Water Equivalent of 1 Gram of Several Metals with % Variation Between 20-100°C

Lead	0.03	(5%)	Zinc	0.09	(3%)
Mercury	0.03	(2%)	Copper	0.09	(2%)
Tin	0.06	(6%)	Iron	0.11	(7%)
Silver	0.06	(1%)	Aluminum	0.22	(5%)

From these, it is possible to compute the results of mixing various amounts of these substances with each other or with water at different temperatures. We can use the mass of substances and our water-mixture formula, if we introduce the appropriate constant for each substance as a multiplier of the mass.

Laboratory exploration:

6.5 As a laboratory exercise to clarify the concept of the water equivalent of a given mass of metal, the student should make mixtures of various hot metals with cold water. Very accurate results cannot be expected without good insulation against unwanted loss of heat. Care taken in measurement of the initial temperatures to insure that they are stable will be rewarded. The temperature of a mixture must be uniform throughout, but one can't wait too long, or an appreciable amount of heat will be lost to the surroundings. Compare the results obtained with the values in Table 6.1 and try to determine whether the discrepancies, if any, are in the right direction to be attributable to unwanted heat loss. If they are in the opposite direction, or are very large in either direction, try to find the cause of the error and correct it. ■

A UNIT FOR MEASURING HEAT

Having found the mass of water equivalent to 1 g of each of a number of substances, we are ready to consider calculating the amount of heat gained and lost in mixtures of different substances. Equation (6.2) has already led to the suggestion (p. 177) that it would be convenient to use, as the unit for heat, the amount of heat required to change the temperature of 1 g of water by 1°C. If we adopt this unit, Table 6.1 tells us immediately how many units of heat would be required to change the temperature of 1 g of each kind of metal by 1°C, and we can easily calculate from that how much heat is required to change the temperature of any amount of a given metal by a given number of degrees Celsius.

Before deciding to accept such a definition of a unit of heat, we should make sure that the *same* amount of heat produces a 1°C change in the temperature of 1 g of water when starting from various initial temperatures: from 30°C to 31°C, as from 67°C to 68°C, and so forth. Our evidence supporting Eqs. (6.1) and (6.2) does show that this is at least roughly so. When a unit of measurement is to be defined, we would like its use to be as reliable as possible so that if discrepancies arise in experimental results we can search for their causes, acting on the assumption that they are not due to the procedures of measurement. It turns out by careful experimentation that the amount of heat required *is* nearly the same, regardless of the initial temperature of the water, but because of a slight variation, an unambiguous definition of the unit of heat must specify the initial temperature. Conventionally, this is taken at 14.5°C. We then have as the precise definition of the unit of heat change, called a **calorie,** the amount of heat required to raise the temperature of 1 g of water from 14.5° to 15.5°C.

For most practical purposes we may regard the calorie as the amount of heat needed to raise the temperature of 1 gram of water from any initial temperature to a temperature 1°C higher. Conversely, each gram of water must lose 1 calorie of heat in order for its temperature to be lowered by 1°C. The number of calories lost or gained by any amount of water is jointly proportional to the mass of water and to the temperature change, and the constant of joint proportionality is unity. To bring to a boil 30 g of water that is initially at 20°C, we must supply it with $(30)(100 - 20) = 2400$ calories of heat. (In practice, a little more heat would be needed, for some of the heat would be absorbed by the vessel and some be radiated into the surrounding space.) Again, for 50 g of water at 95° to be cooled down to 25°C, we must take away (or, the water must lose) $50(95 - 25) = 3500$ calories of heat.

Theoretical practice:

6.6 Consider some applications of the water equivalents listed in Table 6.1 interpreted in terms of the unit, calorie. Calculate the amount of heat, in calories, required to change the temperature of various substances by specified numbers of degrees (Celsius). How many calories are needed to heat 100 grams of copper-shot from 15°C to 65°C? According to Table 6.1, 1 g of copper is equivalent to 0.09 g of water; hence, 100 g of copper is the equivalent of 9 g of water. The required amount of heat is $9(65 - 15) = 9(50) = 450$ calories. Again, if 500 g of mercury is to have its temperature lowered from 40° to 20°C, how many calories of heat must it give off? $(500)(0.03)(40 - 20) = 300$ calories. The student should test his understanding of these calculations by trying some similar calculations himself. How many calories are needed to heat 300 g of lead from 23° to 48°C? How many calories must be lost by an iron skillet of 1-kg mass in order for it to cool down from 200° to 20°C? ■

We may interpret the number listed in Table 6.1 for a given substance as the amount of heat, expressed as a fraction of a calorie, required to change the temperature of 1 g of that substance by 1°C. The calculations given above, and those done as exercises, should convince the student that this interpretation is valid. Interpreted in this way, each entry of Table 6.1 is called the **specific heat** of the particular substance named; it is the quantity of heat specifically required for a standard amount of each substance to undergo a given change. As a variable, specific heat is commonly denoted by the letter s, and we may use a subscript to indicate the particular substance. We write $s_{Al} = 0.22$, $s_{Zn} = 0.09$, using as subscripts the chemical symbols for the substances referred to.

The foregoing discussion may be summarized as follows: given the specific heat, s, of any substance, the heat change, in calories, undergone by m g of that substance when its temperature changes from $t_1°$ to $t_2°$C may be expressed as follows:

$$\Delta H =_{Df} sm(t_2 - t_1)$$

If t_2 is larger than t_1, ΔH is positive and represents *heat gained* by the substance. If t_2 is smaller than t_1, then ΔH is negative and represents heat lost. This equation expresses the relation noted earlier that the amount of heat gained or lost by any given substance undergoing temperature change is *jointly proportional* to the mass m and the magnitude of the temperature change. Note that we could not define "H" but only "ΔH." We may also use the Δ notation for temperature change analogous to the way it was used in Chapter 3, where Δd stood for a change in *distance* and Δt for a change in *time*. When we have no interest in the particular temperatures before and after heat exchange, we write

$$\Delta H =_{Df} sm \Delta t$$

In many experiments, the specific heat s plays the role of a proportionality constant in this relationship. Conventionally, s is written to the left of m, since mass can be easily varied if the substance is in the form of pellets or is a liquid. Δt is, of course, most likely to vary from one trial to another. The mathematical convention of writing constants toward the left and variables toward the right is not always easy to interpret, since what is constant in one experiment may be variable in another. The convention is followed often enough, however, to make it worth remembering. Recall that, if the substance in question is water, the specific heat is unity, that is, $s_{H_2O} =_{Df} 1.0$.

Comparing the expression just written for heat lost or heat gained with the two sides of Eq. (6.2), it is not difficult to see how to write a generalization of this equation which will be applicable to experiments in which any two substances at any two temperatues are mixed. Letting s_H stand for the specific heat of the hot substance and s_C represent the specific heat of the cold substance, the generalized equation is

$$s_H m_H (t_H - t_F) = s_C m_C (t_F - t_C) \tag{6.3}$$

Since the specific heat of water is equal to 1 this equation reduces to Eq. (6.2) in the special case in which the hot and cold substances are both water. We have further generalized our law of heat regarding mixtures of hot and cold substances. We now assert with confidence, as a basic postulate for the construction of a mathematical model of heat exchanges, what we had earlier hypothesized, *the amount of* HEAT

LOST *by the hot substance is* EQUAL TO *the amount of* HEAT GAINED *by the cold substance.* Another way of stating this postulate is: the total amount of heat in an insulated system of objects always remains the same. This postulate is known as the **law of conservation of heat.**

We have tacitly made an important assumption in developing the concept and unit of measurement of heat. We have assumed that, whenever two bodies of different temperatures are brought into contact, heat is always lost by the warmer and gained by the colder—never the other way around. Devices, like refrigerators, have been invented for removing heat from colder objects and transferring it to warmer objects—the air and walls of the room. But our experience confirms that this does not happen without the application of some power from the outside. It is important to note that Eq. (6.3) would still be mathematically true if the hot substance *gained* heat equal to $s_H m_H (t_H - t_F)$ and the cold substance *lost* heat equal to $s_C m_C (t_F - t_C)$. That we do not know of any such cases and regard them as impossible without external sources of power, is a second postulate which is therefore logically independent of the conservation of heat postulate. Another way in which this second postulate has often been formulated is this: *When a system of objects is insulated from the outside, temperature differences within the system are eventually eliminated.*

The two postulates formulated in the two preceding paragraphs are recognized as fundamental to understanding all thermal or heat changes, and they are known respectively as the **first** and **second laws of thermodynamics.** In later chapters, we shall find further applications and still more general formulations of these two laws.

The applications of Eq. (6.3) to heat exchanges are many and varied for, if we know any 6 of the 7 quantities, m_H, m_C, s_H, s_C, t_H, t_C, t_F, we can calculate the remaining one from this equation. If we were to pour 2500 g of boiling water into an iron pan ($s = 0.11$) of mass 1000 g whose temperature was 25°C, we could calculate by how many degrees the water would be cooled (assuming no heat losses such as would surely occur when we pour the water into the pan). Here we are given the values of all the quantities except t_F, which we are to find. Substituting in Eq. (6.3), we have

$$(2500)(1)(100 - t_F) = (1000)(0.11)(t_F - 25)$$

Performing the indicated multiplications, $250,000 - 2500\, t_F = 110\, t_F - 2750$; whence, $2610\, t_F = 252,750$, and $t_F = 97°$ (as a first approximation). That is, the water should be cooled by $100 - 97 = 3°$C. If we now perform the experiment, we may get some idea of the heat losses.

Application exercises:

Work out the following exercises in order to confirm your understanding of specific heat and the interpretation of Eq. (6.3).

6.7 An aluminum pan of mass 500 g is heated to 150°C. How many grams of water at 25°C must be poured into the pan in order to bring its temperature down to 50°C? (Assume this is done so suddenly that almost no water vaporizes.) ■

6.8 A 200 g piece of an alloy, whose specific heat is unknown, is heated to 100°C and put into a beaker containing 50 g of water at 20°C. The temperature of the mixture is 40°C. What approximation to the specific heat of the alloy can you compute from Eq. (6.3)? ■

6.9 An iron rod of 250 g mass was heated to an unknown temperature and placed in a trough containing 500 g of water at 24.3°C. From the final temperature of 30°C, estimate the original temperature of the iron rod. ■

6.10a. If 20 g of copper pellets, heated to 67°C, are mixed with 150 g of mercury at 30°C, what, approximately, is the final temperature?

  b. If the pellets were mixed with mercury in its glass container, which weighed 20 g, what correction would you make to the approximation computed in (a)? (For glass, s is approximately 0.2 cal/g.) ■

LATENT HEAT

In order to broaden still further our developing theory of heat exchanges, we now undertake two experiments in which heat is exchanged between hot and cold objects of the same material but in different **states of matter** (i.e., solid, liquid or gas). We will first examine the cooling effect of *ice* (i.e., water in the *solid state*) when it is mixed with warm water and then the heating effect of *steam* (i.e., water in the *gaseous state*) when it is "mixed" with cold water.

Laboratory explorations:

6.11 To carry out the ice and water experiment, ice cubes are melted in beakers partly filled with hot or warm water. Different numbers of ice cubes and various temperatures of water should be used by different students in order to seek a general relationship. The mass and temperature of the water in each beaker should be recorded before putting in the ice. Then, one or more ice cubes (carefully dried to remove as much of the melted ice as possible) should be quickly put into each beaker and stirred until all the ice has melted. The temperature of each of these "mixtures" should be read immediately, and the new mass determined *as quickly as possible*—for otherwise moisture in the air may condense on the outsides of the beakers and increase the total mass appreciably. The mass of the ice that was put into each beaker can be found by subtracting the original mass of water from the final mass of the mixture. For each beaker, we have the following measurements: m_H (mass of hot or warm water), t_H (temperature of hot or warm water), m_{ice} (mass of ice added), t_C (which is 0°C, the cold substance being ice), and t_F (temperature of the mixture).

Actual experimentation makes it quite evident that t_F is not a simple average of initial temperatures or even an average weighted by mass. Can we approach this situation in a manner analogous to the mixing of various hot metals with cold water, in which we calculated the equivalent masses of hot water? Equation (6.2) may be used here as it was there, except that we now want to find $(em)_C$ for the ice instead of $(em)_H$ for the hot metal. Following the method we used for materials other than water, calculate the equivalent mass of cold water at 0°C that would have produced the same cooling effect as the ice actually did, calculating separately for the mixture in each beaker.

In the case of metals, it turned out that $(em)_H$ is proportional to the mass of the metal. Does a similar proportionality hold here? When $(em)_C$ has been calculated for each beaker, divide this value by the actual mass of ice that was added in that beaker to see if the ratio $(em)_C/m_{ice}$ is constant. The answer turns out to be negative. Check to see what this ratio might be related to. Is $(em)_C/m_{ice}$ dependent upon the initial or the final temperature?

It turns out that a graph of $(em)_C/m_{ice}$ plotted against the corresponding temperature of the mixture, t_F, does show a systematic relationship. Note that t_F is actually the temperature change undergone by the melted ice; that is, since the original temperature of ice was 0°C, $(t_F - t_C) = t_F$. Figure 6.1 shows the graph obtained from an experiment of this type. Combine your data in a graph with those of other students for comparison with Fig. 6.1.

In Fig. 6.1 the actual experimental data are represented by x's; the o's represent hypothetical results which would be obtained from similar experiments conducted with much greater care using better experimental apparatus. Note that only a few of the x's depart seriously from the o's.

We observe from this graph that the ratio, $(em)_C/m_{ice}$ is inversely related to the temperature-change: the larger the temperature-change, the smaller the value of $(em)_C/m_{ice}$. This is in striking contrast to the case in which the water equivalent of 1 g of any given metal was nearly constant no matter what the temperature change. (If that had not been so, there would have been no justification for introducing the concept of specific heat.) In the present case, it seems that we cannot employ a similar tactic and use a simple ratio of the heat added to the mass of ice melted.

Can we express the relationship represented by this graph in a mathematical form? The graph shows that it is quite similar to the graph representing an inverse proportionality relationship. (See Fig. 3.9, p. 93.) The only difference is that the general elevation of the present graph is higher than in a graph for inverse proportionality. *How much* higher is it? It is hard to tell accurately from the graph itself, but the following theoretical consideration suggests that the

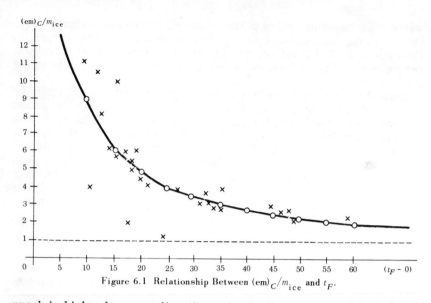

Figure 6.1 Relationship Between $(em)_C/m_{ice}$ and t_F.

graph is higher by *one unit* on the vertical axis than a graph of inverse proportionality would be. As $t_F - 0$ becomes larger and larger (which it does as the amount of hot water mixed with a given amount of ice is increased more and more), $(em)_C/m_{ice}$ gets smaller and smaller, which means the ice has less and less effect as a cooling agent; but it nevertheless stands to reason that the ice will always be at least as effective as water at 0°C. It is therefore reasonable to assume that, as the amount of hot water mixed with a given amount of ice is increased indefinitely, the cooling effect of the ice approaches that of water at 0°C as a limit. This means that, in the limit, m_{ice} and $(em)_C$ are equal, that the ratio $(em)_C/m_{ice}$ approaches unity but never becomes smaller than unity; it will never be the case that a smaller mass of water at 0°C will suffice to produce the same cooling effect as does a given mass of ice.

Contrast this relation with an inverse proportionality relation, $y = k/x$, where y comes closer and closer to *zero* as x gets larger and larger. It seems justifiable to conclude that our present graph has a general elevation one unit higher than has the graph of $y = k/x$. If we had plotted the value of $(em)_C/m_{ice} - 1$, on the vertical axis, instead of $(em)_C/m_{ice}$ itself, then we would have obtained exactly a graph of the form, $y = k/x$. We conclude that the mathematical expression for the relationship represented by the graph is

$$\frac{(em)_C}{m_{ice}} - 1 = \frac{k}{t_F}$$

But what possible physical meaning could be attached to such an equation? Again it turns out that a transformed (but mathematically equivalent) equation is much easier to interpret. Adding 1 to both sides of the above equation and multiplying both sides by $m_{ice} \cdot t_F$ in order to clear the denominators, we obtain

$$(em)_C \, t_F \ = \ (m_{ice}) \, t_F \ + \ k(m_{ice}) \qquad (6.4)$$

The left-hand member of this equation is clearly the heat gained by the ice. Recalling the equation from which we originally calculated $(em)_C$—a modification of Eq. (6.2) in which we replaced m_C by $(em)_C$ and in which we also set $t_C = 0$—we obtain another expression for the same quantity,

$$(em)_C \, t_F \ = \ m_H(t_H \ - \ t_F) \qquad (6.5)$$

We now eliminate the fictitious quantity $(em)_C$ and obtain a simple relation between the observed quantities. Equating the two expressions for $(em)_C \, t_F$ from Eqs. (6.4) and (6.5), we conclude that

$$m_H(t_H \ - \ t_F) \ = \ (m_{ice}) \, t_F \ + \ k(m_{ice}) \qquad (6.6)$$

How do we interpret Eq. (6.6)? The left-hand member is the heat lost by the hot (or warm) water. By the first law of thermodynamics, the conservation of heat, the entire right-hand member of the equation must stand for the heat gained by the ice. This is broken down into two components: the first term, $(m_{ice}) \, t_F$, is precisely the number of calories of heat that would be gained by m_{ice} grams of water being warmed up from $0°$ to $t_F°C$. This is then the heat gained by the *melted* ice which is then warmed up to t_F. The second term $k(m_{ice})$, oddly enough, is *independent* of the temperature change (since t_F is not involved in this term).

The second term of Eq. (6.6) is an essentially new feature in the type of experiment in which the process of mixing brings about a *change of state* (in the present case, from solid to liquid—ice to water) in one (or both) of the materials mixed. Analysis of experiments with the melting of metals supports the conclusion that a change of state from solid to liquid is always accompanied by an extra absorption of heat by the material changing state, which is represented in the heat-exchange equation by a term free of Δt. In general, the extra heat-exchange term represents an absorption if the change of state is from solid to liquid or from liquid to gas, and a release of heat, if the change is from gas to liquid or from liquid to solid. The second component, $k(m_{ice})$, of the total amount of heat gained (i.e., absorbed) by the ice is called the **latent heat** of fusion of the ice that melted. (The term means *hidden heat*—hidden, because it does not produce any change in temperature.)

Once we agree that $k(m_{ice})$ represents the number of calories of heat absorbed by the total mass of ice just for it to melt and become water, we see that the proportionality constant, k, stands for the latent heat of fusion of 1 g of ice. The value of k may be calculated from any point on the graph of Fig. 6.1 by multiplying the value of $(em)_C/m_{ice} - 1$ by the corresponding t_F-value. For the points indicated by an o in the graph, k is 80. In the most careful experiments, 80 calories of heat are absorbed by each gram of ice in order for it to turn into water at 0°C. Conversely, freezing 1 g of water at 0°C into ice requires the removal of 80 calories of heat from the water that is to be frozen.

The second of the two experiments referred to at the beginning of the section involves "mixing" steam with cold water to examine the heating effect of the steam. By analogy with the ice and water experiment, we may expect that the steam experiment will yield results of a comparable nature, for here again the "mixing" brings about a change of state—from the gaseous to the liquid state this time.

Laboratory exploration:

6.12 Apparatus for passing steam into a measured volume of water is shown in Fig. 6.2. The mercury in the U-shaped tube attached to the flask balances the pressure of the steam needed to force it down to the bottom of the cylinder containing cold water; it thereby acts as a safety valve letting steam escape in case it is generated at an explosive rate. *Heat gently* to avoid spraying mercury out of the U-tube. Since we are interested in the heating effect of *steam* on the cold water, it is important to minimize the condensed steam which trickles from the delivery tube into the cold water. While we cannot eliminate condensation in the delivery tube, we can prevent most of the condensed water in it from getting into the cold water. The water trap shown in the diagram on page 189 is for this purpose.

The amount of steam thus mixed into the cold water may most conveniently be measured by the increase in volume which is simple to determine if the experiment is carried out in a graduated cylinder. By varying the amount of steam (relative to the amount of cold water) used, a variety of different values of the final temperature of the mixture, t_F, are obtained. By measuring the amount of water in cubic centimeters, we are directly measuring volumes. The volume in cc of a given amount of water is, numerically, almost exactly the same as its mass in grams, since 1 cc of water has a mass very close to 1 g. So, indirectly, we are measuring mass and we may speak of mass instead of volume. It would be incorrect to speak of the observed increase in volume of water as the *volume of steam* added—the volume of the steam as such is much greater. The increase in volume observed corresponds to the volume *after* the steam has condensed into water. But since the mass of the steam remains unchanged before and after condensation, there is no ambiguity when we speak of the mass of steam in grams—meaning the mass of steam that is condensed in the cylinder.

As in the ice and water experiment, the class may obtain a series of values of t_F by employing various initial temperatures and mixing different amounts of steam. Record the appropriate values of m_C, t_C (mass and temperature of cold water), m_{st} (mass of steam), and t_H

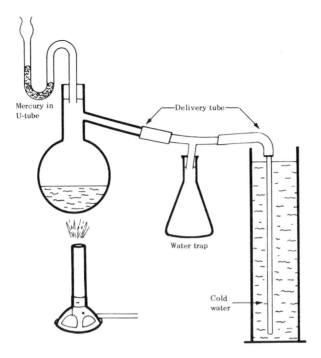

Figure 6.2 Apparatus for Determining the Heating Effect of Steam.

(which is always 100°C) corresponding to each of the values of t_F.
Equation (6.2), suitably reformulated, permits us to calculate the
equivalent mass of hot water at 100°C that would have produced the
same heating effect as the steam actually did, which we shall designate $(em)_H$.

To analyze the results for the class, apply the same method
used in the ice experiment. Each student should calculate the ratio
$(em)_H/m_{st}$ corresponding to the value of t_F he obtained. A graph is then
plotted for the entire set of trials of the steam experiment. To make
the graphs comparable for the two experiments, the horizontal axis
should represent, not t_F, but $(100 - t_F)$—which is the analogue of
$(t_F - 0)$ in the ice experiment. The graph resulting will ordinarily
resemble in general form that obtained for the ice experiment. Exactly
parallel arguments can be used to develop a mathematical equation
which is, term for term, a counterpart of Eq. (6.6). This equation is

$$m_C(t_F - t_C) = m_{st}(100 - t_F) + K \cdot m_{st} \qquad (6.7)$$

The left-hand member expresses the number of calories of heat
gained by the cold water; and the right-hand member represents the
heat, in calories, lost by the steam, broken down into two components: first, the heat given off by the water formed by condensation of

the steam in cooling from 100°C to the final temperature; and second, the heat associated with the process of condensation, which is independent of temperature change and is proportional to the mass of steam. The second part of the heat lost by the steam is the *latent heat* of condensation of steam. The value for 1 g of steam, given by the proportionality constant, K, is found in the most careful experiments to be 540 calories. Each gram of steam must lose 540 calories in condensing into water at 100°C. Conversely, to convert 1 g of liquid water at 100°C into steam, 540 calories must be supplied.

To check the accuracy of his experimental result, each student should compute the ratio of $(em)_H/m_{st}$ using his measured values of m_{st}, t_F and letting $K = 540$. (Review of the ice experiment should provide sufficient reminder of how this may be done.) If the error is large, he should try to find the most likely sources of error. ∎

The concept of latent heat, introduced in this section, is summarized diagrammatically for water in Fig. 6.3. A similar diagram could be drawn for any other substance which is capable of assuming solid, liquid, and gaseous states at normal atmospheric pressure, each with its appropriate latent heat of fusion (or of solidification) and latent heat of vaporization (or of condensation). Changes in the direction

$$\text{Solid} \longrightarrow \text{Liquid} \longrightarrow \text{Gas}$$

involve absorption of heat by the substance changing state; and changes in the opposite direction,

$$\text{Solid} \longleftarrow \text{Liquid} \longleftarrow \text{Gas}$$

involve emission of heat on the part of the substance undergoing the changes. The amount of heat change is independent of the direction in which the change of state occurs.

In the equations developed so far, temperature differences have typically been positive because the smaller temperature was subtracted from the larger. When more than two objects exchange heat, we may not know in advance whether the temperature of a particular object will increase or decrease. It would be desirable, in the interest of formulating the most general sort of equation, to have a notation which does not depend on advanced knowledge of the direction of temperature changes. Following our definition of ΔH (p. 182), if we always subtract the initial temperature of an object from its final temperature, then, if heat is gained by the object, ΔH will be positive and, if heat is lost, ΔH will be negative.

With such a convention, the law of conservation of heat may be written in a more general form. Note that the old form of the law, HEAT GAINED = HEAT LOST, can be rewritten as, HEAT GAINED + (− HEAT LOST) = 0. Since ΔH will be positive or negative depending on whether it represents heat gained or heat lost, a more general formulation of

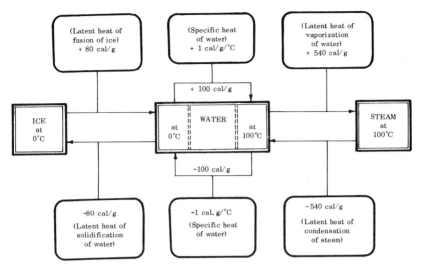

Figure 6.3 Changes of State of Water.

the law for any two objects exchanging heat is possible:

$$\Delta H_1 + \Delta H_2 = 0$$

If three objects exchange heat, we write, $\Delta H_1 + \Delta H_2 + \Delta H_3 = 0$, and so on.

In cases in which the second of two objects undergoes a change of state, we write

$$\Delta H_1 + \Delta H_2 + \Delta H_{2L} = 0$$

Here ΔH_{2L}, meaning latent heat of object number two, will be positive if the change of state is in the direction solid–liquid–gas, and negative if it is in the opposite direction. ΔH_2 is the heat change of object number two apart from that required for its change of state.

Since two changes of state are possible for a single substance, and since changes of temperature can occur in each of the three different states of matter, we could have a situation in which the sum of five ΔH terms represents the total heat change in one substance. This would occur if we started with m_1 grams of ice at $t_1°C$ (a negative temperature) and a metal pot, whose mass is m_2, at a temperature well above $100°C$, t_2. Before the ice can be melted in the pot, it must be warmed up to $0°C$. The specific heat of ice, s_{ice}, is 0.5 calories/ gram/°C. Thus $\Delta H_{ice} = 0.5 m_1 (0_1 - t_1)$. In melting the ice, $\Delta H_{fusion} = 80 m_1$. In heating the melted ice to the boiling point $\Delta H_{water} = 1.0 m_1 (100 - 0)$. In evaporating the boiling water $\Delta H_{vapor} = 540 m_1$. In heating the steam to the final temperature, t_F, the specific heat of steam is 0.1 calories/gram/°C. So $\Delta H_{steam} = 0.1 m_1 (t_F - 100)$. All five of these ΔH values will be positive, if t_F is above 100°C. The pot cools down from t_2 to t_F, so $\Delta H_{pot} = s_{pot} \, m_2(t_F - t_2)$, which is negative. The sum of all the ΔH values should be zero. If we know the values of all the variables except one, we solve the equation and find its value.

A general way to write the law of conservation of heat is as follows:

$$\sum_i \sum_j \Delta H_{ij} = 0$$

The Greek letter Σ (sigma) in this equation signifies summation over all values of the subscript. Here, a double summation is required since ΔH must be summed over all objects and all heat constants applicable to each object. See Fig. 6.4, in which the terms for the above example are arranged in a matrix showing the double summation.

Process (j) / Object (i)	Heating or cooling solid	Fusion	Heating or cooling liquid	Vapori-zation	Heating or cooling gas	$\sum_j \Delta H_{ij}$
Object 1	ΔH_{1ice}	$\Delta H_{1fusion}$	ΔH_{1water}	$\Delta H_{1vap.}$	ΔH_{1steam}	ΔH_1
Object 2	ΔH_{2pot}					ΔH_2
Object 3					ΔH_{3air}	ΔH_3
$\sum_i \Delta H_{ij}$	ΔH_{solid}	ΔH_{fusion}	ΔH_{liquid}	$\Delta H_{vap.}$	ΔH_{gas}	$\sum_i \sum_j \Delta H_{ij}=0$

Figure 6.4 A Matrix for Heat-Exchange Experiments. (Terms are indicated for the vaporization of ice in a hot pot.)

The two laws of thermodynamics relate this equation in the following way. The first law asserts, as the equation says, that the sum of all heat changes is zero; the second law tells us what the equation does not explicitly say, that is, heat flows from objects at higher temperatures to objects at lower temperatures and continues to flow until all temperatures are the same.

Practice exercises:

The following exercises are provided in order for the student to check his understanding of latent heat. (Whenever one of the phrases, "just to melt," "just to freeze," etc., is used in the questions below, it means that no change in temperature occurs.)

6.13 How many calories of heat must be supplied in order just to melt 50 g of ice at 0°C? ■

6.14 How many calories of heat must be supplied in order just to vaporize 5 g of water at 100°C? ■

6.15 How many calories of heat must be removed from 40 g of water at 0°C just to freeze it? ■

6.16 How many calories of heat must be removed from 12 g of steam at 100°C just to condense it to water? ■

6.17 How many calories of heat must be supplied to 30 g of ice at 0°C in order to convert it into water at 25°C? ■

6.18 How many calories of heat must be supplied to 4 g of ice in order to convert it all into steam at 100°C? ■

6.19 Fill in the terms required in a matrix like Fig. 6.4 for an experiment in which superheated steam is blown over subzero ice cubes resulting in water at room temperature. ■

DULONG AND PETIT'S LAW

To draw another parallel with the history of astronomy, we can compare the laws we have now developed for heat phenomena with Kepler's first two laws of planetary motion. Just as Kepler's first two laws give a fairly complete and concise description of the motions of planets taken one at a time, once certain constants of the planets are known, the first and second laws of thermodynamics enable us to describe and predict the thermal behavior of any substance for which we have already found such constants as specific heat and the two types of latent heat. We are unable to predict anything quantitatively about heat phenomena involving new substances, whose heat constants we do not know—just as Kepler's first two laws did not permit any quantitative predictions about the motion of a planet whose period *and* orbit size had not both been observed. Kepler's Third Law was the first law in astronomy that allowed predictions to be made concerning motions of planets on which only partial data (either the orbit size or the period of revolution) were available. Can we find a law for heat phenomena that would have a similar degree of generality?

To seek a law of such generality, we must look for relationships between specific heat and some *more basic* property of matter. We have have already seen that specific heat is not related to mass and volume; so these variables are ruled out. Regarding elements, the most efficient search for some property which is related to specific heat can be conducted by using the periodic table, for in it many properties of elements are related. A study of Table 6.1 reveals that the order in which the metals are arranged (from small to large in specific heat) turns out also to be the order of decreasing atomic weight. This is an interesting relationship. To study it we plot a graph of the specific heats of various elements against their respective atomic weights. The atomic weights are obtained from the table on page 156, and the specific heats from Table 6.1; the resulting graph is as shown in Fig. 6.5. Two elements of low atomic weight have been added to show the range of the relationship. A greater variation of their specific heats with temperature (S 28% and Li 20% from 20 to 100°C) is shown by vertical bars.

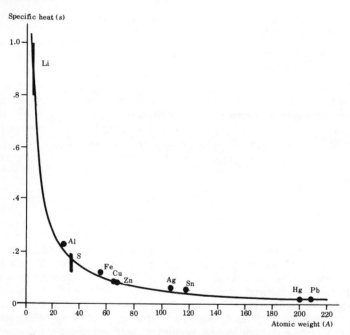

Figure 6.5 Relationship Between Atomic Weight and Specific Heat.

We recognize immediately that the graph in Fig. 6.5 resembles an inverse proportionality relationship. If specific heat is denoted by s and atomic weight by A, the equation for such a relationship between s and A would be $s = k/A$. Multiplying both sides by A, we obtain

$$s \cdot A = k \qquad (6.8)$$

The student should determine the value of the proportionality constant, k, for each element, by multiplying the specific heats of the elements by the corresponding atomic weights, to see how nearly true Eq. (6.8) is. The law expressed by Eq. (6.8) is called **Dulong and Petit's Law** after the two men who first found this relationship.

It turns out that Dulong and Petit's Law does need an important qualification. It holds only for substances whose molecules are monatomic—one atom per molecule. Equation (6.8) is applicable to compounds such as H_2O or to those few elements such as hydrogen (H_2) and oxygen (O_2), whose molecules consist of more than one atom each. We shall later see why this is so. (See p. 266.) Our question is whether, within the scope to which it applies, Dulong and Petit's Law is a law of thermodynamics that is comparable in generality with Kepler's Third Law in the field of astronomy. Using Eq. (6.8), we can predict the specific heat of any monatomic element, provided we know its atomic weight. Is this, however, merely trading another constant for specific heat?

What further conclusions may be drawn from this law by application of what we have already learned about heat? It would prove enlightening if we could replace s in Eq. (6.8) by an equivalent mathematical expression containing terms which are theoretically more basic—by a theoretical definition of *specific heat*. Recall the equation,

$$\Delta H = s \cdot m \Delta t$$

where ΔH represents the change in heat (either gain or loss), in calories, which takes place when m g of a substance with specific heat s undergoes a temperature change of Δt (°C). Solving the above equation for s, we obtain, as an explicit definition of s,

$$s =_{\text{Df}} \frac{\Delta H}{m \cdot \Delta t} \tag{6.9}$$

Substituting the right-hand member of Eq. (6.9) for the s in Eq. (6.8), we have

$$\frac{\Delta H}{m \cdot \Delta t} \cdot A = k$$

Let us explore this relationship further. A regrouping of terms in the left-hand expression may prove enlightening. ΔH and Δt seem closely related as do A and m, so we write

$$\frac{\Delta H}{\Delta t} \cdot \frac{A}{m} = k$$

We recognize this equation as an inverse proportion between ratios. Multiplying both sides of this equation by m/A, however, we obtain an equation in standard form for a direct proportion of two ratios,

$$\frac{\Delta H}{\Delta t} = k \cdot \frac{m}{A} \tag{6.10}$$

This equation tells us that the ratio of heat change to temperature change is proportional to the ratio of mass to atomic weight.

What interpretation can we give to the ratio m/A? From the meaning of atomic weight, we see that if we knew the *number of atoms*, N, contained in a piece of metal, we could write the mass of the piece of metal as $m = k'NA$, where k' is a proportionality constant. (The relationship is one of proportionality rather than of direct equality, since the unit we use in assigning atomic weights and the unit we use in measuring the mass of ordinary objects are not the same.) From this equation, it follows that $m/A = k'N$. Equation (6.10) may then be written as

$$\frac{\Delta H}{\Delta t} = kk'N$$

whence

$$\Delta H = KN\,\Delta t \tag{6.11}$$

where $K = kk'$, a new proportionality constant.

We have now reached a very remarkable conclusion. For Eq. (6.11) tells us that, regardless of what monatomic element we use, the heat lost or heat gained is proportional to the *number of atoms* in the object, multiplied by the temperature change. This consequence of Dulong and Petit's Law provides an interesting comparison with Kepler's Third Law in generality. If we could only measure the number of atoms in an object, we would need no special constants in order to apply the law to new monatomic elements.

A little thought convinces us that we have now also answered the question raised earlier in the chapter: what measure of the amount of a substance will preserve the law of average temperature regardless of whether we mix same or different substances? It has turned out that this measure (for monatomic substances) is the *number of atoms contained in the substances mixed*. This result implies that heat is contained equally by atoms of different kinds, and the amount of heat that can be obtained from a given number of atoms of a chemical element depends only on the temperature change, not on any property of the particular element. This is not true for changes in state, and we must pass up the far more difficult task of analyzing latent heat. In the next two chapters we shall develop in more detail a theory of the relationship between heat and atoms and molecules which is opened up by the present analysis.

METHODOLOGICAL REVIEW

In this chapter we saw a line of scientific investigation proceeding from the level of simple, common-sense observation to that of a relatively sophisticated theoretical model, developing certain new concepts in the process. That our line of investigation moved more directly to its climax than any actual investigation ever does is primarily a consequence of the ease with which we were able to select theoretical quantities and measures of them which have proved fruitful and supply precise data. We make no apologies for this use of hindsight.

The concept of *specific heat* illustrates the logical formation of a concept rather well. *Specific heat* entered the investigation simply as a computational device, enabling us to enlarge the scope of applicability of a formula, Eq. (6.2). Later, for convenience, values of specific heat were listed for various substances. Specific heat was recognized as a property, relatively constant for any given substance, which preserved the two laws of thermodynamics we had postulated. It was subsequently found that the specific heat of elements was closely related to a more basic property of matter, namely, their atomic weights. This discovery (by Dulong and Petit) tied together concepts that had developed in two then widely divergent areas of science, heat and chemistry. Dalton himself had earlier given consideration to the heat capacities of atoms, but he had no way to measure them, and he was unable to arrive at any law concerning thermal properties of the elements. It is interesting that the successful approach he introduced to the determination of atomic weights eventually did open the way to determining heat capacities.

The relationship between specific heat and atomic weight has introduced a certain connection between two branches of physical science, chemistry and physics. This relationship permitted the remarkable conclusion that the amount of heat exchanged between monatomic substances depends only upon the number of atoms of each substance and the temperature change and not on the elements involved, as Dalton assumed. Specific heat was reduced to a measure of the number of atoms per unit mass in monatomic substances. This explanation has added very greatly to the confidence we place in the theory developed, including its two fundamental postulates, the law of conservation of heat and the law that heat flows from warmer to colder objects. It has also pointed the way to an even greater degree of integration of different branches of science.

Throughout the development of the theory of heat, problems of measurement have been very much in evidence. Although measurement is obviously required for the application and testing of mathematical models of the sort we have been considering, we have seen that measurement is not always a simple matter. There are four somewhat interrelated problems concerning measurement which occur in most fields of science as they have in the investigations of the present chapter. These are: the problem of standards and scaling, the problem of choice of technique for a particular purpose, the problem of reliability, and the problem of selecting quantities to be measured that have the most fruitful theoretical relationships. The way each of these problems has arisen and been dealt with in this chapter is now briefly reviewed.

We first encountered the problem of standards and scaling in connection with temperature measurement. Three standards were required (as against one in the case of length or mass measurements): two standard temperature-stabilizing conditions (freezing and boiling water) and a standard thermometric substance (mercury). Also the measurement of temperature differed from that of length and mass in that no physical interpretation could be given to the sum of two temperatures (although difference between two temperatures could be interpreted). Addition of two quantities is possible only if the initial point on the scale is known. Since the complete absence of temperature could not be meaningfully defined (a difficulty which is later resolved), units of temperature had to be defined in terms of the difference between two temperatures. The Celsius unit is defined as a one-hundreth part of the difference between the two standard temperatures.

This kind of scale, in which differences but not ratios of two scale values can be obtained, is often called a **"difference scale"** (or an *interval scale*) in contrast to a **ratio scale** such as found in measuring distance and mass. Note that even with difference scales, we may meaningfully speak of the ratio of two differences. The difference between 30°C and 10°C is twice the difference between 90°C and 80°C.

The problem of choosing a thermometric substance also illustrates the need, which is common in scientific research, to make practical decisions in the absence of a completely rational basis for them. Thermometers made with different thermometric substances, calibrated at the standard conditions designated as 0°C and 100°C, and subdivided evenly in terms of length, do not ordinarily agree perfectly at other temperatures. The only standard way of subdividing them that would produce agreement would involve adopting one substance as standard. Figure 6.6 shows the type of disagreement that is to be expected. Subdividing one thermometer in terms of another is a very difficult process, so uniform subdivision seems the most reasonable way to make thermometers. For this reason, if one wishes to be very precise in reporting temperature measurements, he indicates the type of thermometer used. Fortunately, the practical choices (mercury and alcohol) do not produce temperature values that differ greatly. The theoretical significance of the choice of thermometric substance is therefore not very large. Mercury is usually preferred as the standard substance for the practical reason that it remains a liquid over a very wide range of temperatures.

The problem of reliability arose in several ways. Temperature measurements may vary if the amount of a thermometer immersed in the substance to be measured is not kept reasonably constant. Even the usually very reliable procedure of determining mass on a pan balance may become most erratic because of condensed moisture, if the substance to be weighed is cold and there is appreciable humidity in the air. In this case, the usually less reliable volume measurements may have better reliability than weighing on a balance. It is very important for an experimenter to report his measurement techniques and give an estimate of their reliability so that sources of error can be estimated and experimental results checked. As more sensitive techniques become available, experiments may need to be repeated to discover how precisely the conclusions hold. The student experimenter can appreciate how difficult it would be to develop theory from *his* data alone.

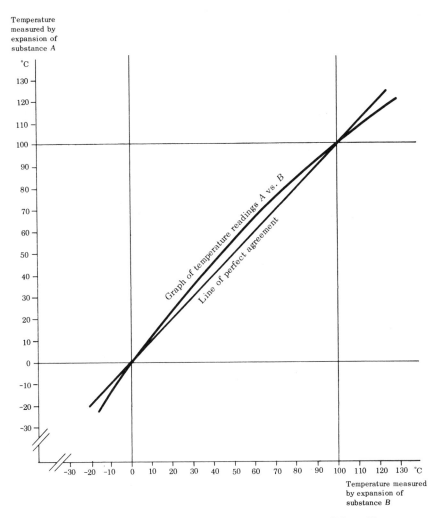

Figure 6.6 Illustration of the Kinds of Relationships Found Between Celsius Thermometers Using Different Thermometric Substances.

The problem of finding the quantities that have the most fruitful relationships for the development of theory is a difficult but interesting one. It appeared explicitly in this chapter as we sought, and eventually found, a measure of the amount of substance involved in heat exchanges that removed our dependence on the additional constant, specific heat. A useful guide was the search for a measure which preserved the simple weighted-average relationship for mixtures. The quest for a general theory that would minimize the need for specific constants found great encouragement in Dulong and Petit's

Law, which made the direct measurement of specific heat unnecessary for monatomic substances. Although we had earlier selected mass as having greater theoretical importance than volume, because of the fact that volume was dependent on temperature, the "number of atoms" turned out to be the measure which removed our dependence on specific heat. The key to unlocking this measure, the Dulong and Petit relation between specific heat and atomic weight, was a connection we might never have suspected at the outset.

At the beginning of an investigation into a new, or relatively new, field, one cannot reasonably hope to select the quantities that will yield the most fruitful relationships. It is precisely at this point that a scientist must rely on his hunches. In the social and behavioral sciences, much attention is often given to the validity of measures, i.e., the degree to which a procedure measures what it is said to measure. This question has no relevance to scientific investigation in the absence of a theory, for how else can one tell whether what a measure measures is worth measuring? Obviously, the more fundamental question is that of the theoretical import of a measure or set of measures. To answer this at all, one has to participate creatively in at least sketching a possible theory.

In the investigation reconstructed in this chapter, in place of hunches, we tacitly drew on the long tradition of thermometry in selecting our first new quantity. In proceeding directly to the mixture type of heat-exchange experiment, we eliminated in one step a dozen difficult problems in the experimental control of variables. In the actual development of a scientific theory finding out what to measure is one of the most significant kinds of breakthrough possible.

PROBLEMS

1. The initial data for three experiments are given in Table 6.2. In each experiment a given amount of heat is applied to a given mass of water or ice. Calculate, for each case, the final temperature and the amount of water remaining in liquid state, if any, after the heat has been applied.

Table 6.2 Data for Problem 1

State	Mass in grams	Initial temperature	Heat applied in calories
Water	25	$35°$	1000
Water	10	$50°$	3200
Ice	50	$-20°$	14,900

2. a. Derive the heat equation for an experiment in which different amounts of two metals having different specific heats are heated and then placed in cold water (that is, an equation from which you could calculate the final temperature). Use the symbols shown in Table 6.3 for your equation.

Table 6.3 Symbols for Problem 2

	Metal A	Metal B	Water
Mass	m_A	m_B	m_W
Specific heat	s_A	s_B	(1)
Initial temperature	t_A	t_B	t_W

Final temperature $= t_F$

 b. Calculate the final temperature if 200 g of metal A ($s_A = 0.1$) at 100°C and 400 g of metal B ($s_B = 0.05$) at 100°C are together placed in 500 g of water at 20°C.

3. By plotting a graph, study the relationship between t_F and ΔH for the data given in Table 6.4 and express the relationship in the form of a mathematical equation. Also state the relationship in words.

Table 6.4 Data for Problem 3

t_F (°C)	ΔH (cals)
10	900
20	1000
35	1150
55	1350
75	1600

4. Two identical metal pans, each weighing 200 g, were placed on a shelf in the sun. One pan contained 260 g of water, and the other was empty. The pans were both initially at 26°C, but after a short while the pan containing water had a temperature of 30°C, while the empty pan was at 56°C. These data are summarized in Fig. 6.7.
 a. Calculate the number of calories of heat gained by the water alone.
 b. Representing the specific heat of the metal by s, write an expression for the number of calories of heat gained by the pan containing water (not counting the heat gained by the water in it).
 c. Write an expression for the number of calories of heat gained by the empty pan, again letting s stand for the specific heat of the metal.

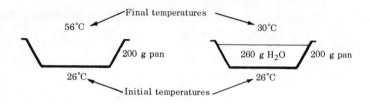

Figure 6.7 Diagram for Problem 4.

d. Write an equation expressing the fact that the heat gained by the filled pan together with its water is equal to the heat gained by the empty pan, and solve the equation for s.

SUPPLEMENTARY READINGS

Conant, James Bryant and Nash, Leonard K. (eds.). *Harvard Case Histories in Experimental Science*. Cambridge, Mass.: Harvard University Press, 1957.
Case 3, "The Early Development of the Concepts of Temperature and Heat," gives the historical background of the concepts of specific heat and latent heat.
Davis, Kenneth S. and Day, John Arthur. *Water, the Mirror of Science*. Garden City, N. Y.: Doubleday (Anchor Books), 1961.
A fascinating, popular account of the discovery and explanation of the physical properties of a most remarkable substance.
Holton, Gerald and Roller, Duane H. D. *Foundations of Modern Physical Science*. Reading, Mass.: Addison-Wesley, 1958.
Chapter 19 covers the same materials from a more historical point of view than the present chapter.
Woolf, Harry (ed.). *Quantification; A History of the Meaning of Measurement in the Natural and Social Sciences*. Indianapolis: Bobbs-Merrill Co., 1961.
Thomas S. Kuhn's chapter entitled, "The Function of Measurement in Modern Physical Science," provides an interesting, but different, point of view on the role of measurement in the development of physical theory.

7

A MECHANICAL-MOLECULAR
MODEL OF GASES

The remarkable discovery which climaxed the last chapter was that the *heat lost or gained* by a sample of any monatomic substance not undergoing a change of state is jointly proportional to the *number of atoms* in the sample and to the *temperature change*. This strongly suggests that both heat and temperature are intimately related to *some* property of atoms, but, since $s \cdot A = k$ for all monatomic substances, this relationship is independent of the particular kind of atom. The mass and, presumably, also the size of atoms would seem to be ruled out. When Dulong and Petit discovered this law, the idea had already suggested itself to a number of thoughtful scientists, that heat and temperature may be related to molecular *motion*. If so, it would be important to know precisely how they are related, that is, to be able to write mathematical equations expressing heat and temperature as functions of molecular velocities. To the investigation of this problem we address ourselves in this chapter and the next.

That the atoms or, more generally, the molecules composing matter are in constant random motion is vividly demonstrated by *Brownian motion*—a phenomenon seen in particles suspended either in gaseous or liquid states of matter. This phenomenon (discovered in 1827 by the Scottish botanist Robert Brown) can readily be observed by viewing illuminated particles of cigarette smoke through a microscope. The smoke particles are seen to display a rapid zigzag motion, and we infer that this motion is the result of constant, irregular bombardments by rapidly moving molecules of air. Similar effects of the molecules of a liquid can be observed by viewing a drop of some suspension, such as unhomogenized whole milk, through a microscope. Suspended fat particles in the milk can be seen to undergo erratic motion—a motion which is much more pronounced in the smaller particles than in the larger ones. This observation also is explainable by the assumption of incessant bombardments by the surrounding water molecules. The larger the particle, the more numerous would be the molecular collisions on all sides and hence the more steady their total effect on the particle would be. The smaller the particles, on the other hand, the more susceptible they would be to jostling because collisions with molecules from one side are less likely to be balanced by simultaneous collisions from the opposite side.

HEAT AS ATOMIC–MOLECULAR MOTION

Granting that atoms and molecules are in constant agitated motion, what evidences do we have that this motion is the key to explaining heat and temperature? The familiar process of producing heat by friction provides one such evidence. A convenient way of producing a lot of heat by friction in one spot is to bore a hole. Count Rumford, an American expatriate in Europe, once found himself assigned the task of supervising the boring of cannon for the Bavarian army and turned the job into an experiment in physics. The duller the bit, the more heat he got, so he undertook to measure the heat produced by the friction of a very dull bit. A shallow hole was drilled in the front part of a newly cast brass cannon. In this hole he placed a dull bit and near this hole he drilled a small hole in which he placed a thermometer. The number of calories produced in a given time could be determined, to a close approximation, by the change in temperature of the cannon, knowing the specific heat of the brass. Rumford found that change in temperature, and hence the number of calories produced, was proportional to the time during which a pair of horses turned the drill by walking on a treadmill, which implied that it was proportional to the distance that the horses walked.

Rumford reasoned that the rubbing of one object against another increased the vibratory motion of their atoms. Even though atoms are too small to be sensed individually, contact between two objects must involve an interaction between some of the surface atoms of the two objects. The motion of one object across another, then, must produce collisions between surface atoms of the two objects, increasing their vibratory motion. Since heat generated by friction is transmitted through an object, it must be that the surface atoms of an object, which are set into more rapid motion by collision with atoms of another object, also collide with neighboring atoms in the same object and cause them to vibrate more rapidly too. In this manner, the speed and the force with which two objects move across one another could be transmitted to and distributed among all the atoms which compose the objects.

Rumford had found that a single horse could pull his drill, but generally had used two to make the task easier. In retrospect, we can obtain a rough estimate of the force required to turn Rumford's drill, for James Watt, the inventor of the steam engine, had found that a "mill horse" could exert a steady pull of 150 lbs (662 newtons) while walking at a speed of 2.5 mi/hr (1.18 m/sec). If Rumford's horse had pulled with similar force and speed, it would have been capable of lifting a weight of 780.6 (662 × 1.18) newtons 1 meter in 1 second. Although Rumford did not report, and presumably did not measure, the force exerted by the horse or horses, he clearly recognized that the force and motion of the horse were the source of the heat. He did report that pulling continuously for 30 min could heat a brass cylinder enough to raise its temperature 39°C. Its mass was 51.3 kg and specific heat .11. His data for this experiment show that heat was produced at the rate of about 120 cal/sec. His work helped to make plausible his conclusion that "heat is vibratory atomic motion," but it remained for later scientists to develop quantitatively the mechanical theory of heat suggested by his arguments.

To illustrate the quantitative determination that Rumford's experiments would have permitted, we note that, if Rumford's horse had pulled with a force of 780.6 newtons, walked at a rate of 1 m/sec, and produced heat at the rate of 120 cal/sec, then every calorie required a force of 6.5 newtons acting through a distance of 1 meter. Any other pair of values for force and velocity whose product equals 1755.6 nt-m/sec would produce just as much heat, if the rate of heat production is jointly proportional to force and velocity. Other investigators, notably J. P. Joule, by the middle of the nineteenth century had determined more precisely what came to be known as the **mechanical equivalent of heat.** Such work showed that a force of 4.18 newtons acting through a distance of 1 meter generates one calorie of heat by friction. More generally, for each calorie of heat produced by friction, the product of force and distance equals 4.18 newton-meters.

The idea of defining mechanical energy by the product of the force acting and the distance through which it acts, turned out to be an extremely valuable one in mechanics generally. It led ultimately to the more general **law of conservation of energy** governing transformations between mechanical, thermal, and chemical forms of energy. A unit of measurement was introduced representing the amount of energy equivalent to a force of one newton acting through a distance of one meter. This unit is called the **joule,** honoring Joule's studies of the mechanical equivalent of heat. Since one joule is equivalent to one newton-meter, the mechanical equivalent of heat is 4.18 joules/cal.

The experiments of Rumford, Joule, and others had shown clearly that heat and mechanical energy were related, but a mathematical, mechanical explanation of heat and temperature in terms of the vibratory motions of atoms and molecules required the efforts of many investigators, working independently, who followed up experimental results from several different areas of physical science. One of the areas whose theoretical investigation proved most fruitful is the study of physical properties of gases. This should not be too surprising, since it is in the gaseous state of matter that molecules are most free to move about.

One of the earliest studies made on the properties of gases concerns the effect on the volume of a sample of gas confined in a cylinder by a movable piston when the piston is subjected to various forces that compress or expand the gas. In this investigation, temperature is kept constant in order to isolate the variables, volume and force. Thus it would not appear to involve heat exchanges. Before we undertake to apply Newtonian mechanics to the motion of molecules in hopes of developing a theory of heat, it would be desirable first to determine whether the laws of Newtonian mechanics, which hold as closely as they can be checked for medium-sized objects, will continue to hold for the motion of molecules. We can determine this best by first trying to develop a mechanical model which adequately accounts for the observed relationship between properties of a gas such as volume and pressure. These can be defined in terms of distance and force measurements reflected directly by the container in which a gas is held. If we are successful in this, then we can approach the matter of finding a mechanical explanation of heat and temperature with greater confidence, because we will have a common set of basic concepts with which to describe gas phenomena and motion.

BOYLE'S LAW

The relationship between the volume and pressure of gas in a container was discovered in the results of experiments, which Boyle had performed using a hand-operated vacuum pump. His results were published in 1660, and later confirmed by more extended studies. The mathematical formulation of this relationship was first made by an acquaintance who had read of Boyle's experiments. Boyle then devised a simpler apparatus which demonstrated this relationship more precisely. That the relation was formulated by another person, rather than Boyle himself, should remind the reader of the difficulties of finding mathematical relations for any given set of data. (See p. 123.)

Boyle had performed his first experiment because of his dispute with scientists who supported Aristotle's principle that "nature abhors a vacuum." As an illustration of the rather indirect process of scientific inquiry it will be useful to look briefly into the relation of this dispute to the demonstration of the principle that came to be known as Boyle's Law.

The dispute between Boyle and his opponents centered around an instrument known as a *mercurial barometer* (invented by Torricelli *c*. 1640). If a glass tube over 80 cm long is sealed off at one end and filled with mercury, it may then be stood upright in a dish of mercury without having all of the mercury run out. In fact, the mercury left in the tube stands very close to 76 cm above the level of mercury in the dish, if the air bubbles have previously been carefully removed from the mercury-filled tube. If the tube is tilted to one side, the *vertical* difference in height remains the same, usually 76 cm at sea level. The height of mercury in the barometer drops off markedly at higher altitudes. (It is about 52 cm high at 10,000 ft elevation.) It also fluctuates a few centimeters with changes in the weather.

The space above the mercury surface in the barometer tube was thought to be a vacuum by Boyle and many of his contemporary scientists. But others argued that this space was full of some subtle, aetherial fluid. The vacuuists believed that what held up the mercury in the tube was the weight of the atmosphere pressing down on the mercury in the dish. Their opponents in the dispute, called the plenists, believed that nature was always filled with matter, as Aristotle had argued. They attempted to explain the appearance of the barometer by postulating an invisible *funiculus* or threadlike substance which supported the column of mercury. To this funiculus, then, had to be assigned the property of holding up a column of mercury just 76 cm high at sea level in good weather. This is another example of the adaptability of subtle-fluid hypotheses—a characteristic that sometimes had more valuable consequences for the development of science than it did in this dispute.

Boyle developed a variation on the barometer in which the height of the open surface of mercury could be made much greater than that in the closed end of the tube. His apparatus consisted of a J-shaped tube with the short end sealed off, as shown in Fig. 7.1. The long end could be extended higher and higher by adding on more and more straight pieces of tubing. With a little air trapped in the short side, he poured mercury in the long side until it was many meters high. He found that the trapped air was compressed to a small fraction of its original size. This showed him the strength of the "spring of the air" when it was compressed by an applied force and convinced him that the mercury levels were controlled by this compression of the air and not by any kind of funiculus. The highly compressed air in the short

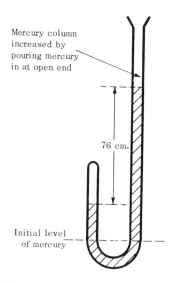

Mercury column
increased by
pouring mercury
in at open end

76 cm.

Initial level
of mercury

Figure 7.1 Boyle's J-tube Apparatus.

side was able to hold up a high column of mercury plus the weight of a column of the atmosphere pressing down on it through the open end. In this experiment, Boyle obtained measurements which he published. His friend discovered that the total weight pressing against the confined air multiplied by the length of the air column in Boyle's experiment was constant within 2 per cent.

The relationship which Boyle's experiment demonstrated may be studied over a wider range with the modified form of Boyle's apparatus depicted in Fig. 7.2 (c) and (d). An L-shaped tube with an inverted U-shaped extension at the end of the long arm is used. The shorter arm, whose end can be shut off by a stopcock, is clamped horizontally on the table so that it can be rotated all the way around. Mercury is poured into the open end of the U-tube leaving some air trapped in the closed end of the horizontal arm. The advantage of this apparatus over Boyle's is that the trapped air can be greatly expanded as well as compressed. By rotating the longer arm of the L-tube to vary its angle with the edge of the table, we can observe the trapped air in various degrees of compression and expansion: maximum compression obtains when the longer arm is vertically upright; maximum expansion, when it is pointed vertically downward. The volume of the trapped air can be determined simply by measuring the length of the mercury-free portion of the horizontal tube.

As compared with Boyle's J-tube apparatus, measurement of the force exerted on the trapped air in this apparatus is not quite so obvious. This force is a function of the angle of inclination of the long arm. It is also a function of the height of the surface of mercury at the open end of the tube, relative to any fixed horizontal surface such as the table top or the floor. The height of the outer surface of mercury minus the average height of the inner surface (since the inner surface is often not horizontal) would seem most closely related to the measurements made by Boyle. Measured in this way, the force on the trapped air will sometimes be negative, indicating an expansion, and sometimes positive, indicating a compression.

After making measurements of the length of the column of trapped air and the pressure to which it is subjected at each of a series of different inclinations of the long arm, we plot a graph, using the horizontal axis for the length and the vertical axis for relative height. Figure 7.3 shows such a graph. It somewhat resembles the graph showing the relationship between t_F and the ratio, $(em)_C/m_{ice}$, which we discussed in the previous chapter. (See Fig. 6.1.) An inverse proportionality relationship is again suggested. This time the graph extends *below* the horizontal axis; in other words, the general elevation is *lower* than in a graph for inverse proportionality. We need to find out how many units lower it is and whether any physical reason might be found for shifting it upwards by that amount so the mathematical formulation of inverse proportionality can be used.

When the long arm is pointed vertically downward (and the U-tube is open upward), our apparatus functions very much like a barometer. (Compare Fig. 7.2 (b) and (d).) It is the weight of the atmosphere

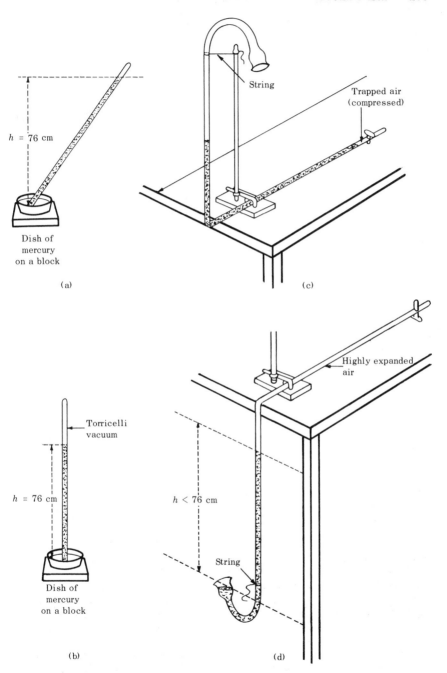

Figure 7.2 Mercury Barometer (a) and (b) Compared with Boyle's Law Apparatus (c) and (d).

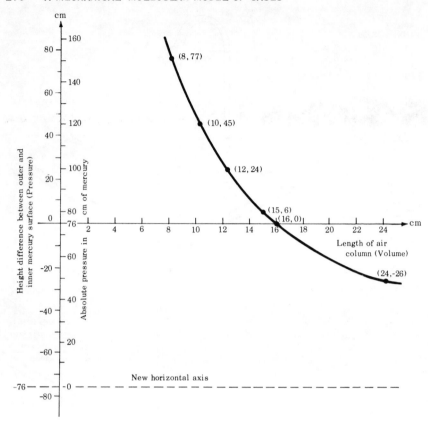

Figure 7.3 Relationship Between Pressure and Volume of a Gas.

pressing down on the mercury at the open end of the U-tube that keeps
the mercury from gushing out. As Boyle had seen, the atmospheric
pressure counterbalances the weight of the mercury in the long straight
part of the L-tube. (In the curved part, the mercury in the two sides
of the "U" balance each other.) The surface of the mercury at the
open end of the U-tube cannot be more than 76 cm below the level of
the mercury in the closed arm of the tube.

If there were no air trapped in the end of the tube, but a vacuum
instead, then we would expect the height difference between the inner
surface of the mercury and the outer surface to be exactly the same
as the height of a nearby barometer, that is, 76 cm. Since there is
some trapped air and, no matter how much it is expanded, it still
pushes back on the mercury, the height difference between the inner
and outer surfaces of mercury will never quite attain 76 cm, no matter how much the trapped air is expanded. If the apparatus were made
larger, permitting the trapped air to expand more and more, the lower

end of the graph would come closer and closer to the horizontal straight line passing through the point − 76 on the vertical scale, but never quite touching it.

The foregoing discussions lead to two conclusions. First, if the horizontal axis is lowered by 76 units, the graph will be asymptotic to the new horizontal axis. (This shift of axis has the same effect as plotting the sum of the observed height difference between the two mercury surfaces and 76 cm.) Second, it makes physical sense to perform this translation of the horizontal axis. What we originally took as the zero point in our measure of the force exerted on the trapped air corresponds to normal atmospheric pressure, i.e., 76 cm of mercury. By adding this amount to the observed height difference, we have a new measure of the force exerted on the trapped air. This measure of force on the trapped air, in units of cm of mercury, has the characteristics of a ratio scale, which make it most desirable for purposes of theory development. It has an absolute zero, corresponding to a vacuum, and physical meaning can be attached to sums and ratios of its values. Therefore we may refer to it as absolute pressure. This measure has still another aspect of theoretical importance: the experimental results are independent of the cross-sectional area of the tubing used. If several different pieces of apparatus with different cross-sectional areas of tubing were used, then height difference plus 76 cm could *not* be interpreted as a measure of the *force* on the confined air. For the larger the bore of the tubing, the larger the force produced by a given height difference. The law of inverse proportionality, however, holds for height difference of mercury plus 76 cm, so we must have been measuring a more appropriate quantity than force. This quantity we may call *pressure*, to distinguish it from force, and we must now rephrase our statement of the relationship represented by Boyle's Law as that of an inverse proportionality of pressure and volume of a confined gas.

We shall not undertake here to show that the manner in which we have measured the pressure on the confined gas corresponds with the usual sense of *pressure*, defined as *force per unit area*. It is sufficient for present purposes that we have a procedure which gives results that are comparable from one experimental apparatus to another.

One final theoretical consideration is necessary before we can justifiably conclude that the relationship is an inverse proportionality of pressure and volume. We have checked only one asymptote of the graph, and we must make sure that the other also has a satisfactory physical interpretation. What would happen if we could lengthen the vertical arm of the L-tube, while in the upright position, as much as we pleased, and were to add more and more mercury? It is not difficult to see that, with greater and greater pressure thus exerted, the column of trapped air would become smaller and smaller in volume. But the volume should never quite become zero. Ultimately, if the molecules themselves prove incompressible, the graph may stop approaching the vertical axis. We may reasonably assume that, even though the range of actual data plotted in Fig. 7.3 is far too small to show this, the graph would be very nearly asymptotic to the vertical axis if larger pressures were used. (Such an assumption then poses a challenging problem for further investigation: to design experiments for testing Boyle's Law at very high pressures.)

From the foregoing evidence and arguments we can express the relationship between volume (V), and pressure (P) of a gas at constant temperature by the equation for inverse proportionality:

$$P = \frac{K}{V}$$

or, equivalently,

$$PV = K \tag{7.1}$$

Theoretical exercise:

7.1 The student should perform a numerical check to see how constant the product of the P-value (ordinate *plus* 76) and V-value is for each of the six data points shown in Fig. 7.3. ∎

A MECHANICAL MODEL OF BOYLE'S LAW

Our next task is to construct an imaginary mechanical model of a gas by which the inverse-proportionality relationship between pressure and volume can be explained by means of the laws of mechanics applied to postulated motions of molecules. This task provides a check on the feasibility of applying mechanical principles to molecular motions and should be carried out before we try to construct a mechanical model of heat phenomena, since we lack the necessary terminology. Before we invoke mathematical formulas, let us see if we can provide some sort of mechanical explanation of Boyle's Law at an intuitive level. We should try to represent our experimental situation as closely as we reasonably can, but it may be helpful to make some simplifying assumptions. The mass of air trapped in the glass tube of our apparatus was cylindrical for the most part, although the ends of it were often peculiarly shaped. Assume that the relationship would be unaltered if the trapped air were in the shape of a perfect cylinder, for that will simplify the geometry. It may be helpful in accepting the hypothetical cylindrical form if we imagine a frictionless piston which separates the mercury from the air. In Fig. 7.4, a diagram representing this simplified arrangement is shown.

Consider two positions of the piston, at distances d_1 and d_2 from the end wall of the cylinder, as shown in Fig. 7.4. The number of gas molecules trapped in the tube should not change when the piston is moved from the one position to the other, provided the tube is well sealed. What *does* change when the piston is moved is the separation of the molecules. We should speak of the *average* distance separating the molecules, since we have no reason to believe that the separations would be uniform. Since we think of the molecules as undergoing rapid, irregular motion, the separation between any two probably varies widely from time to time. On the average, the molecules must be closer together when the gas is compressed than when it is expanded.

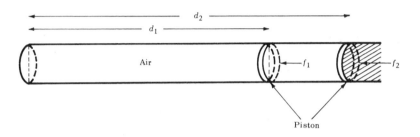

Figure 7.4 The Trapped Air in Boyle's-Law Experiment Represented in Cylindrical Form.

What can we say about the interaction of the gas and the piston in terms of the conception of a gas as a lot of tiny molecules flying around? There will surely be more frequent collisions of the gas molecules against the piston when the gas is compressed than when it is expanded. To explain Boyle's Law in terms of a mechanical model, we must show mathematically that a *higher frequency of collisions with the piston is associated with greater pressure* on the gas. That this can be done seems plausible enough, because each time a gas molecule collides with the piston, it must exert some force (and pressure) on the piston. We also need Newton's Third Law, which implies that the force of a molecule on the piston is equal to the oppositely directed force of the piston on the molecule.

A reasonable beginning on our task would be first to make a detailed analysis of a *single* collision, write an expression for its force, and then try to formulate the sum of the forces exerted by a multitude of collisions. Figure 7.5 depicts the path of one molecule before and after collision with the piston. Here we have assumed that the angles between the path of the molecule and the piston–surface before the collision and after collision are equal. Equality of angles of incidence and reflection holds true for collisions between billiard balls and the billiard table cushions and between steel balls and rigid steel surfaces, for example, and for all collisions of a moving object with a fixed object in which no permanent deformation of either object takes place. Such collisions are called **perfectly elastic collisions**, and will serve as our model of the interaction between the molecules of a gas and the walls of its container.

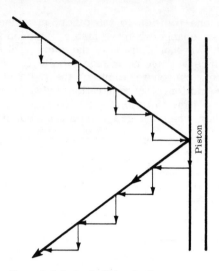

Figure 7.5 Path of a Molecule Colliding with Piston.

As we did with trajectories, we may analyze the motion of the molecule into two components: one, a motion parallel to the surface of the piston and the other, a motion perpendicular to that surface. We see from Fig. 7.5 that, if we assume the collision to be perfectly elastic, the velocity of the parallel component motion is exactly the same before and after collision and that the velocity of the perpendicular component motion undergoes a reversal in direction but is unchanged in magnitude. Since the parallel component does not contribute to the force exerted on the piston, we restrict our attention to the perpendicular component motion.

Figure 7.6 is an enlarged diagram of a collision between a molecule and the piston, showing more detail than Fig. 7.5. Here we have made the assumption that the only change from before to after the collision is a reversal of direction of the perpendicular component of the motion. But we have here indicated that this reversal is not instantaneous but occurs over a small interval of time, Δt sec, during which the perpendicular component motion is gradually slowed down and then accelerated again in the opposite direction. During this time it is assumed that the molecule is flattened somewhat and that the piston surface acquires a temporary dent. Since we assume that the parallel component motion is unaffected by the collision, it can serve as a measure of time during the collision. This means that the path of the molecule is a d–t graph. In Fig. 7.7, we have rotated the graph to correspond with the usual orientation of a d–t diagram. For any collision, the path becomes a d–t diagram of that component of the motion which is changed during the collision.

The first objective of our analysis of molecular collisions with the piston is to determine the force of interaction in such a collision. For

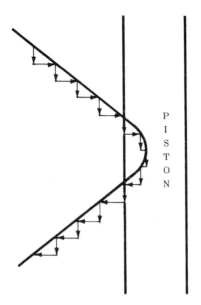

Figure 7.6 Enlarged View of a Collision.

this purpose a d-t diagram does not suffice. We need the corresponding v-t diagram, because the force producing a given acceleration is
expressed by the equation $f = ma$ and a is the slope of a v-t graph. To
construct a v-t diagram corresponding to the d-t diagram of Fig. 7.7
is our next step.

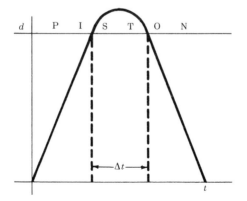

Figure 7.7 d-t Diagram of a Collision.

The straight-line portions of our d-t graph offer no problem—their
counterparts in the v-t graph are horizontal steps. A difficulty arises
in determining the v-t counterpart of that portion of our d-t graph

which represents the duration of impact—the curved part bounded by dashed lines in Fig. 7.7. To be technically precise in constructing this part of our v–t graph would require a detailed analysis of the collision process, involving the choice of an appropriate model from the theory of elasticity. This would carry us too far afield, so we merely point out that such an analysis would show that it is not unreasonable, as a first approximation, to assume that the velocity of a colliding molecule changes at a uniform rate. This assumption is also a convenient one since it will permit us to use the theory of uniform acceleration developed in Chapter 2. The central part of our v–t graph, on this assumption, becomes a sloping straight line. Figure 7.8 (a) shows the resulting v–t diagram. (The student should check that the height of the sloping line changes like the slope of the curved part of Fig. 7.7.) In Fig. 7.8 (a), positive and negative numbers are used to represent the two directions of the perpendicular component velocity. A positive velocity is taken as directed *away* from the piston, and a velocity *toward* the piston is plotted as negative. In a collision the velocity changes

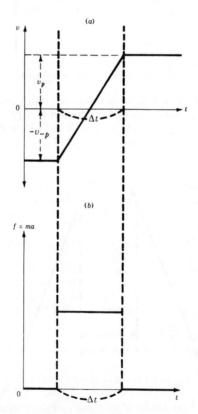

Figure 7.8 (a) v-t Diagram and (b) f-t Diagram of a Collision.

from a negative to a postive value, and the slope of the v–t graph is that of a uniformly increasing velocity.

We can now write an expression for the force exerted by the piston on a colliding gas molecule. Since the mass of a single molecule is a constant, so long as we are dealing with a single gas, the force given by the equation $f = ma$ is proportional to the molecule's acceleration, which is represented by the slope of our v–t diagram. Our model of the collision process, therefore, yields the conclusion that the force is zero before and after the collision and has a constant positive value during the collision. This is shown in Fig. 7.8 (b). (The student should note, as before, that the height of the lower graph corresponds, point for point, with the slope of the upper graph.) More quantitatively, if we let v_p denote the velocity (in magnitude only) of the perpendicular component motion, it can be seen from Fig. 7.8 (a) that the change in velocity, $v_2 - v_1$, during a collision of a single molecule is $v_p - (-v_p)$, or $2\,v_p$. Since this change takes place in the time interval Δt, the acceleration is, by definition,

$$a = \frac{2\,v_p}{\Delta t}$$

Letting m be the mass of a molecule, the force ($f = ma$) of a *single* collision is given by

$$f = \frac{2\,mv_p}{\Delta t} \tag{7.2}$$

We have obtained from our theoretical model a formula for the force exerted by the piston in a single collision on a single molecule. We must discover how to combine the effects of many collisions by each of a great many molecules. (Note the double plurality in this task.)

First, how may we represent the cumulative effect of repeated collisions by a single molecule? The collisions occur intermittently, and we cannot simply multiply the force given by Eq. (7.2) by the number of collisions that take place in a certain length of time, since there is a gap of time between collisions.

Figure 7.9 illustrates the correct procedure for obtaining an average force in separate collisions. The forces exerted during three successive collisions are here represented by three short, horizontal lines, at the height f as given by Eq. (7.2), each extending over a time interval of length Δt. We do not want the average of the forces of the three *separate* collisions but the average force during the *whole* time represented in the graph. Such an average force would be obtained by averaging all the forces taken during equal intervals of time, some of these forces being f and others being 0. In the diagram, three f-intervals and six 0-force intervals are shown, so the average force would be $(3f + 6 \cdot 0)/9 = f/3$. Because an average value is a fictitious value that can replace each of the individual values and leave the total

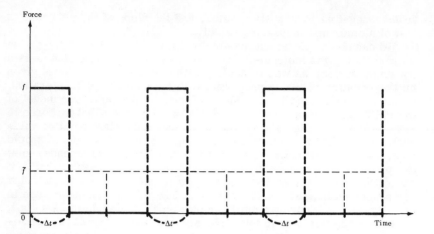

Figure 7.9 Averaging-out the Forces Exerted by Three Collisions (t_r is the interval during which a single molecule exerts a force on the wall. See Figure 7.8.)

unchanged, we replace the three collisions together and the three pairs of intervals following them by 9 fictitious collisions whose durations fill the whole time without overlapping. The force of each of these 9 fictitious collisions must be equal to the average of the 3 actual forces exerted by the molecules during the same time. In effect, by averaging, we imagine a continuous force. Any number of intermittent collisions can be represented by a single *continuously acting* force, if we average out the actual forces to fill in the gaps between collisions.

Theoretical exploration:

7.2 We have seen before, in connection with v-t diagrams, that the total area under a changing graph (here the area under the solid horizontal lines), is equal to the area under the average graph (here the area under the horizontal dashed line in Fig. 7.9). As an exercise, the student should show that the horizontal dashed line defines a rectangular area of 3 $f\, \Delta t$ newton-seconds. ∎

The average force $\bar{f}$ can be calculated algebraically, in the general case of n collisions, as follows: We may calculate $\bar{f}$ by dividing $nf\Delta t$ by the length of time that spans n collisions. If we find the number of collisions, say n_1, which a single molecule undergoes with the piston in one second, then, $\bar{f}$ is given by the formula

$$\bar{f} = n_1 f \Delta t$$

since dividing by one second does not change the expression on the right. It would be convenient if we could find an expression for $\bar{f}$ in terms of directly measurable quantities. Substituting for f from Eq. (7.2) helps by getting rid of Δt, measurement of which seems out of the question. We obtain

$$\bar{f} = n_1 (2mv_p)$$

or, more conventionally,

$$\bar{f} = 2n_1 mv_p \tag{7.3}$$

Next we need to find a replacement for n_1, the number of collisions per second. To simplify this task, suppose the distances between molecules are so great that collisions among molecules themselves are negligibly rare compared to collisions with the piston. Consider the path of a single molecule traveling back and forth along the length of the tube, colliding with the sides and the ends along the way, and making many round trips before ever colliding with another molecule. (See Fig. 7.10.) In making this and other simplifying assumptions we are attempting to build a bridge of theory between two sciences, mechanics and thermodynamics. Although our first bridge may be weaker than we would like, the first objective is to connect the two sciences. Later the bridge can be strengthened by supporting our assumptions or eliminating them.

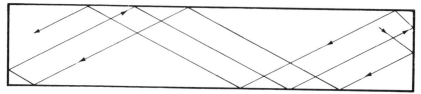

Figure 7.10 Path of a Molecule Not Colliding with Any Other Molecule.

The number of collisions per second by each molecule depends on the component of the motion of a molecule perpendicular to the piston which, according to our assumption of perfect elasticity, will not be affected during collisions with the sides, since these are at right angles to the piston. The component of the motion parallel to the piston will not affect the time taken by the molecule to go from one end of the tube to the other. That time is given by $t = d_l/v_p$, where d_l is the length of the tube and v_p is the component of velocity perpendicular to the piston. Since one collision with the piston occurs in each *round trip*, the time between collisions is $2t$ and the number of collisions per second is given by

$$n_1 = \frac{1}{2t}$$

and, by substitution for t, we obtain,

$$n_1 = \frac{v_p}{2d_l} \tag{7.4}$$

We now substitute from Eq. (7.4) in Eq. (7.3) to obtain the *average force due to repeated collisions by a single molecule*, thus:

$$\bar{f} = 2 \, \frac{v_p}{2d_l} \, mv_p$$

This simplifies, yielding

$$\bar{f} = \frac{mv_p^2}{d_l} \tag{7.5}$$

The final step remaining is to add up the average forces given by this formula for each of an enormous number, say N, of the gas molecules in the cylinder. The standard way of representing such an addition is to use the mathematical symbol for summation, Σ. Let us denote by $\bar{F}$ the sum-total of the N average forces, $\Sigma\bar{f}$, which is the total force exerted by all N molecules averaged over the course of their repeated collisions with the piston. We have from Eq. (7.5),

$$\bar{F} = \Sigma \frac{mv_p^2}{d_l}$$

But d_l, the length of the cylinder occupied by the gas, is a constant and $1/d_l$ can be factored out of the N terms standing in the above sum. Multiplying both members by d_l gives

$$\bar{F}d_l = \Sigma mv_p^2$$

Assuming that we are working with a pure gas so that the mass of every molecule would be the same, we can then factor m out of the right-hand expression. We are not actually making a restriction on the generality of the model, because, in a mixture of gases like air, we substitute for m the weighted average of the masses of the different kinds of molecules.

A further simplification is possible by making use of the relationship between a sum and an average. The average of the squares of the perpendicular components of the velocities may be expressed as follows:

$$\overline{v_p^{\,2}} = \frac{\Sigma v_p^2}{N}$$

Multiplying both sides of this equation by N, we get, as the left-hand member, an alternative expression for Σv_p^2. Substituting this in the previous equation, and factoring out m, we get the following equation relating average force with the average of the squares of the perpendicular components of the molecular velocities:

$$\bar{F}d_l = Nm\overline{v_p^2} \tag{7.6}$$

We leave the externally measurable quantities on the left side of the equation and the hypothetical, internal quantities on the right side to remind us of our dependence on a theoretical model. It is important also to recall that we are still focusing our attention on a hypothetical, frictionless piston that confines the gas in a cylinder. This assures us that the expression containing a force and the expression containing velocity are not incompatible—as they would be if the force and velocity were in different directions.

In finding an expression for the number of collisions per second on the piston (Eq. (7.4)), we made the assumption that the collisions among molecules themselves are negligibly infrequent compared to their collisions with the piston, and we now reexamine this assumption. It is perhaps more realistic to suppose that intermolecular collisions are at least as frequent as molecule-piston collisions, if not more frequent. Analysis of molecular collisions, assuming them to be perfectly elastic collisions, shows that the velocities of individual molecules are changed by such collisions but the sum-total of velocities of the whole system of molecules remains unchanged. Consequently, the *average* velocity of the perpendicular component motion is also unaffected. The average of the squares of v_p is not strictly invariant during collisions between molecules, but is approximately so. Although a somewhat unrealistic assumption was made in the course of deriving Eq. (7.6), the conclusion can be shown to be reasonably accurate, even if that assumption is discarded.

We have now taken our mechanical analysis as far as we can by using the familiar concepts of distance, velocity, and force. In order to derive Boyle's Law, we must introduce the concept of *pressure*, which, as mentioned earlier, is defined as the **force per unit area.** That is,

$$P =_{\text{Df}} \frac{f}{A}$$

where A is the total area over which the force is exerted.

Empirical exploration:

7.3 If the student is unfamiliar with the above definition of pressure, he should explore various situations in which the effects of equal forces are applied to unequal areas. Try the following simple experiment: place two blocks of wood having different bottom areas on damp clay, and place heavy equal weights on them. Which block makes a deeper dent in the clay?

More important for our purposes, *pressure*, so defined, is proportional to the difference h in height of mercury in a J-tube. This is easy to see for vertical tubes, for the excess weight of mercury in one side of such tubes is $f = khA$. Therefore, $P =_{\text{Df}} f/A = kh$. In the case of slanting tubes the geometry becomes complex but the result is the same. Expressing force in terms of pressure and area from this definition, we have

$$f = PA$$

Substituting the product PA for the force, $\overline{F}$, in Eq. (7.6), we get

$$PAd_l = Nm\overline{v_p^2}$$

The product Ad_l, in our present context, is precisely the *volume* of the air in our cylinder, so the above equation may be rewritten as

$$PV = Nm\overline{v_p^2} \tag{7.7}$$

Examine the right-hand member of this equation. Since N is the number of molecules and m the mass of each molecule (in the case of mixed gases, the average mass), Nm is simply the total mass of the gas in the cylinder, which is constant throughout the experiment. If we make the plausible assumption that v_p^2 does not change when the temperature is fixed (an assumption which is consistent with Rumford's conclusion that changes in heat content are changes in the rapidity of molecular motion), then Eq. (7.7) agrees with Boyle's Law (Eq. (7.1)): that the volume and pressure of a gas at constant temperature are inversely proportional to each other. From Eq. (7.7) we can derive a further conclusion: if the mass Nm of the gas is doubled—if we use twice as much gas, measured in terms of mass—and the temperature and pressure are held constant, then the volume of the gas will also be doubled. This conclusion is not only extremely plausible, it is also in agreement with experimental fact. Rumford's mechanical explanation of heat has now been formulated in terms of a mathematico-mechanical model which is consistent with at least two well-established empirical laws.

The validity of Eq. (7.7), and, hence, of the approach of applying Newtonian mechanics to molecular motion hinges on whether or not, in a gas, v_p^2 is constant for a given temperature, that is, whether it is functionally related to temperature. This is another instance of the by-now-familiar pattern in physics and chemistry, in which an assumption is made in the course of developing a theoretical model for which direct experimental verification is not possible. As pointed out earlier, on page 140, what the scientist typically does in such a case is to suppose that the assumption is valid, develop the theory further, and then try to find new, experimentally verifiable consequences of the whole theory. Good theories are usually valued for their fruitfulness in guiding subsequent research.

Having achieved some success with our mechanical model of a gas which assumes elastic collisions of a simple sort, we now undertake to apply the same model to properties of gases in which heat and temperature are directly involved.

THE CONSTANT-VOLUME EXPERIMENT
AND THE GENERAL GAS LAW

To investigate phenomena of gases which explicitly depend on temperature changes, we have two principal choices. We could study either the relationship between volume and temperature with pressure held constant or that between pressure and temperature with volume held constant. The choice is largely dictated by the apparatus one has available since the two relationships are quite similar. Once we determine the nature of one of these two relationships and combine that result with Boyle's Law, it would be theoretically possible to derive the other. The simple apparatus, shown in Fig. 7.11, is easy to construct and is quite adequate for a study of the pressure-temperature relationship. We shall consider this relationship first. The student should undertake this as a laboratory exercise in order to convince himself of the phenomenon and to practice the application of theoretical analysis.

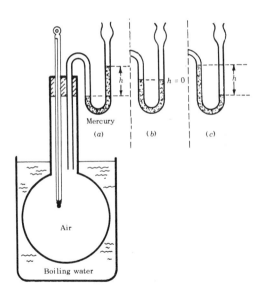

Figure 7.11 Constant-Volume Experiment.

Laboratory exercise:

7.4 A flask of air with a thermometer inside and mercury pressure guage attached is placed in a water bath which is heated to boiling and then allowed to cool gradually. Periodic examinations are made of the temperature and the height difference in centimeters between the levels of mercury in the two arms of the U-tube. The latter quantity is converted to absolute pressure in the same way as in the Boyle's-Law experiment. If the outer surface of mercury is the higher of the two (as in Fig. 7.11 (a)), the height difference is added to the atmospheric pressure; but when the inner surface is higher (as in Fig. 7.11 (c)), the height difference is subtracted from the atmospheric pressure. ∎

There is a slight change in the volume of the air with temperature as the inner surface of mercury moves. However, if a sufficiently large flask is used, the resulting volume change of the air is negligible and we may regard this as a constant-volume experiment showing the relationship between pressure and temperature. (If a 500-ml flask is used

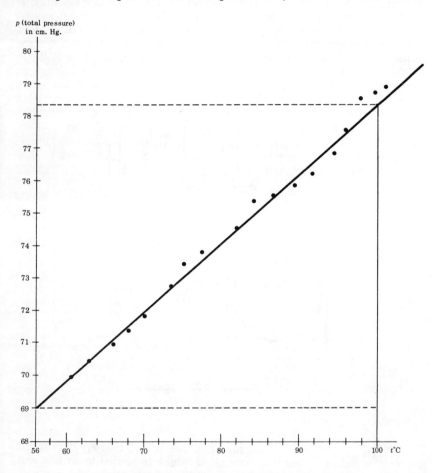

Figure 7.12 Results of Constant-Volume Experiment.

with 5 mm-bore tubing, the variation in volume would be only about 0.1% when the temperature ranges from 100° to 20°C. This change is smaller than most fluctuations in temperature and pressure measurements of a random nature, so it can safely be neglected.)

After a series of temperature and pressure observations are made, the data may be plotted on a graph. Figure 7.12 shows a typical set of data from this experiment. The resulting points are seen to fall very nearly on a straight line. The wandering from one side of the line to the other can be reduced by continuous tapping of the U-tube, since the mercury tends to stick to the walls and changes level somewhat irregularly if left alone. The straight line reminds us that a direct proportionality relationship would be useful if an appropriate constant were added to or subtracted from one of the two variable quantities. As in previous cases in which we successfully used this strategem, we must find a satisfactory physical interpretation of the new measure defined as the old measure plus or minus a constant. We have made such a theoretical redefinition of the convenient pressure scale. Can we meaningfully add a constant to the temperature scale so that the pressure-temperature graph would pass through the origin?

In the upper right-hand corner of Fig. 7.13 is a very much reduced representation of the original graph, which indicates how far the

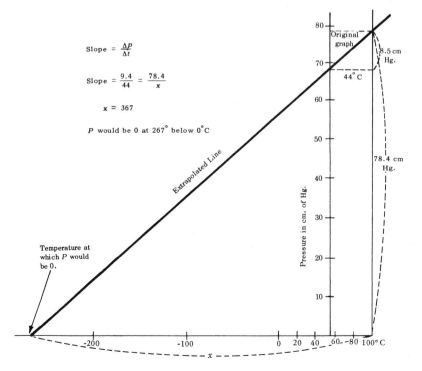

Figure 7.13 Extrapolation of Constant-Volume Results to Give a Direct Proportion.

Celsius temperature scale would have to be extended to the left in order that the straight line passing through the dots representing experimental data reach the level of zero pressure. Although 0°C is reached by a smaller translation of the pressure axis, this temperature scale is a difference scale and has an arbitrary zero, whereas pressure is measured on a ratio scale whose zero is absolute. We should, therefore, consider temperatures below 0°C and determine what physical circumstances theoretically might occur at the negative temperature for which the extrapolated graph reaches zero pressure.

The intersection of the extrapolated graph and the temperature axis represents the temperature at which the pressure of the gas would be zero. In terms of the mechanical explanation of pressure, developed in the previous section, this means that the number of collisions per second of the gas molecules with the piston is zero. Presumably the average squared perpendicular velocity of the molecules is zero. This temperature would correspond to a state of *absolute rest*, a cessation of all molecular motion. In terms of our mechanical theory of gas pressure, then, no lower temperature is conceivable. For this reason, this point on the temperature scale has been designated **absolute zero**, and a measure of temperature which assigns the value zero to this point is called an **absolute temperature scale**.

Can we estimate from Fig. 7.13 how far below 0°C this absolute zero temperature is? By assuming a uniform slope of the graph (a consequence of the direct-proportion assumption already made), we set up the equation displayed in Fig. 7.13. Solving that equation, we find the graph intersects the horizontal axis at the point − 267°C. Considering how far we were forced to extrapolate from the original data, this value is in very good agreement with the accepted value of − 273.16°C.

The absolute-zero temperature has been determined from many other experiments besides this one, for many other quantities turn out to be closely related to temperature measured on an absolute scale. The huge gap, which we jumped over in extrapolating from temperatures of hot water to absolute zero, has been well explored by all sorts of experiments and, except for the fact that most gases including air liquefy well before absolute zero is reached, our extrapolation has been fully justified. The idea of absolute zero and its relative position on the Celsius scale remain valid, and the gas laws from which they were derived hold down to the very low temperature where gases begin to liquefy.

The absolute temperature scale which uses Celsius degrees as its unit of measurement is known as the **Kelvin scale** after Lord Kelvin, who first introduced it. (If Fahrenheit degrees are used, the resulting absolute scale is called the Rankine scale.) It is conventional to use an upper case T to designate temperature measured on an absolute scale in order to distinguish it from that measured on a difference scale, for which a lower case t is used. So we have the conversion formula, $T = t + 273.16$, which is used to determine the Kelvin-scale value $T°K$ from the Celsius-scale value $t°C$ for a given temperature, or vice versa. The relationship of absolute and difference scales of temperature is graphically portrayed in Fig. 7.14.

By using the Kelvin scale for measuring temperature, we may express the empirical relationship between the pressure and temperature of a gas which is maintained at constant volume, in the form of a direct proportionality:

$$P = kT \tag{7.8}$$

The student might well begin to wonder whether every law of nature will turn out to be either a direct or an inverse proportionality. In the next two chapters we shall encounter a few that are not expressible in this form.

Let us now combine this pressure-temperature relationship with the pressure-volume relationship stated as Boyle's Law (Eq. (7.1)). The latter asserted that, when T is constant, P is inversely proportional to V. In conjunction with Eq. (7.8), we conclude that P is jointly proportional to T and $1/V$. That is,

$$P = K \cdot T \cdot \frac{1}{V}$$

or

$$PV = KT \tag{7.9}$$

This relationship between the pressure, volume, and temperature of a given sample of gas is known as the **general gas law.** It includes both Boyle's Law and Eq. (7.8) as special cases, for it reduces to the former when T is constant, and to the latter when V is constant.

Another special case of the general gas law is worthy of brief mention. If P is held constant, Eq. (7.9) reduces to

$$V = k'T$$

asserting that the volume of a confined gas, whose pressure is held constant, is directly proportional to its absolute temperature. This is known as the **Law of Charles and Gay-Lussac,** after the names of the French scientists, Jacques Charles and Louis Gay-Lussac who, independently, discovered this property of gases.

This concludes our survey of thermal properties of gases. It is now time to return to Eq. (7.7), $PV = Nm\overline{v_p^2}$, which we obtained as a result of our mechanical analysis of the Boyle's Law experiment, to

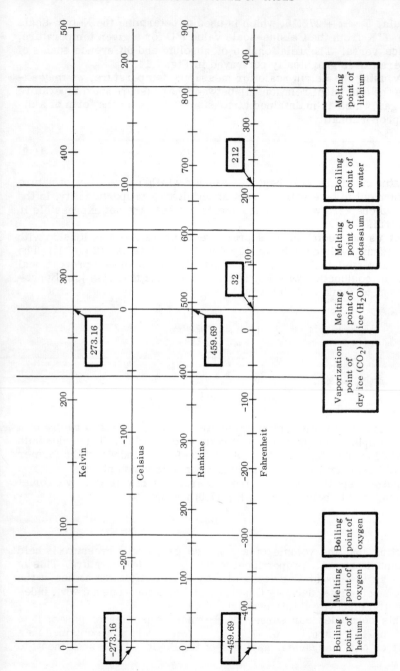

Figure 7.14 The Relationship Between Absolute and Difference Scales of Temperature. (The top two scales, Kelvin and Celsius, have the same size degrees. The bottom two scales, the Rankine and the familiar Fahrenheit, have degrees that are 5/9 of the Kelvin and Celsius degrees.)

see if we are in a better position to evaluate Count Rumford's hypothesis that molecular velocity varies with temperature and our converse assumption that $\overline{v_p^2}$ is constant when temperature is.

THE MECHANICAL CONCEPT OF TEMPERATURE

Before proceeding to an analysis of the relationship we have hypothesized between $\overline{v_p^2}$ and temperature, it would be helpful to develop a more general concept of the average squared velocity of gas molecules. The expression $\overline{v_p^2}$ lacks generality in that it refers to some particular surface toward which the component velocity is directed. We introduced the component, v_p, as a device for finding expressions for acceleration and force. Can we express net force in terms of the original and more general quantity v? To do so, we require a mathematical relationship between v_p and v that enables us to eliminate the former in terms of the latter. We must consider the geometry involved in analyzing the velocity of a molecule into components.

It should be recalled that, in our mathematical model of mechanics, the concept of velocity has a magnitude and a direction—that changes of a velocity in either magnitude or direction (or both) are accelerations. (See p. 57.) To remind us of this characteristic, the variable for velocity is often written as $\vec{v}$ or v, and is referred to as a **vector** quantity. Because a single component of molecular velocity, e.g., v_p, has a fixed direction although its magnitude may vary, it could be confusing to use an arrow or other vector notation for v_p; consequently the arrow has been omitted heretofore. But a component velocity should not be thought of as a scalar quantity as temperature and mass are. To avoid confusion, in vector notation, unit vectors in specified directions may be multiplied by the scalar magnitude, and a more complete symbol for the perpendicular component velocity might be

$$v_p \cdot \vec{u}_p$$

where $\vec{u}_p$ is the unit vector in the direction perpendicular to the piston. In subsequent discussion, it will be most important to keep clear the directional aspect of vector quantities, but we will not use the arrow or other vector notation since to do so would require a new arithmetic and algebra. Instead, we will base our developments on geometric considerations as a guide to the correct algebraic handling of magnitudes of components.

Figure 7.15 illustrates the analysis of velocity into three components: *horizontal* (H), *vertical* (V), and *perpendicular* (P). When we analyzed molecular motion in Figs. 7.5 and 7.6, we had arbitrarily disregarded one component by working in the plane of the paper. In general, three components are required to analyze any particular velocity in space. In a particular case, any of the three component velocities might be zero.

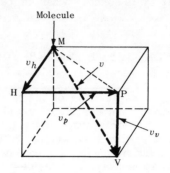

Figure 7.15 The Three Components
of Molecular Velocity.

Component velocities of molecular motion are most conveniently taken at right angles to each other. This means that any two component velocities can be represented by the perpendicular sides of a right triangle. In Fig. 7.15 two such right triangles are MHP and MPV. The three components, v_h, v_p, and v_v and the velocity itself, v, are sides of one or the other of these two triangles. We should be able to find a relationship between them by using the well-known theorem of Pythagoras, that the square of the hypotenuse of a right triangle is equal to the sum of the squares of the other two sides. Writing this theorem out for the two triangles we have,

$$\overline{MP}^2 = v_h{}^2 + v_p{}^2 \qquad \text{for the first,}$$

and

$$v^2 = \overline{MP}^2 + v_v{}^2 \qquad \text{for the second.}$$

Substituting from the first equation in the second we get:

$$v^2 = v_h{}^2 + v_p{}^2 + v_v{}^2$$

which is a 3-dimensional extension of the Pythagorean theorem that expresses the square of the magnitude of any given velocity in terms of three perpendicular components.

Mathematical exploration:

7.5 The student should write a verbal formulation of this three-dimensional Pythagorean theorem (that is, a counterpart of the statement, "the square of the hypotenuse is equal to the sum of the squares of the other two sides") in order to gain experience in the interpretation of mathematical results. ∎

Imagine that the component expansion above has been written out for every one of the N gas molecules in our cylinder. By adding together all the left members of the N equations and all the right members, noting that the summation of the right members may be performed component by component, we obtain the equation,

$$\sum v^2 = \sum v_h^2 + \sum v_p^2 + \sum v_v^2$$

Dividing all four terms of this equation by N and making use of the definition of an average (see p. 220), we obtain the following relationship:

$$\overline{v^2} = \overline{v_h^2} + \overline{v_p^2} + \overline{v_v^2} \tag{7.10}$$

Since our purpose is to obtain an equation containing only $\overline{v_p^2}$ and $\overline{v^2}$, we need to rid Eq. (7.10) of the other component velocities. To do so, consider whether there is any reason why the average values of the three squared component velocities should be different from one another. If one of the three average values were different from the others the pressure in that direction would be different; but experiments involving surfaces larger than those of particles in Brownian motion show uniform pressure in all directions. We reasonably assume that the average squared component velocities are *all equal*. In Eq. (7.10), we may replace both $\overline{v_h}^2$ and $\overline{v_v}^2$ by $\overline{v_p}^2$, and write:

$$\overline{v^2} = \overline{v_p^2} + \overline{v_p^2} + \overline{v_p^2} \qquad \text{or} \qquad 3\,\overline{v_p^2}$$

From this it follows that

$$\overline{v_p}^2 = \frac{1}{3}\overline{v^2}$$

which, substituted in Eq. (7.7), yields the more general equation,

$$PV = \frac{Nm}{3}\overline{v^2} \tag{7.11}$$

Comparison of this theoretically derived equation with the empirically developed general gas law,

$$PV = KT \tag{7.9}$$

strongly suggests that we should identify the K and T of the latter with factors of the right hand member of the former. Which factors should be assigned to K and which factors should be assigned to T? We have seen ample evidence that $\overline{v^2}$ should be included in a definition of T, but what about the other quantities? Would it work, for example, to let $K = 1/3$ and $T = Nm\overline{v^2}$?

Four possibilities seem immediately open to us. They are listed in Table 7.1. If we can answer the questions listed in the table, that is, decide where N and m go, we can choose one of these four possibilities. If N occurred as a factor in the expression defining T, as either $T = Nm\overline{v^2}$ or $T = N\overline{v^2}$, we would have the absurd conclusion that temperature is increased by adding to the number of molecules. This would mean that combining two samples of a gas having the same temperature, volume and pressure, would double their absolute temperature. We must reject the first two possibilities in Table 7.1 and consider the next two. Which of the two questions about m can we answer?

Table 7.1 Possible connections between $PV = KT$
and $PV = \dfrac{Nm}{3}\overline{v^2}$

$K =$	$T =$	Questions	
$\dfrac{1}{3}$	$Nm\overline{v^2}$	N in T?	m in T?
$\dfrac{m}{3}$	$N\overline{v^2}$		m in K?
$\dfrac{N}{3}$	$m\overline{v^2}$	N in K?	m in T?
$\dfrac{Nm}{3}$	$\overline{v^2}$		m in K?

If m were a part of K, the general gas law would have to read

$$PV = \left(\frac{Nm}{3}\right)T$$

But this would mean that, under constant pressure and temperature, the ratio N/V for a gas (the number of molecules per unit volume) would be inversely proportional to its molecular weight, that is,

$$\frac{N}{V} = \left(\frac{3P}{T}\right) \cdot \frac{1}{m}$$

This consequence is contradicted by Avogadro's principle that equal volumes contain equal numbers of molecules, regardless of the molecular weight, a principle which is highly confirmed in its chemical applications. Since we cannot absorb m into the constant of Eq. (7.9), we must admit it as an explicit factor in the definition of T and write $T = mv^2$. This might appear to contradict our conclusion from Dulong and Petit's Law that the heat content of objects made of monatomic elements is independent of atomic weight. This is not necessarily a contradiction because we have no experimental measure of v^2. In a joint proportionality, one variable may vary in such a way as to conceal dependence on the other. We must seek other means of determining v^2 to check on this possibility. Although we are left with a plaguing doubt about this seemingly unlikely possibility, we have no simpler alternative open to us and must choose $m\overline{v^2}$ for T and $N/3$ for K.

Actually, we must allow for the arbitrary choice we have made of the size of a degree on the Kelvin scale, so we require a scaling constant in our definition which we shall call k_1. Using this constant, we tentatively adopt as our definition,

$$T =_{Df} k_1 m\overline{v^2} \tag{7.12}$$

whereupon K becomes $N/(3k_1)$ and the equation for the general gas law (7.11) becomes

$$PV = \frac{N}{3 k_1} T = k_2 NT \tag{7.13}$$

where $k_2 = 1/3 k_1$. Let us return briefly to the starting point of our search for a mechanical model of heat and temperature to see how this result looks from that perspective.

Rumford had suggested that heat and temperature were aspects of molecular motion, and our present definition of T has sharpened his hypothesis considerably by specifying exactly what aspect of molecular motion temperature is. But Rumford demonstrated that heat is produced by physical work, and Joule and others actually determined the mechanical equivalent of heat, 4.18 joules/calorie (or newton-meters/calorie). If the measurable work expended is simply divided among all the molecules of an object that has been heated by friction, the energy imparted to each atom should be expressible in the same units, newton-meters, even if it is not actually measurable.

For purposes of comparison we may change the units, newton-meters, to the units of the primitive terms in our m-kg-sec (M.K.S.) system. The force unit, the newton, we have defined by the equation, $f =_{Df} ma$, so its basic units are $(kg \cdot m/sec^2)$. Energy, which can be represented as the product of force and distance, is measured in the units $(kg \cdot m/sec^2)$ (m), or more simply in $kg (m/sec)^2$. The mechanical units for the quantity of heat should be the same. Since $\Delta H = KN \Delta T$ (Dulong–Petit's Law) and K and N have no units, the units for temperature on a mechanical interpretation should *also* be the same as for heat, $kg (m/sec)^2$. Since k_1 is merely a scaling factor, examination of Eq. (7.12) shows that these are precisely the units needed for our expression defining T. This result is gratifying since a theoretical definition of temperature should have consistent units, but it may be puzzling in another way since heat and temperature turn out to have the same units. We return to this latter question in the next chapter.

The type of checking of theory just carried out, utilizing units of measurement, is closely related to *dimensional analysis*—an aspect of scientific thought first developed by Fourier, the scientist who showed how to analyze periodic motion. While it offers no quantitative verification of our mechanical model of gases, it is very useful as a first check to see if newly defined concepts make "physical sense" in the light of known empirical relationships involving them. We shall see other examples of this type of unit analysis.

METHODOLOGICAL REVIEW

In this chapter we have developed a mathematico–mechanical model of a gas which yields conclusions that agree with the empirical laws of gases and heat. This model, together with its empirical interpretation through the definition of new scales of measurement, constitutes **the kinetic theory of gases**. The steps we took in developing it have been far simpler and far more direct than the actual historical development of any theory ever is. But our study has taken us through a succession of different levels of development which are characteristic of the levels found in the actual development of theories in many fields of science. This succession of levels is often found in scientific thought and our development of kinetic theory has illustrated several important points concerning theory development in general.

The first level we have examined is that characterized by the simplification of an empirical relationship. As we have seen repeatedly in earlier chapters, and in this one, we can recognize the form of some kind of proportionality in a graph of measurements made on two aspects of a given phenomenon, for example, the pressure and temperature of a gas during thermal contraction. The relationship can often be simplified by translating the axes in one direction or another in order to make the relationship expressible in a simple equation. It might seem astonishing that it so often makes physical sense to perform such a translation. It would be even more astonishing if the measures which appeared the most obvious ones to use at the outset of an investigation usually turned out to be the most fruitful as theory developed.

Many persons have expressed surprise that the world really seems to be such that a great many of its properties are precisely expressible in simple equations like, $PV = K$, and $P = KT$. Our mathematical number system, which we tend to take for granted, actually developed over thousands of years as a consequence of man's struggle to find order in his environment. These more recent discoveries of mathematical order are a natural extension of the concepts of distance, time, and weight with which we started our study of mechanics and which must originally have grown up in conjunction with the number system at a much earlier stage of development of intellectual processes.

The technique, so essential to the scientific endeavor, of extending mathematical relations to the physical world would seem to be primarily that of trying to fit different mathematical relations to observed physical relations. From this point of view, the better a scientist's knowledge of mathematical relations, the more likely he is to succeed from time to time in finding "models" that fit his data. There is, however, a problem of developing new mathematical concepts to fit other aspects of man's experience. As new fields of knowledge are researched, new tools of thought will have to be invented before a theoretical science of the sort we have been studying will be possible. We may not be able to reap much more of the harvest of the algebra and geometry of proportion that grew out of man's first successful measurements of the world in which he lives. This kind of interaction of observation, manipulation, efforts at representation, and deduction of consequences is the earliest stage of science which we have overlooked because length, time, weight, and the associated mathematics of proportion are familiar components of our civilization. This stage probably cannot be bypassed in new fields of research.

The next level in theory development beyond that of empirical laws is the level of a rough conceptual model. An intuitive realization that the physical characteristics of gases might be explained in terms of the motion of their molecules illustrates this level. After much thought and study one comes intuitively to see that the force of collisions against the walls of a container may be a reasonable way to account for the pressure of a gas on its walls; and the temperature, it seems, could represent the speed of motion. On this model, pressure can be increased either by compressing the gas so that more numerous collisions occur with the walls or by increasing the temperature so that the collisions are more forceful. This sort of explanation lacks mathematical precision but does suggest mathematical relationships that can be set up on the next level.

The highest level of theory development began as we undertook to apply mechanical laws to individual molecules. We discovered that from such beginnings, a reasonable, quantitative picture could be obtained of the collective behavior of a container full of gas. Assuming elastic collisions with the walls and assuming the total conservation of velocities of molecules, we were able to find an equation for the same relationship between pressure and volume that had been observed empirically. In order to do so, it was necessary to make a series of assumptions of generally increasing specificity and strength: (a) that temperature increases as the speed of molecular motion increases (Rumford, p. 204); (b) that $\overline{v_p^2}$ is constant when temperature is constant (p. 222); (c) that T is directly proportional to $\overline{v^2}$ (p. 232); and finally (d) that $T = k_1 m v^2$. Note that (a) and (b) are implied by (c) but not vice versa, and that (c) is implied by (d) but not vice versa. There are other ways in which (a) and (b) could be true and (c) not true, and there are more ways for (c) to be true than there are for (d).

We have successively made the model more general by referring to additional experiments. We note that greater generality means stronger assumptions, which would seem undesirable except that we are increasing the possibilities of testing the theory by connecting it to a wider range of phenomena. This point is related to that made in the first chapter where it was pointed out that simplicity of theories is only sought relative to a certain scope of phenomena explained. We recall the subtle fluid for which assumptions had to be added to account specifically for each new phenomenon. There was insufficient return for those assumptions; there was no "economy of thought," to use a phrase from Ernst Mach, an Austrian physicist-philosopher, who curiously failed to appreciate the "economy" provided by the kinetic theory of gases.

One final point is that we have seen an example of the reduction of a law in one science to laws of another science—in this case, the reduction of the general gas law of thermodynamics to the laws of mechanics. The accomplishment of such a connection between two sciences is of great interest not only because it provides an explanation of the reduced law, but because it also greatly extends the range of the basic science. The situation is closely parallel to the reduction of Kepler's laws (from the science of astronomy) to Newton's laws of mechanics. In both cases, Newtonian mechanics was greatly increased in scope and hence became more highly esteemed as a theory. The basic laws of mechanics are designed for ideal situations with an absence of friction. Consider the law that an object in motion continues moving indefinitely in a straight line in the absence of external forces. This law could not be checked directly because friction is not really eliminable in ordinary laboratory experiments. In the solar system and in the motions of molecules in a gas we have reason to regard these applications of mechanics as frictionless cases. The reduction of astronomy and the gas laws to mechanics thus helps confirm basic assumptions of the latter science.

A necessary condition for performing the reduction of a law of a first science to laws of a second science is that the terms of the first science in which the reduced law is formulated must all be either found in the second science or must be defined by means of terms of the second science. The terms T and P of the general gas law had to be defined in terms of the purely mechanical concepts, f, d, t, m and the usual mathematical signs. V also was defined in terms of d. This condition of definability is necessary in order to derive the gas laws from the laws of mechanics. It is interesting to note that we were forced to use some undefined terms from mechanics in a way for which we had no procedures of measurement to tie them to experience. The duration of a molecular collision, Δt, gets no empirical interpretation in the kinetic theory of gases. We cannot always hope either to define or to specify measurement procedures for every term used in a theory. At this stage of the development of the theory, we have no way to check the hypothetical velocities of molecules. As we shall see in the next chapter, somewhat more direct ways have been found to check the assumptions made about velocities of molecules. The sacrifice of empirical concreteness which we made in introducing concepts like Δt and v—themselves not connected with experience— was rewarded by the great unification and general simplicity achieved. One may hope eventually to be able to interpret every concept as directly as possible, that is, avoid introducing uninterpretable concepts. It is unrealistic to rule such concepts out of theory development altogether, as some scientists have advocated, because the creation of worthwhile theories would be stifled. We can insist that concepts not directly interpretable be so labeled, in order to preclude our being led into an unwarranted sense of objective reference. This is what we have just done for Δt and v, as applied to molecules, and this is one of the functions which the philosophy of science usefully plays in the scientific endeavor. But the general concept of a model is also a useful reminder of the uncertainties that always remain in scientific theories.

PROBLEMS

1. A large metal cylinder, sealed tightly at one end, has a freely movable piston sealed in with oil. The whole cylinder is placed in a steam bath long enough to bring it and the gas inside to the boiling point of water. Its volume is then 2.5 liters. Next it is immersed in a liquefied gas until the piston stops moving inward. The new volume is found to be 1.2 liters. What is the temperature of the liquefied gas in degrees Kelvin? In degrees Celsius?

2. Air is confined in a cylinder with a frictionless piston. When the volume occupied by the air is 0.12 m^3, the pressure it exerts is found to be 50,000 newtons/m^2. The piston is now slowly pulled out until the volume of the air is 0.30 m^3. Assuming that the temperature does not change in the process of expansion, find the new pressure.

3. A gas thermometer is an apparatus in which a given mass of confined gas is free to expand when the temperature is raised, without change in pressure. If the volume of the confined gas is 250 cm^3 when the temperature is 27°C, what will the volume be when the temperature rises to 54°C?

4. A tire on a semi-trailer truck is pumped up until the tire gauge, which indicates the difference between inside and outside pressure, reads three times the atmospheric pressure (3.0 atm). The temperature is 20°C. After prolonged driving on a highway, the temperature of the tire rises to 70°C. Assuming that the volume of the air in the tire does not increase appreciably and that the external atmospheric pressure remains at 1.0 atm, calculate what a reading of the tire gauge would now show.

5. A balloon containing 12 liters of hydrogen at 27°C and 1 atm rises to a height where the temperature is − 23°C and the pressure is

0.25 atm. Assuming that the balloon bag can expand freely, what is its new volume?

6. Air contains N_2, O_2, and often considerable amounts of H_2O molecules. According to our definition of temperature in Eq. (7.12), which of these kinds of air molecules would have the highest velocity on the average? Which the lowest?

SUPPLEMENTARY READINGS

Boorse, Henry A. and Motz, Lloyd. *The World of the Atom*, Vol. I. New York: Basic Books, Inc., 1966.
    Selections 3 (Boyle), 7 (Bernoulli), 14 (Herapath), 15 (Brown), 16 (Waterston), and 17 (Joule) are recommended original scientific writings appropriate for this chapter.

Brown, Sanborn C. *Count Rumford, Physicist Extraordinary*, Garden City, N.Y.: Doubleday (Anchor Books), 1962.
    A biography of the American-born scientist and soldier of fortune.

Conant, James Bryant and Nash, Leonard K. (eds.). *Harvard Case Histories in Experimental Science*. Cambridge, Mass.: Harvard University Press, 1957.
    Case 1, "Robert Boyle's Experiments in Pneumatics," and Case 3, "The Early Development of the Concepts of Temperature and Heat," give valuable historical background on the gas laws and the mechanical concept of heat.

Danto, Arthur and Morgenbesser, Sidney (eds.). *Philosophy of Science*. New York: Meridian, 1960.
    Part Two, Laws and Theories, contains several selections particularly relevant to the present chapter. Selections 1 (Duhem), 3 (Presley), and 9 (Nagel) deal respectively with physical law, laws and theories, and reduction of one science to another.

Holton, Gerald and Roller, Duane H. D. *Foundations of Modern Physical Science*. Reading, Mass.: Addison-Wesley, 1958.
    Chapters 14, 15, 21 and 25 provide a valuable extension of both the methodology and the content of the present chapter.

Sandforth, John F. *Heat Engines*. Garden City, N.Y.: Doubleday (Anchor Books), 1962
    Recommended for further study of thermodynamics.

Schwartz, George and Bishop, Philip W. (eds.). *Moments of Discovery, Vol. I, The Origins of Science*. New York: Basic Books, 1958.
    Three brief selections by Torricelli, Pascal, and Boyle are recommended reading.

Wiener, Philip P. *Readings in Philosophy of Science*. New York: Scribner's, 1953.
    Selections 38 (Duhen, Meyerson, and Schlock) and 44 (Nagel, also included in Danto and Morgenbesser) provide valuable methodological remarks on physical theory and reductionism.

HEAT AND THE RANDOM
MOTION OF MOLECULES

In the preceding chapter we defined the kinetic-theory concept of absolute temperature of a gas as a quantity proportional to mv^2 for its molecules. The importance of this concept lies in the fact that, if this relationship between observed gas temperature and hypothesized molecular velocities can be shown to hold in general, we should be able to explain all phenomena associated with temperature as effects of molecular motions. The differential sensation of high and low temperatures on the skin would, in some way, be explainable as due to a sensitivity of cutaneous nerve endings to different molecular velocities. The expansion of objects when heated must be due to their molecules taking up more room as a result of the increased velocities with which these particles vibrate. Similar explanations may be expected to hold for all other phenomena associated with an increase or decrease in temperature.

The relationship in question has not yet been demonstrated in such a general way. The only experiments that have so far been explained quantitatively by means of the kinetic-theory model are the two experiments with gases described in the previous chapter. In those experiments, we dealt only with molecular velocities on the average and did not (or could not) consider differences in the velocities of various molecules. Furthermore, we have not yet understood how heat content is independent of atomic weight if $T = kmv^2$. We have very little of the knowledge that is needed in order to consider such questions and to determine how generally the model serves to explain temperature phenomena. For this purpose, we need to know not only the average squared velocities at different temperatures, but also the range of velocities and their **distribution** (i.e., the percentages of molecules whose velocities fall in different portions of the range).

Under some circumstances it is possible to measure molecular velocities directly. If a piece of silver wire is heated intensely, some of it will evaporate. Some of the silver atoms will escape from the surface of the wire. These escaping atoms can be admitted through a narrow slit into a partially evacuated, rapidly rotating chamber and collected on its wall. (See Fig. 8.1.) In this way the faster-moving silver atoms entering the chamber strike a part of the wall different from that on which their slower moving companions are collected. The percentage of the atoms with different speeds can be calculated by measuring the density of the deposit at different distances from the slit. This method does not give us direct information about the distribution of molecular velocities in gases at ordinary temperatures.

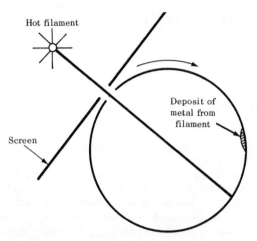

Figure 8.1 A Device for Measuring Molecular Velocities.

An indirect method for determining the distribution of molecular velocities was successfully made before any direct measurement of molecular velocities became possible. Because of the great importance of indirect methods of measurement in the growing stages of a science, and because the direct approaches to this particular problem are quite limited in their applicability, it is worth our while to consider in some detail one of the successful indirect approaches to finding the distribution of molecular velocities in a gas at ordinary temperatures. Before doing so, we need to clarify further the notion of a frequency or percentage distribution, and to develop some basic rules for working with distributions.

SOME ELEMENTARY RULES FOR DERIVING PROBABILITY DISTRIBUTIONS

The nature of a statistical distribution can best be understood by considering a concrete example in which actual experimentation is possible. Imagine that two coins are repeatedly tossed and the number of heads observed is recorded each time. The possible numbers of heads are, of course, 0, 1 and 2. One result of such an experiment is that, in 200 trials, 0 heads occurs 45 times, 1 head 103 times, and 2 heads 52 times. These frequencies are listed in Table 8.1, which also shows the corresponding percentages of the three outcomes. The frequency and percentage values of this table illustrate an empirically observed statistical distribution. If the total number of tosses had been much larger, say 1000, then in all likelihood the percentages of the respective outcomes would have been much closer to 25%, 50%, 25%, which is the theoretical distribution for the results of tossing two coins. The reason for these theoretically expected percentages is found in the following sequence of arguments.

Table 8.1 One Outcome of Tossing Two
Coins Two Hundred Times

No. of heads	Frequency	Percentage
0	45	22.5%
1	103	51.5%
2	52	26.0%

Suppose that the two coins are distinguishable in some way, for instance, one being a penny and the other a dime. If each coin is perfectly balanced, the chance of its landing heads on a given toss is exactly one half; likewise, the chance of its landing tails is also one half. The penny would be expected to land tails on half of the tosses; and similarly for the dime.

If the number of tosses is large enough, we may expect that, among those times when the penny lands tails, there will be a fifty-fifty split into cases in which the dime also lands tails and those in which it lands heads. In one half of half of all the tosses (that half in which the penny shows tails) we would expect that both coins will show tails. The percentage of tosses in which we observe 0 heads should be 1/2 of 1/2, or 25%. By exactly similar reasoning, we would expect that the percentage of tosses in which 2 heads are observed should also be 25%. The two extreme outcomes, 0 or 2 heads, therefore, together account for 1/4 + 1/4, or 50% of all the tosses. Consequently, the remaining 50% would be expected to show exactly 1 head. Although in our argument we imagined the two coins to be distinguishable, it should be evident that the distribution of expected number of heads thus obtained, 25%, 50%, 25%, would still hold even if the coins are not distinguishable. The percentage (expressed as a fraction) of times an event is expected to occur is called the **probability** of that event. Thus the probability distribution of number of heads when two coins are tossed is .25 for 0, .50 for 1, and .25 for 2.

The foregoing argument exemplifies two important principles of probability theory. First, if we know the percentage with which each of two **independent events** (i.e., events that have no influence on each other) may be expected to occur, i.e., their probabilities, the *product* of these two probabilities gives the probability with which both events occur together. If we denote the probability of any event or combination of events by $p(\ldots)$, the above principle may be formulated as follows:

If A and B are independent events, then
$$p(A) \cdot p(B) = p(A \text{ and } B)$$
(8.1)

This is known as the **multiplication rule for independent events**.

Second, if we know the probability with which each of two **mutually exclusive events** (i.e., events that cannot both occur together) occurs, the *sum* of these two probabilities gives the expected percentage of times in which *one or the other* of the events occurs. Using the probability notation, this principle may be formulated as follows:

If A and B are mutually exclusive events, then
$$p(A) + p(B) = p(A \text{ or } B)$$
(8.2)

This is known as the **addition rule for mutually exclusive events**.

These two principles may be used for constructing new distributions from distributions already found. Consider an experiment in which four coins are tossed, say two nickels and two quarters. We already know the distribution of expected number of heads for each pair of coins. How can we derive the probability distribution of the total number of heads among all four coins?

In deriving the distribution of numbers of heads among all four coins, it is useful, as an intermediate step, to obtain the probability of each possible combination of numbers of heads for the two kinds of coins. Consider the combination in which both nickels show heads but only one of the quarters shows heads. We may denote the probability of this combination by $p(2,1)$, where the first number in the parentheses indicates the number of heads in the nickels and the second number indicates the number of heads in the quarters. This notation is an abbreviation for p (2H among nickels *and* 1H among quarters). Using Eq. (8.1), we calculate this probability from p (2H among nickels), which is 1/4, and p (1H among quarters), which is 1/2. Thus

$$p(2, 1) = \frac{1}{4} \cdot \frac{1}{2} = \frac{1}{8}$$

Similarly,

$$p(1, 1) = \frac{1}{2} \cdot \frac{1}{2} = \frac{1}{4}$$

and

$$p(0, 2) = \frac{1}{4} \cdot \frac{1}{4} = \frac{1}{16}$$

We may collect the probabilities of all the combinations in a chart like that shown in Fig. 8.2. The fractions shown outside the square, along the top and right-hand margins, represent the number of heads among the nickels and that among the quarters, respectively. The student should note that the fraction entered in any one of the small squares, which represents the probability of a particular combination, may be obtained by multiplying the two corresponding probability values in the margins. This is an application of the multiplication rule. It should also be noted that the sum of the entries in any row or column is equal to the corresponding marginal probability. This is in accord with the addition rule, extended for three mutually exclusive events, because for example, two heads among the nickels can occur in combination with either two, *or* one, *or* zero heads among the quarters, so the probability of two heads among the nickels is equal to the sum, $p(2, 2) + p(2, 1) + p(2, 0)$.

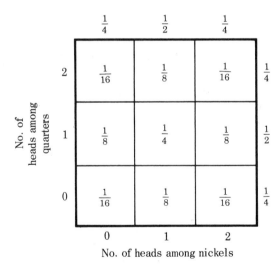

Figure 8.2 Probabilities of Heads when Tossing Four Coins.

We now obtain from Fig. 8.1 the probabilities of getting 0, 1, 2, 3, and 4, respectively, as the total number of heads among all four coins. Zero heads can be obtained only by having zero heads in both nickels and in quarters. Thus, $p(0) = p(0, 0) = 1/16$, the entry in the lower left-hand cell of the chart in Fig. 8.2. One head among the four coins can be obtained by either having one head among the nickels and zero heads among the quarters *or* having zero heads among the nickels and one head among the quarters. Thus $p(1) = p(1, 0) + p(0, 1) = 1/8 + 1/8 = 1/4$, the two "1/8's" being the middle entries of the leftmost column and the lowermost row in the Fig. 8.2 chart. Again, two heads among the four coins may be obtained in any one of the following three ways: two heads among the nickels and zero heads among the quarters, *or* one head among the nickels and one head among the quarters, *or* zero heads among the nickels and two heads among the quarters. Hence, $p(2) = p(2, 0) + p(1, 1) + p(0, 2) = 1/16 + 1/4 + 1/16 = 3/8$. Similarly, $p(3) = p(2, 1) + p(1, 2) = 1/4$, and $p(4) = p(2, 2) = 1/16$. The theoretical probability distribution for the results of tossing four coins is $1/16, 1/4, 3/8, 1/4, 1/16$ for obtaining $0, 1, 2, 3, 4$ heads, respectively.

Exploration exercises:

To gain familiarity with the use of addition and multiplication rules for probabilities, the student should carry out the following exercises. Note that the conditions stated in these rules (exclusiveness and independence, respectively), hold for the situations described below.

8.1 Consider a simple roulette wheel which is divided into eight equal sectors numbered $1, 2, \ldots, 8$, as shown in Fig. 8.3. The sectors are alternately colored black and red, sector number one being black. When the wheel is spun, a ball rolls around inside the rim, and the probability that it will stop in any given sector is $1/8$. Calculate the probability of each event described below.

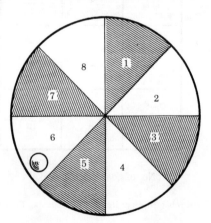

Figure 8.3 An Eight-Sector Roulette Wheel.

a. On a given spin of the wheel, the ball stops on a red sector.
b. On a given spin, the ball stops on either 5, 6, or 7.
c. On both of two successive spins, the ball stops on black.
d. In two successive spins, the ball stops on a number less than 4 on the first spin and on a number greater than 4 on the second.

e. In two successive spins, the ball stops on numbers such that their sum is 4.

f. In two successive spins, the ball stops on numbers which total 9. ∎

8.2 Suppose we have a pair of dice, one of which is a regular die and the other a loaded one. In one throw of the regular die, the probability of getting any one of the numbers of spots, 1, 2, 3, ... , 6 is equal to 1/6. The probability that the loaded die lies showing each of the six faces is as given below.

Face	1	2	3	4	5	6
Probability	$\frac{4}{9}$	$\frac{2}{9}$	$\frac{1}{9}$	$\frac{1}{9}$	$\frac{1}{18}$	$\frac{1}{18}$

Calculate the probability of each of the outcomes for a single throw of the pair of dice.

a. Both dice show 3 spots.

b. The regular die shows 6 spots and the loaded die shows 1.

c. The total number of spots showing on the pair of dice is 11.

d. The total number of spots showing on the pair of dice is 7. ∎

THE DISTRIBUTION OF MOLECULAR VELOCITIES

The probability distribution of molecular velocities was originally derived for a theoretical model of gases by James Clark Maxwell and Ludwig Boltzmann, independently. Maxwell, a Scottish physicist, did his work in England and Boltzmann worked in his native Austria. Although both derivations employed mathematics beyond the scope of this text, the gist of Maxwell's derivation may be understood by an application of the two principles of probability discussed in the preceding section.

Maxwell's approach is based on an analysis of velocities into three mutually perpendicular components, just as our derivation of Boyle's Law was. However, unlike that case, in which we identified one of these components as perpendicular to a particular surface (the surface of the piston), we are here completely free to orient the three mutually perpendicular axes in any manner.

Imagine a sample of gas in a spherical container. Of the multitude of molecules in the sample, now consider those whose velocities at a given instant are all of the same magnitude, say, 7 hm/sec. (1 hectometer = 100 meters.) The molecules under consideration will be moving in various directions. By selecting three mutually perpendicular axes, designated by subscripts 1, 2, and 3, we can, however, analyze all these variously directed velocities into components that are parallel respectively to the three axes. In accordance with the three-dimensional Pythagorean Theorem (p. 230), these three component velocities must be such that the sum of their squares is equal to the square of the actual velocity magnitude, 49 (hm/sec)^2 in this case. The three component velocities, v_1, v_2, v_3, might be the ordered triple, 2, 3, 6; since $2^2 + 3^2 + 6^2 = 7^2$. If the order of this triple were different the molecule in question would have a different direction but its velocitiy magnitude would still be 7. But the component velocities could just as well be 2, 6, -3; -6, -2, 3; 4, 5, $\sqrt{8}$; or 6, 0, $-\sqrt{13}$; or any of an enormous number of triples, most of which would be far more difficult to check than these, even if we should agree on the number of decimal places to be specified in each value.

We have no reason to assume that, among all the molecules having a given velocity magnitude, there are more whose velocities lie in one direction rather than another. As a first step, it is reasonable to expect a uniform probability distribution of the directions in which molecules move. Among the molecules whose velocity is 7 hm/sec, the proportion of molecules whose component velocities were 2, 3, 6 would equal the proportion whose velocities were 4.5, 5.0, $\sqrt{4.75}$, and also equal the proportion having every other possible combination of component velocities. However, it *might* be reasonable to assume that there are more (or fewer) molecules whose velocity is 10 hm/sec than 7 hm/sec, that is, the probability distribution of the velocity magnitudes themselves may not be uniform.

Denoting by $p(v_1, v_2, v_3)$ the probability of molecules having the triple of values, v_1, v_2, v_3, for the magnitudes of their three component velocities (i.e., the proportion, *among all the molecules*, of those having just those values),[1] we may state the above conclusion as follows: Although we would not expect $p(2, 3, 6)$ to equal $p(2, 3, 5)$, etc., we would expect equal probabilities, e.g., $p(2, 3, 6) = p(2, 6, -3) = \ldots = p(6, 0, -\sqrt{13}) = \ldots$, where the velocity magnitudes themselves, computed by the three-dimensional Pythagorean Theorem, are all equal. Stated more generally, the probability, $p(v_1, v_2, v_3)$, of molecules having any particular combination of velocity components *depends only on the magnitude of the velocity v, or its square, which is the sum*, $v_1{}^2 + v_2{}^2 + v_3{}^2$. This probability, we assume, is not dependent on the direction of the motion.

If we adopt the customary mathematical notation $f(x)$ for a quantity that depends only on the value of x, called a *function* of x, this conclusion may be formulated as follows: For any v_1, v_2, and v_3,

$$p(v_1, v_2, v_3) = f(v_1^2 + v_2^2 + v_3^2) \qquad (8.3)$$

The probability of molecules having a particular ordered triple of component velocities v_1, v_2, and v_3, is a function only of the sum of the squares of these velocities.

In deriving the probability distribution of number of heads among four coins, we saw that it was useful to consider, as an intermediate

---

[1] Strictly speaking, we would have to specify just how close each component velocity has to be to a given value in order to be counted as having that value. For simplicity, we have omitted such specification here.

step, the joint distribution for the number of heads among each of two pairs of coins (see Fig. 8.2). To find these joint distributions, we used the multiplication rule for independent events and expressed the probability of each particular composite outcome (for example, two heads on one pair and one head on the other) as the product of the probabilities of the separate "component" outcomes. In other words, we made use of the fact that

$$p(n_1, n_2) = p(n_1) \cdot p(n_2)$$

where n_1 and n_2 were, respectively, the numbers of heads on the first and second pairs of coins.

In a similar manner, *assuming that the component velocities of the molecules of a gas are independently distributed,* we use the multiplication rule to express the joint probability $p(v_1, v_2, v_3)$, which is the left member of Eq. (8.3), in a different manner, i.e., as the product of the probabilities of the component velocites. Thus,

$$p(v_1, v_2, v_3) = p(v_1) \cdot p(v_2) \cdot p(v_3) \tag{8.4}$$

With regard to the question of whether or not the component velocities are indeed independent, if we were to take into consideration only those molecules having a given velocity magnitude, the answer would be negative. When two of the components have been determined, the third is also known by virtue of the three-dimensional Pythagorean theorem, $v^2 = v_1^2 + v_2^2 + v_3^2$. (See p. 230.) Since we are interested in the distribution of velocities in the entire gas sample, we defined the function, $p(\ )$, as the proportion among all possible molecular velocities. If we should pick any molecule at random and determine any two of its velocity components, that information would tell us nothing about the velocity of the third component. Therefore, the three component velocities of the entire collection of molecules may be regarded as independently distributed, and we may apply the multiplication rule and its consequence, Eq. (8.4). Substituting from Eq. (8.4) in Eq. (8.3), we may also write

$$p(v_1) \cdot p(v_2) \cdot p(v_3) = f(v_1^2 + v_2^2 + v_3^2) \tag{8.5}$$

This equation presents an interesting mathematical property of the probabilities of the component velocities: their product is a function of the sum of the squares of the component velocities themselves. This mathematical relationship, as we shall see later, provides a clue for finding the probability distribution of the component velocities, and this result will enable us to find the distribution of the velocity magnitudes themselves.

We have already noted that the choice of axes is completely arbitrary because the pressure of the gas is uniform in all directions. This gives us another important relation: the distribution of the component velocities in the direction of one axis must be identical to the distribution of those along either of the other axes. For any two component velocities at right angles to each other and having equal values, the probabilities of these component velocities are also equal. Considering all three axes at once, for any triple of component velocities, v_1, v_2, v_3 (not necessarily belonging to one molecule),

$$\text{if} \quad v_1 = v_2, \quad \text{then} \quad \mathbf{p}(v_1) = \mathbf{p}(v_2);$$

$$\text{if} \quad v_1 = v_3, \quad \text{then} \quad \mathbf{p}(v_1) = \mathbf{p}(v_3);$$

and

$$\text{if} \quad v_2 = v_3, \quad \text{then} \quad \mathbf{p}(v_2) = \mathbf{p}(v_3).$$

A more convenient representation of this fact is to say that the probabilities of component velocities in each of the three directions chosen are all given by the same mathematical function—a function of the component velocity values.

We may derive one further conclusion from the fact that the pressure of a gas is uniform in all directions; at any time, the proportion of molecules traveling in a given direction with a particular velocity magnitude is equal to the proportion of molecules traveling in the diametrically opposite direction with the same speed. With respect to the three components of a molecule's velocity (for which opposite directions are indicated by positive and negative signs), this means that there is just as great a probability of finding a molecule for which v_1 is equal to, say, − 5 hm/sec as there is of finding one for which $v_1 = + 5$ hm/sec. That is,

$$\mathbf{p}(-v_1) = \mathbf{p}(v_1)$$

$$\mathbf{p}(-v_2) = \mathbf{p}(v_2)$$

$$\mathbf{p}(-v_3) = \mathbf{p}(v_3)$$

The positive and the negative component velocities of a given magnitude yield the same value when squared. The previous conclusion that the probability of any component velocity is given by the same function of the component velocity value (which may be positive or negative) can now be restated as follows: *the probability of a component velocity is uniquely determined by the square of its magnitude.* This function may be represented by the symbol g( ). The foregoing conclusion is expressed mathematically by writing

$$\mathbf{p}(v_1) = g(v_1^2)$$

$$\mathbf{p}(v_2) = g(v_2^2)$$

$$\mathbf{p}(v_3) = g(v_3^2)$$

Using this new function, g( ), Eq. (8.5) is rewritten as

$$g(v_1{}^2) \cdot g(v_2{}^2) \cdot g(v_3{}^2) = f(v_1{}^2 + v_2{}^2 + v_3{}^2) \tag{8.6}$$

Our task now is to find the mathematical functions that we have denoted as f( ) and g( ) which determine the probability distributions of the velocity magnitudes and of the component velocities. Lacking any means for determining these distributions physically, Eq. (8.6) is our principal guide in seeking the appropriate mathematical functions. There is one familiar group of mathematical functions that satisfies the requirement of Eq. (8.6): the family of exponential functions, $h(x) = a^x$. The student may readily see that at least one of these functions satisfies Eq. (8.6) by taking $a = 2$, for example, and choosing three values for x. The product $2^3 \cdot 2^2 \cdot 2^5$, which is $h(3) \cdot h(2) \cdot h(5)$, is, by the law of exponents, equal to 2^{3+2+5}, which is $h(3 + 2 + 5)$. If we choose any positive number a and any three numbers x, y, z,

$$a^x \cdot a^y \cdot a^z = a^{x+y+z}$$

If we let

$$g(x) = a^x \tag{8.7}$$

so that $g(y) = a^y$, $g(z) = a^z$ and $g(x + y + z) = a^{x+y+z}$, then

$$g(x)\,g(y)\,g(z) = g(x + y + z)$$

If we take the squares of three component velocities, $v_1{}^2, v_2{}^2, v_3{}^2$ as the x, y, z, we have

$$a^{v_1{}^2} \cdot a^{v_2{}^2} \cdot a^{v_3{}^2} = a^{v_1{}^2 + v_2{}^2 + v_3{}^2} \tag{8.8}$$

We see that choosing g( ) from the family of functions, $g(v_1{}^2) = a^{v_1{}^2}$, satisfies Eq. (8.6) with f( ) turning out to be the same function as g( ).

Since the functions f( ) and g( ) in Eq. (8.6) need not have the same form, we may choose g( ) from the larger family,

$$g(x) = Ca^x \tag{8.9}$$

and then

$$f(x) = C^3 a^x$$

where C is some constant. These functions also satisfy Eq. (8.6), as may readily be confirmed by forming the product $Ca^{v_1{}^2} \cdot Ca^{v_2{}^2} \cdot Ca^{v_3{}^2}$. Using the law exponents again, we see that

$$Ca^{v_1{}^2} \cdot Ca^{v_2{}^2} \cdot Ca^{v_3{}^2} = C^3 a^{v_1{}^2 + v_2{}^2 + v_3{}^2} \tag{8.10}$$

By means of advanced mathematics, it can be shown that Eq. (8.9) specifies the only family of appropriate functions that satisfies Eq. (8.6).

Our previous g( ), defined by Eq. (8.7), is a special case of expression (8.9) with $C = 1$. Had the earlier definition of g( ) been taken, we would have been arbitrarily assigning the value 1 to the constant C. We have no grounds for choosing this or any other value for C. We should therefore take the more general function, Eq. (8.9), from which the following expressions are written for the proportions of molecules with particular values[2] for the three component velocities:

$$p(v_1) = Ca^{v_1^2}$$

$$p(v_2) = Ca^{v_2^2} \qquad (8.11)$$

$$p(v_3) = Ca^{v_3^2}$$

Our task of determining the probability distribution of component velocities reduces to that of finding the appropriate values of the constants C and a. Recalling that the temperature of a gas and the molecular velocities and masses are related by the equation, $T = kmv^2$, we expect that the velocity distribution will depend on the kind of gas and its temperature. The values of the constants C and a should be different for samples of gas of different molecular mass and temperature.

Taking different values of C merely has the effect of changing the vertical scale of the graph of the distribution. The graph of the distribution takes on quite different shapes depending on whether a is greater than 1, equal to 1, or less than 1. This can be easily understood by recalling that raising a number between zero and one (e.g., 1/2, 1/3, 0.8, .065) to successively higher powers gives successively *smaller* values, whereas raising a number larger than 1 to successively higher powers gives successively *larger* values. Raising 1 to any power always gives 1. The effect of the value of a on the shape of the resulting graphs is shown in Figs. 8.4, 8.5, and 8.6, which have been plotted for a equal to 1.1, 1, and 0.9, respectively. The effect of a change in the constant, C, is seen in these figures by comparing the solid-line graphs, labeled C, with the broken-line graphs labeled C'.

By a suitable choice of the value of C, the area under a distribution graph can be made numerically equal to 100%, representing the totality of molecules in a given sample of gas. In order to do this in the case of $a \geq 1$ (Figs. 8.4 and 8.5), it would be necessary to set definite limits on the values of v_1. The choice of such limits would have to be arbitary and the existence of limits would conflict with our conceptual model of a gas. In our model there is nothing, in principle, to prevent a molecule, whose component velocity is at some hypothetical limit, from acquiring an even larger velocity by an appropriate

---

[2]Each component velocity value must be taken to represent a certain range of values whose center has that value.

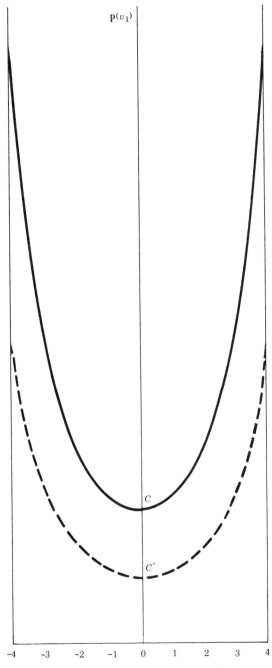

Figure 8.4 Graph of $\mathbf{p}(v_1) = C(1.1)^{v_1^2}$.

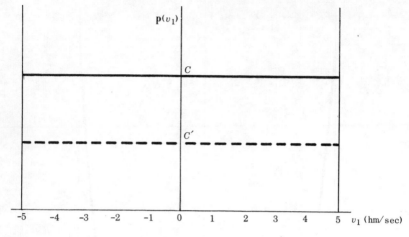

Figure 8.5 Graph of $p(v_1) = C(1)^{v_1^2}$.

collision with another molecule. Examining Fig. 8.6, we note that as we consider larger and larger numerical values of v_1 the percentage of molecules becomes very small. It can be shown that the area under this graph is limited even though the range of v_1 values is not.

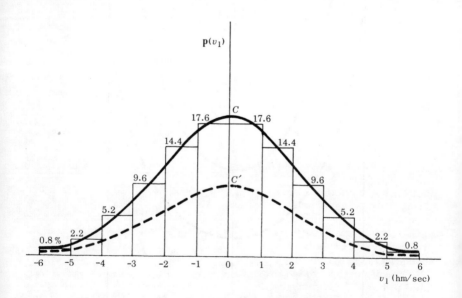

Figure 8.6 Graphs of $p(v_1) = C(0.9)^{v_1^2}$ (for C and C') and the Binomial Distribution for $n = 19$. (Total areas are equated for the continuous line and bar graphs).

Mathematical exploration:

8.3 By methods of advanced mathematics it may be proved that the areas under graphs that asymptotically approach the horizontal axis are limited in certain cases and not in others. The area under the graph of an inverse-square proportionality, $y = k/x^2$ (see Fig. 4.4), approaches a limit as x increases indefinitely; but there is no limit that the area under the graph of an inverse proportionality, $y = k/x$ (see Fig. 4.3), does not exceed. In Table 8.2 the student should compare the ratios of pairs of values of $p(v_1)$ with the ratios of the corresponding pairs of values of k/v_1^2. He should convince himself that the smooth graphs of Fig. 8.6 drop off much more rapidly at the extremes than does the graph of an inverse-square proportionality. This means that the area under each of the smooth graphs of Fig. 8.6 is also limited. By appropriate choice of the value of C, the area of such a graph can be made equal to 100% without limiting the range of v_1.

Table 8.2 Heights of the Smooth Graphs of Fig. 8.6 Compared with those of a Graph for the Inverse Square Proportionality

v	$p(v_1)$	k/v_1^2
0	C	indeterminate
1	$.90\,C$	$k/1 = k$
2	$.66\,C$	$k/4 = .25\,k$
3	$.39\,C$	$k/9 = .11\,k$
4	$.19\,C$	$k/16 = .06\,k$
5	$.07\,C$	$k/25 = .04\,k$
6	$.023\,C$	$k/36 = .03\,k$

We see that only a graph like Fig. 8.6, for which a is a positive number less than 1, can represent the distribution of component velocities of molecules in a gas. This conclusion gains even greater plausibility when it is realized that distribution graphs of this form repeatedly occur in connection with a variety of phenomena in science—phenomena which reflect a large number of underlying random processes. Distributions having this form are known as *normal* or Gaussian distributions.

The step or bar graph in Fig. 8.6 depicts a distribution closely related to the normal distribution. It is one of a family of distributions—the *symmetrical binomial distributions*—two other members of which we have already studied. They were the distributions describing the outcomes of tossing two coins and of tossing four coins. In a similar manner, the binomial distribution, the central portion of which is graphed in Fig. 8.6, would serve to represent the outcomes of tossing 19 coins repeatedly. As the number of coins is increased without limit (and the width of the bars is correspondingly decreased) the resulting sequence of binomial distributions approaches the normal distribution curve as a limit. Consequently we can use the binomial distributions as convenient approximations to the normal distribution. ∎

The next question to be considered concerns the relation of the constant a to the molecular weight of a given sample of gas and to its temperature. This question is answered by application of more mathematics than we care to undertake here to results already obtained in this chapter and the preceding one. The conclusion of such analyses is that $a = (0.548)^{M/T}$ where M is the molecular weight and T is the absolute temperature of the gas sample in degrees Kelvin. Substitution of this expression into Eqs. (8.11) yields the probability distributions of component velocities, for any of the three components and for any sample of gas, as expressed in the following equation:

$$p(v_i) = C[(0.548)^{M/T}]^{v_i^2}$$

where $i = 1, 2,$ or 3. It is more compactly written as

$$p(v_i) = C(0.548)^{(M/T)v_i^2} \tag{8.12}$$

The value of a [i.e., $(0.548)^{M/T}$] used in plotting Fig. 8.6, that is 0.90, happens to be the appropriate value for a gas sample in which $M/T = 0.175$. If a sample of oxygen ($M = 32$) were used, Fig. 8.6 would give the distribution of component velocities for a temperature of $T = 183°K$ (or $-90°C$). For sulfur dioxide ($M = 64$), and $T = 366°K$ (93°C). For chlorine ($M = 71$), the component velocity distribution shown in Fig. 8.6 would correspond to a temperature of $406°K$ (133°C). By means of a table of logarithms it is a routine process to calculate the appropriate value of a for any gas at any given temperature and plot out the component velocity distribution. Note that, since T has as its basic units kg $(m/sec)^2$, the units in the exponent of Eq. (8.12) cancel out. Since exponents are interpreted as pure numbers, it would have been awkward had this not been so.

Our final task is that of determining the distribution of the molecular velocities from the distribution of the component velocities. We need to assign, to a large set of molecules, values for each of the three component velocities that are distributed in accordance with Eq. (8.12) and then compute the resultant velocities of the molecules. In view of the assumption that the directions of molecular velocities are randomly distributed, we assign component velocities to each molecule by selecting three values at random from a set of component velocities having the prescribed normal distribution. To use the normal distribution for computing this new distribution would require advanced mathematics. We shall take the binomial distribution of

Fig. 8.6 as the basis for selecting component velocities. Since the two distributions resemble each other closely, this procedure should yield a reasonably good approximation to the desired result. This procedure can only give us the velocity distribution for a particular value of a, but one case will suffice to exhibit the general relationship between the distribution of component velocities and the corresponding distribution of molecular velocities.

Theoretical exploration:

8.4 As a class or laboratory exercise, it will be instructive for students to produce an approximation to the Maxwell–Boltzmann distribution. To do this, a sizeable number of magnitudes of v should be calculated from component velocity magnitudes selected at random from a "population" based on the binomial distribution, which was shown in the bar graph of Fig. 8.6. One can easily create a "population" of component magnitudes from which to sample by copying each magnitude a number of times in proportion to the areas of the bars in the right half of the graph. If such numbers are written on some kind of easily shuffleable tags or cardboard chips,[3] they can be mixed in a bowl or hat and drawn out at random.

The velocity magnitude for each bar of the positive half of the graph is written on a number of tags which is proportional to the relative area indicated in that bar. For a total of 200 tags, the velocity value 0.5 should be written on $17.6/50 \times 200 = 17.6 \times 4$ or, when rounded off, 70 tags. The appropriate number of tags on which to write each of the other central values can be calculated in the same way. These tags will then constitute a "population" distributed very much like half of the normal distribution. Only one half of the distribution needs to be used, because it is symmetrical, and because the positive or negative signs of the component velocities are immaterial in considering their squares.

The "population" of tags is thoroughly mixed in a container and three tags are drawn at one time. Their numbers are recorded, and the tags are replaced.[4] The three numbers obtained in each drawing are squared, summed, and recorded. The process is continued, the population of tags being thoroughly mixed between drawings.

The sums of squares, or v^2 magnitudes, obtained in this manner, should be grouped according to which of the ranges, 0–0.99, 1–3.99, 4–8.99, 9–15.99, etc., they fall into. These are the ranges of v^2 magnitudes which correspond respectively to unit intervals of v, 0–0.99, 1–1.99, 2–2.99, 3–3.99, etc. The frequency distribution of v-values

---

[3]The easiest kind of "chip" to shuffle is a metal-rimmed cardboard tag which sometimes comes with strings attached. The strings should be removed.

[4]Strictly speaking, the tags should be drawn one at a time and each tag replaced before drawing the next—otherwise the population distribution is changed slightly. The effect of non-replacement on the result seems too small to be of much concern, if only three tags are drawn before being replaced.

thus obtained may be expected to approximate the theoretical Maxwell-Boltzmann distribution. Before a reasonable approximation of the theoretical distribution is obtained, the total number of drawings may have to be more than 100. ∎

The method just described is an application of the Monte Carlo method for finding approximate solutions to complex problems involving probability. Its name derives from the fact that it employs a random sampling procedure as do games of chance. Use of the method is often the only feasible approach when purely mathematical methods of solution cannot be found. Although such is not the case in the present problem, the purely mathematical methods available go beyond the limits set for this book. Accordingly we have used the Monte Carlo method described above to derive a much more accurate distribution (for a = 0.9) by carrying out the calculations for a very large number of "drawings," and with a minor refinement in the original binomial distribution. This refinement consisted in subdividing the bar covering the interval from 0 to 1 into two bars of equal widths, whose midpoints were 0.25 and 0.75. The reason for doing so is that the distribution of v-values is especially sensitive to variations in component-velocity values falling within the 0-to-1 interval. Subdividing all the bars would have made the entire distribution more precise, but only slightly so, while the calculations would have become considerably more complicated.

A high-speed digital computer was used to produce 10,000 velocity magnitudes, each magnitude being calculated from three component velocity values selected at random from the binomial distribution of Fig. 8.6 modified as just indicated. The resulting velocity magnitudes, when grouped in intervals of 1 hm/sec, yielded the distribution shown in the bar diagram of Fig. 8.7. This is an approximation to a distribution of the type for which Maxwell and Boltzmann, independently, derived the general formula. The instance of their general formula, with a = 0.9, may be most simply written as follows:

$$\mathbf{p}(v) = Cv^2(0.9)^{v^2}$$

For comparison with the bar diagram of our Monte Carlo results, the appropriate value of the constant C for 10,000 molecules is 771. The smooth curve of Fig. 8.7 is a graph of the resulting equation. The closeness of the Monte Carlo approximation for 10,000 v-values to this exact curve is evident. It may not be intuitively evident why the distribution of v-magnitudes is so different from that of v_1. The difference hinges on the fact that component molecular velocities will be negative as often as they are positive, while velocity magnitudes can only be positive. Thinking through the "experiment" of drawing tags should help make the relationship of the two distributions intuitively clear.

The reader will recall that in Eq. (8.12) a was replaced by the expression $(0.548)^{M/T}$, where M is molecular weight and T is absolute temperature. Making the same substitution here will yield an equation with greater experimental applicability. This equation becomes

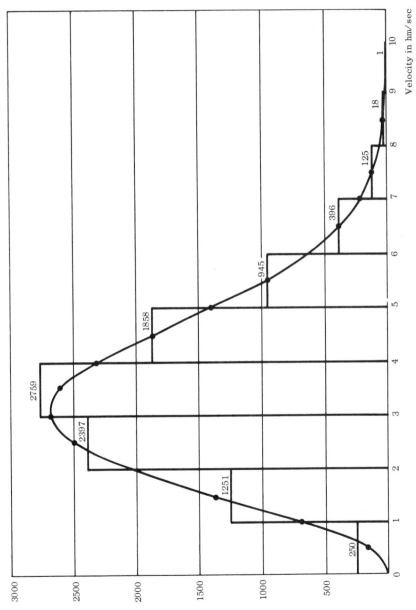

Figure 8.7 A Distribution of Molecular Velocities.

$$\mathbf{p}(v) = Cv^2(0.548)^{(M/T)v^2} \tag{8.13}$$

The value of the ratio M/T for Fig. 8.7 is 0.175, as it was for Fig. 8.6. So Fig. 8.7 could be taken to represent the velocity distribution in a sample of oxygen at 160°K (− 113°C) or a sample of chlorine at 406°K (133°C).

COOLING BY EVAPORATION

It is a commonplace observation that liquids kept in an uncovered container will gradually evaporate, some more rapidly than others. In terms of the well-established atomic-molecular model of matter, the process of evaporation of a liquid consists in the escape of some of its molecules.

The familiar cooling effect of evaporation may very easily be explained qualitatively. First, it is reasonable to suppose that the molecules which escape from a liquid are predominantly the faster-moving ones. The result would then be a reduction of the average squared velocity for the remaining molecules (just as the class average on a test would be lowered if the ablest students left school before the test). This reduction in the average squared velocity would, in view of the kinetic-theory definition of temperature, imply a lowering of the temperature.

This *qualitative* explanation is supported by the further observation that liquids which evaporate more rapidly produce a greater cooling effect than do those whose rate of evaporation is slower. It is well known that alcohol evaporates faster than water and also has a greater cooling effect.

To attempt a *quantitative* explanation of the different cooling effects produced by the evaporation of different liquids, we find the distributions of molecular velocities for alcohol and water. Since the main assumptions made in deriving the Maxwell-Boltzmann distribution were that the molecular velocities are distributed homogeneously and that their component velocities are independent, there is no apparent reason to believe that the molecular velocities in liquids would have any different distribution. Let us proceed by taking the same general-distribution law. (The advancement of scientific thought often requires the making of such assumptions, based mainly on plausibility, but always subject to revision in case new evidence demands it.)

Four liquids which are readily available in most laboratories and which have noticeably different cooling effects are: acetone, ethyl alcohol, ethyl ether, and water. Their molecular weights are: 58.08, 46.07, 74.12, and 18.00. To measure the cooling effects of such liquids, it is desirable to have them initially at the same temperature. Since they differ in molecular weights, the exponent M/T in Eq. (8.13) will be different for each substance. We will need four different instances of the Maxwell–Boltzmann distribution. Assuming $T = 300°K$ (or $23°C$—a suitable temperature for laboratory conditions) we have the following values of M/T:

acetone $\quad \dfrac{58.08}{300} = 0.1936$

ethyl alcohol $\dfrac{46.07}{300} = 0.1536$

ethyl ether $\quad \dfrac{74.12}{300} = 0.2471$

water $\quad \dfrac{18.00}{300} = 0.0600$

In the same manner we used for gases, starting from the binomial distribution ($n = 19$), we have plotted, in Fig. 8.8, the Maxwell–Boltzmann distributions and appropriate bar graphs of molecular velocities for these four liquids. From each of the four bar graphs, we have computed the average of v^2 for the 10,000 molecules. Note that the average squared velocities tend to be higher for substances with lower molecular weights. Let us see if this result is consistent with our definition of absolute temperature as proportional to the average of mv^2 for the molecules.

It is more convenient to rewrite our mechanical definition of temperature, Eq. (7.9) using molecular weight, M, rather than the molecular mass in grams, m, when we are dealing with different chemical substances. Thus:

$$T =_{\mathrm{Df}} KM\overline{v^2} \tag{8.14}$$

Our next step is to determine the value of K, the constant of proportionality in this equation. From Fig. 8.8 (a) we find that $\overline{v^2}$ for acetone at $23°C$ is $12.96 \ \mathrm{hm^2/sec^2}$. By rearranging Eq. (8.14) the required value is obtained as follows:

$$K = \frac{T}{M} \cdot \frac{1}{\overline{v^2}} = \frac{300}{58.08} \cdot \frac{1}{12.86} = 0.402$$

Naturally, there is no need to check this graph against our definition. However, what would be the result if we check the others?

Theoretical confirmation:

8.5 As an exercise, the student should verify that the values of $\overline{v^2}$ and M shown in Fig. 8.8 (b), (c), (d), for their three substances, when substituted in Eq. (8.14) yield essentially the same value of T. ∎

Equation (8.14) gives us the relation between T and $\overline{v^2}$ for any value of M. Having determined K, we write the proper equation for each of

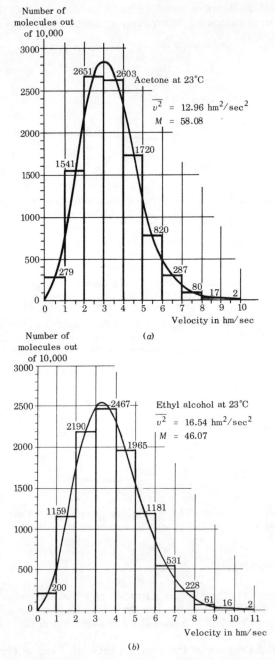

Figure 8.8 Distributions of Molecular Velocities at $T = 300°K$ for Four

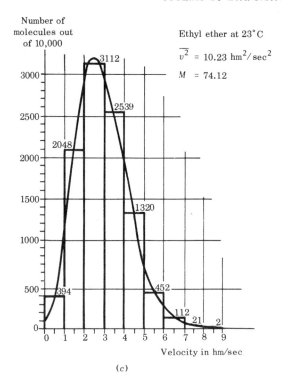

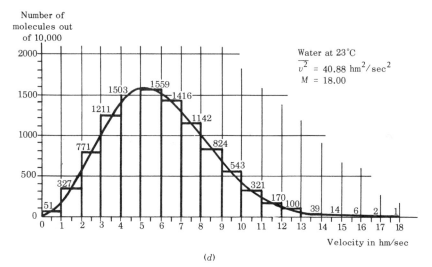

Liquids: (a) Acetone, (b) Ethyl Alcohol, (c) Ethyl Ether, and (d) Water.

the four substances by using the appropriate molecular weights. These equations are:

$$
\left.
\begin{aligned}
T &= 23.33\ \overline{v^2}\ \text{(acetone)} \\
T &= 18.14\ \overline{v^2}\ \text{(ethyl alcohol)} \\
T &= 29.50\ \overline{v^2}\ \text{(ethyl ether)} \\
T &= 7.34\ \overline{v^2}\ \text{(water)}
\end{aligned}
\right\}
\tag{8.15}
$$

The graph of each of these equations is shown in Fig. 8.9.

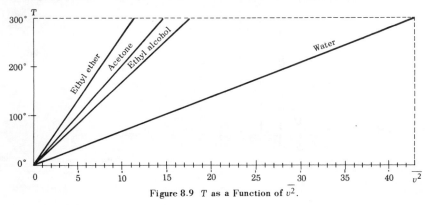

Figure 8.9 T as a Function of $\overline{v^2}$.

With these equations, we may predict the change in temperature that would occur in each substance, if some of the fastest molecules escape. Then we may try to find an experimental procedure to test our predictions. In the case of ether, if all of the molecules represented by the rightmost bar in Fig. 8.8 (c) (velocities of 8-9 hm/sec) should instantly escape, $\overline{v^2}$ for the remaining liquid could be calculated as follows: The total v^2, prior to escape, is $N\overline{v^2}$ or $10,000 \times 10.17 = 101,700$ hm^2/sec^2. From this value, we must subtract the total v^2 of the escaping molecules. Using the midpoint of their velocity range, the total v^2 of the escaping molecules is $(8.5)^2 \times 2 = 145$ hm^2/sec^2. So the total v^2 of the remaining molecules is $101,700 - 145 = 101,555$, or approximately $101,600$. The $\overline{v^2}$ of the remaining molecules is $101,600/9,998$ or 10.16 hm^2/sec^2. Substituting in the third of Eq. (8.15), we obtain, as the value of T, $299.7°$K, representing a drop of only about $0.3°$C.

If all molecules with velocity magnitudes of 7 hm/sec or more should instantly escape, the total v^2 of the remaining 9977 molecules would be $101,700 - 145 - 1,181$ or approximately $100,400$ hm^2/sec^2. The $\overline{v^2}$ for the remaining liquid would be $100,400/9,977$ or 10.66 hm^2/sec^2, for which we find $T = 296.8°$K. The instantaneous escape of the molecules in the top two blocks would thus produce a temperature drop of 3.2°C. Continuing in this manner, the temperature drop that would be produced by the escape of all the molecules in the top three blocks, the top four, and so forth, may be determined. From these calculations the graph of Fig. 8.10 is plotted showing the temperature drop that would result from a hypothetical sudden escape of all molecules with velocities exceeding a given magnitude.

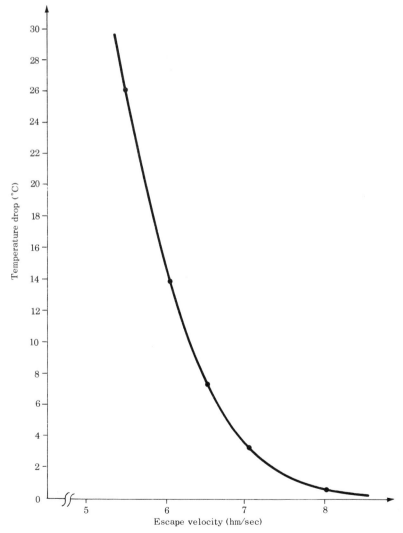

Figure 8.10 Temperature Drop (°C) as a Function of Molecular Escape Velocity for Ethyl Ether at 23°C.

Theoretical development:

8.6 The graph in Fig. 8.10 was plotted from the velocity distribution for ethyl ether, Fig. 8.8 (c). To prepare a basis for analysis of different cooling effects, the student should construct the corresponding graphs for the other three substances. Once these graphs have been plotted, they may be used the other way around to ascribe a hypothetical "escape velocity" to the molecules of each substance that would explain an observed temperature drop. Is it possible that all four liquids could have the same "escape velocity"? If so, what would the relative cooling effects be? ■

Since the graphs just obtained are constructed under the assumption that all molecules escape at a given instant whose velocities exceed a given magnitude, they are applicable only when this assumption is at least approximately sustained by the experimental conditions. This assumption will often be far from true. Molecules near the bottom of a container of liquid will be unable to reach the surface within any very small time interval even if their velocities are very high. Only the molecules moving in an upward direction will have a chance to escape, so evaporation from the flat surface of liquid in a container would be better explained in terms of the distribution of component velocities—the component velocities perpendicular to the surface of the liquid. Evaporation from the surface of liquids in a container does not produce as marked a temperature difference as we might obtain in some other way. The cooling occurs at or near the surface, and the effect is diffused through the liquid making it difficult to determine experimentally how much cooling occurred in a surface layer of given thickness—unless one could arrange to measure the temperature of a very thin layer of liquid.

One convenient arrangement employs cloth wicks which are kept saturated with a liquid. To keep wicks equally wet with different liquids, they are enclosed in glass tubes up to the part that is draped around the thermometer bulb. The wicks and tubes are placed in narrow-necked containers as shown in Fig. 8.11. The temperature of a liquid evaporating from a wick depends on currents of air and other external conditions, but the fibers of the wicks allow escape in all directions.

If four wicks are set up with four liquids under identical conditions, any different cooling effects observed may be ascribed to the different velocity distributions of the liquids. If all the liquids have the same initial temperature, the lowest temperature attained at the exposed end of each wick may be regarded as indicating the temperature drop because of the escape of those molecules which were moving faster than the hypothetical "escape velocity" of that liquid. Assuming an initial temperature of $300°K$, hypothetical "escape velocities" for all four liquids could then, on this model, be read off from graphs like Fig. 8.10. We note that these "escape velocities" are not the same

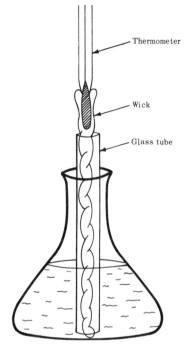

Figure 8.11 Arrangement of Cloth Wick and
Thermometer for Evaporation Experiment.

for all four liquids and we may presume that they depend on the structures of the different molecules. So this procedure cannot be used to
check our predictions.

In introducing the concept of a unique escape velocity for each
liquid, we have undoubtedly adopted an oversimplified model of the
process of evaporation. It has served a useful purpose in providing a
quantitative explanation of cooling be evaporation. If further refinement of the statistical model of evaporation is desired, we may, without making any fundamental changes, replace the concept of a unique
escape velocity by a range through which the probability of a molecule's escape increases with velocity. The student may see for himself how such a concept would function in the model by carrying out
the following exercise.

Another simplification deserving notice is one made in the previous
chapter in our "billiard-ball" model of molecular collisions. We
have analyzed the translational motions of molecules and ignored the
possibility that they rotate (which is an important motion in billiards)
or that the shapes of molecules change rhythmically like a vibrating
tuning fork. If several types of molecular motions are possible, there
may be an interaction between them as, for example, when the spinning
of a billiard ball affects its angle of translation after a collision, or

when the vibration of a tuning fork sends a ball of pith touching it into violent flight. In the cases which our theory explains successfully, these other forms of molecular energy must either be of small effect or must compensate each other so that the overall behavior of matter is as though they were not present.

Perhaps, however, there are other phenomena in which these other forms of molecular energy make themselves known. We cannot examine such phenomena here, but we have already examined one case, which we ought now to recall. Dulong and Petit's Law (see p. 195) holds only for monatomic elements and not for substances whose molecules have two or more atoms. This restriction of the law is explained qualitatively by considering that monatomic substances cannot exchange energy in as many different ways as those whose molecules have two or more atoms. The latter substances should be able to exchange energy of rotation and of internal vibration more readily than the former. A mechanical model of heat exchanges for such substances would have to analyze these forms of energy and their interactions.

We have already noted (p. 258) that progress in theory construction is often made by beginning with simple models and then learning from their successes and failures how to procede in the development of more refined models. We now find, as scientists often do, that we are using a model that is clearly oversimplified and therefore, strictly speaking, wrong. It could serve as a stepping stone to a better model, if one chose to go on. For our purposes, it is still very useful. (See the problems at the end of the chapter for other uses.)

Theoretical exercise:

8.7 The percentage distribution of molecular velocities in a certain liquid at 30°C is as shown in Table 8.3. Suppose that the "escape range" is 3.5 hm/sec and above, and that 25% of the molecules escape in the interval whose midpoint is 4 hm/sec, 40% in the 5 hm/sec

Table 8.3 Percentage Distribution of Molecular
Velocities for Exercise 8.7

Velocity range (hm/sec)	Midpoint velocity (hm/sec)	Percentage
0 − 0.5	0.25	2
0.5 − 1.5	1.00	12
1.5 − 2.5	2.00	35
2.5 − 3.5	3.00	30
3.5 − 4.5	4.00	12
4.5 − 5.5	5.00	7
5.5 − 6.5	6.00	2

interval, and 60 percent in the 6 hm/sec interval. Compute the temperature of the remaining liquid. ■

We can see from this exercise that, if the concept of a unique escape velocity is superseded by a range with associated escape probabilities, the calculations necessary for relating this range to observable phenomena can still be carried out. We have opened up the possibility of relating the Maxwell–Boltzmann distribution to new kinds of phenomena, but have not yet discovered new laws governing them. These would appear to depend on a study of intermolecular forces. Other applications are suggested in the problems at the end of this chapter.

METHODOLOGICAL REVIEW

One of the key ideas in the development of this chapter has been that of a probability distribution. This concept was first introduced in connection with discrete trials with two or more unpredictable outcomes, such as tossing one or more coins or rolling one or more dice. In estimating the probability of a given outcome on a particular trial, such as the probability of obtaining two heads when two coins are tossed, it was necessary to consider some total set of outcomes of the simplest event. The probability of each particular one among the entire set of possible outcomes of a trial, could be computed from the probabilities of elementary events by using the multiplication and addition rules. One distribution obtained in this way was the binomial distribution which specifies the probabilities of 0, 1, 2, 3, or 4 heads, respectively, when four coins are tossed.

Calculations with discrete events of such familiar sorts were carried out in order to clarify the multiplication and addition rules, which are the elementary principles of probability theory. When we turned to the distribution of magnitudes of molecular velocities, by interpreting this as a probability distribution, we found an approach via component velocities that opened up a solution. The multiplication rule provided the key to solving the problem of the component velocity distribution, and by assuming a uniform distribution of velocity directions independent of the distribution of velocity magnitudes, we obtained the Maxwell–Boltzmann distribution of velocity mangitudes. It is surprising indeed that the mathematical expression giving the distribution of velocities in a gas could be obtained from just these two assumptions: (1) that the velocities in any direction are distributed in the same manner and (2) that the multiplication rule for the probabilities of independent events holds for the molecular velocities of a gas.

Such developments leading from simple assumptions to the explanation of complex phenomena are not uncommon in theoretical sciences using mathematical models. This is generally true, whether or not such models make use of probability distributions, although this example may be more surprising than most to persons not accustomed to thinking in terms of probability distributions. Earlier, the assumption of the conservation of heat (heat lost equals heat gained) as understood from mixtures of water enabled us to derive explanations of more complex heat phenomena including heat exchange between different substances and changes in heat content accompanying changes of state. This is one instance of the many applications of the law of conservation of energy in solving complex problems.

Perhaps the most frequent use of the probability concept in science generally occurs in connection with the testing of theoretical predictions by observations. It cannot be expected that measurements and other observations provide precise agreement with theoretical predictions. The question arises as to how close an agreement is required for confirmation of the theory. The inevitable residue of disagreement between theory and observation is attributable to random errors of measurement, specific factors not taken into consideration in the theoretical model, or both. Given an estimate of the probability distribution of errors, the science of statistics enables us to determine the amount of confidence that can be placed in a given conclusion when that conclusion is based on the amount of agreement between theory and observation. The frequency distributions of stellar parallax measurements, depicted in the bar graphs of Fig. 1.15, could be examined by techniques of statistics, if one wanted to determine how likely it is that the differences between them have arisen by random errors of measurement. In practice, if the agreement between theory and observation is obviously good and remains so over several experiments, the value of performing such statistical calculations may be less than the cost of doing so. One always comes to a point in scientific research at which a judgment must be made as to whether further checking of a given conclusion is worth taking the time and effort away from the investigation of other questions.

At the end of Chapter 1 we discussed three criteria for the evaluation of theoretical models: simplicity, scope, and precision. We now reformulate the last two of these criteria in a way which further clarifies them. To increase the precision with which a theory fits the evidence, either the measurements must be made more reliably or the theory must take more factors into consideration, or both. The causes of fluctuations in the observations that were previously unrecognized, must be discovered and either controlled by better measurement techniques or else accounted for by a broader theory. Increasing the scope of a theory requires either that we incorporate into it more factors pertaining to a given set of phenomena or that we extend it so as to account for new phenomena as well.

The direction in which scientific inquiry should proceed is the reduction of uncertainties. In this connection, it has sometimes been remarked that the object of employing statistics in science is to eliminate the need for further statistics. In the light of the foregoing discussion, this statement makes sense if it refers to the techniques of statistical testing of the fit between theory and observation—a field which is usually known as statistical inference—but only if there is the beginning of a quantitative theory to guide the redefinition of variables and measurements that will make their significance clearer. Newtonian mechanics is often taken as the ideal of science, and certainly was for most pre-twentieth-century scientists. Given a start, statistical inference may serve as an aid in reaching such a theory by helping to sort out strong from weak influences in the determination of measured quantities. New quantities may then be definable which enter into mathematical laws that accurately predict observed values.

In the Maxwell-Boltzmann distribution we find probability distributions entering into the theory itself and not just in the testing of hypothetical relationships in the data. When this happens, as is commonplace in twentieth-century physical science, one no longer hopes to predict exactly what values measurement will produce in given situations. Instead, the theory predicts the distribution which the measurements may be expected to take in the long run.

Consider the problem of testing the theoretical prediction that the molecular velocities of a given gas, under specified conditions of temperature and pressure, have a certain probability distribution. Whatever technique we may employ to measure individual molecular velocities—for example, the rotating drum described on p. 240 or some refinement thereof—we must expect to get slightly different results on different trials. Testing a theory which incorporates a probability distribution resembles checking a prediction of the results of throwing dice. No matter how many throws are made in a trial, exact agreement with the theoretical distribution would hardly ever be obtained and the distributions of different outcomes actually obtained would differ from trial to trial. We have considered three sources of discrepancies between theoretical predictions and observational data: (1) uncontrolled factors, (2) random errors of measurement, and (3) random processes at a fundamental level which do not permit exact predictions from theory. It is interesting to speculate whether these sources of uncertainty in scientific research may not ultimately all reduce to the same set of statistically distributed properties of the elementary particles of which all matter in the universe is composed. Such a reduction would have to meet the stringent conditions previously set forth (p. 236), but, it serves, meanwhile, as a highly motivating goal for scientists in many fields of investigation.

PROBLEMS

1. In the cylinder illustrated in Fig. 8.12, gas is confined by a movable piston. Experiments in which the gas is compressed rapidly by means of the piston show that such compression produces a change in the temperature of the gas. This is because the moving

piston affects the gas molecules that collide with it in much the same way as does a baseball bat striking a pitched ball: the colliding molecules are sent back with greater velocities than they had before collision.

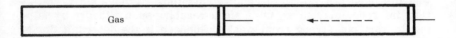

Figure 8.12 Cylinder With Piston Positions Shown Before and After Compression.

To facilitate calculation of the temperature–change resulting from such an experiment, assume the simplified frequency distribution of molecular velocities shown in Fig. 8.13.

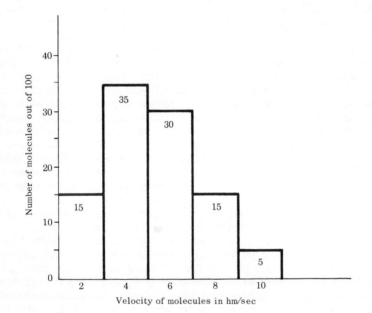

Figure 8.13 Frequency Distribution of Molecular Velocities for Problem 1.

Assume, further, that the piston moves in such a way that the velocities of 20 out of every 100 gas molecules are increased by 1 hm/sec. This means that 1/5 of the molecules in *each* velocity interval are affected in this way.

In Table 8.4 the average squared velocity has been calculated for the 100 gas molecules *before* compression. To facilitate calculating the effect of the compression on the temperature, tables have been started for those molecules whose velocities are changed (20 out of every 100), and for the remaining molecules whose velocities are unaffected (80 out of every 100).

Table 8.4 Calculation Forms for Problem 1

100 molecules *before* compression				20 molecules *affected* by compression				80 molecules *unaffected* by compression			
v	v^2	n	nv^2	v	v^2	n	nv^2	v	v^2	n	nv^2
2	4	15	60	3	9	3	27	2			
4	16	35	560	5				4			
6	36	30	1080	7				6			
8	64	15	960	9				8			
10	100	5	500	11				10			
		100	3160			20	?			80	?

$\overline{v^2} = 31.60 \text{ hm}^2/\text{sec}^2$

    a. Complete the two forms provided, and calculate from them the average squared velocity of the gas molecules *after* compression.

    b. Given that the temperature of the gas *before* compression was 43°C, determine the value of the proportionality constant in the equation $T = kv^2$. Calculate the temperature of the gas *after* compression.

2. Using a cylinder similar to that described in Problem 1, experiments on sudden expansion may be conducted. In one such experiment, the piston is suddenly released, so that the compressed gas inside the cylinder pushes it outward until the gas has expanded to twice its original volume. While the piston is moving, molecules striking it rebound with reduced velocities. The result is that 1/4 of the molecules in each velocity range have their velocities decreased by 1 hm/sec, while the others are unaffected. Given that the distribution of molecular velocities for this gas was as shown in Fig. 8.14 and that its initial temperature was 320°K *before* the expansion, find the temperature of the gas *after* the expansion.

    As in problem 1, the first part of Table 8.5 has been worked out and forms have been provided for the other calculations.

3. Many phenomena in chemistry and biology can be also explained in terms of kinetic theory. Genetic mutations, according to one widely accepted theory, may be caused by the removal of certain parts of the complex DNA molecules in chromosomes resulting from exceptionally energetic collisions by surrounding molecules in thermal motion. The colliding molecules would commonly be the water molecules which are most abundant in the surrounding medium. A rise in the temperature will, by speeding up the motion of water molecules, lead to an increase in the rate at which mutations occur.

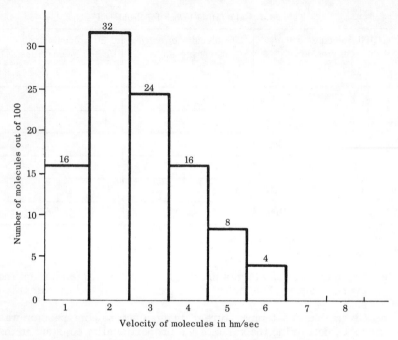

Figure 8.14 Frequency Distribution of Molecular Velocities for Problem 2.

Table 8.5 Calculation Forms for Problem 2

100 molecules *before* expansion				Molecules *affected* by the expansion				Molecules *unaffected* by the expansion			
v	v^2	n	nv^2	v	v^2	n	nv^2	v	v^2	n	nv^2
1	1	16	16	0	0	4	0	1			
2	4	32	128	1				2			
3	9	24	216	2				3			
4	16	16	256	3				4			
5	25	8	200	4				5			
6	36	4	144	5				6			
		100	960								

A certain mutation A occurs at the rate of 0.8% (that is, 8 out of every 1000 organisms undergo this mutation during the experimental period) when the environmental temperature is 25°C. Assume that a velocity of 9 hm/sec or greater is required for a colliding molecule to produce mutation A, regardless of temperature.

a. Now suppose that the velocity distribution of water molecules at 25°C and 35°C is as shown by the solid-line and dotted-line graphs in Fig. 8.15. Calculate the rate of mutation A at 35°C.

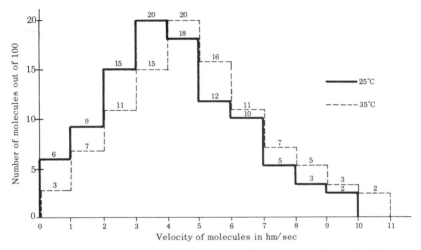

Figure 8.15 Percentage Frequency Distributions of Velocities for Every 100 Molecules of Water at 25°C and 35°C.

b. Next, suppose there is another mutation, B, whose rate at 25°C is 2%. What is the minimum velocity of colliding water molecules capable of producing mutation B?

c. Assuming that this minimum velocity holds for all temperatures, what is the rate of mutation B at 35°C?

4. In order for anything to leave the field of the earth's gravitational attraction, it must have speed exceeding the critical velocity of 112 hm/sec. This applies to rockets and molecules alike. The specific critical velocities can be determined for other attracting objects such as the sun and moon. These depend upon the mass of the attracting object but are independent of that of the escaping object. By comparing these critical velocities for different bodies in the solar system with the average velocities of various gas molecules, one can partially explain why some gases are more abundant than others around a given body and why certain bodies have a larger atmosphere of gases than others.

In Table 8.6 the critical velocities of three objects are given together with the temperatures of the outermost regions containing molecules. For each gas, calculate (using Eq. (8.14) and the constant, K, on p. 259) $\overline{v^2}$ at the temperatures given. In order to compare the molecular velocities with the critical velocities, compute the square root of the $\overline{v^2}$ values obtained. $\sqrt{\overline{v^2}}$ may be taken as an average of the molecular velocities of a gas.

Table 8.6 Data for Problem 4

Object	Critical velocity	Temperature in outermost region	Average velocity $\sqrt{\overline{v^2}}$ in outermost region		
			H_2	N_2	O_2
Earth	112 hm/sec	300°K			
Sun	10^8 hm/sec	6000°K			
Moon	25 hm/sec	500°K (maximum)			

Referring to the completed table, answer the following questions.

a. Which of the three gases may be expected to remain longest in the earth's gravitational field and which to leave it most readily?

b. Which of the three objects may be expected to retain H_2 longest and which to lose it most rapidly?

c. What would the molecular weight of a gas have to be in order for it to be retained by the moon as permanently as N_2 is retained by the earth?

d. Formulate the general principle governing the chances of different gases being retained by a given object.

e. Formulate the general principle governing the chances of different objects retaining a given gas.

SUPPLEMENTARY READINGS

Boorse, Henry A. and Motz, Lloyd. *The World of the Atom*, Vol. I. New York: Basic Books, Inc., 1966.
Selection 18 (Maxwell) is recommended reading for this chapter.

Born, Max. *The Restless Universe*. New York: Dover Publications, 1951.
An ingeniously illustrated treatment of molecular and atomic physics. Chapter I, "The Air and Its Relatives" is especially relevant as a supplement to the present chapter.

Braithwaite, R. B. *Scientific Explanation; A Study of the Function of Theory, Probability and Law in Science*. Cambridge, England: University Press, 1953. (Reprinted in paperback by Harper and Brothers.)
Chapters V, VI, and VII treat, in a precise technical fashion, the logical basis for the use of probability distributions in science.

Bronowski, J. *The Common Sense of Science*. Cambridge, Mass.: Harvard University Press, 1955.
 Chapters VI and VII expound the idea of chance and its role in the progress of scientific thought.

Gamow, G. *Mr. Tompkins Explores the Atom*. New York: Macmillan, 1945.
 The "First Dream" and the "First Lecture" cleverly elucidate some startling consequences of the statistical nature of molecular motions.

Lindsay, Robert Bruce and Margenau, Henry. *Foundations of Physics*. New York: John Wiley & Sons, Inc., 1936 (reprinted in paperback by Dover, 1959).
 Chapters IV and V present the theories of probability and statistical mechanics from a moderately advanced point of view.

Moroney, M. J. *Facts from Figures*. Baltimore: Penguin Books, 1953.
 A very clearly written layman's introduction to statistics.

Nagel, Ernest. "Principles of the Theory of Probability" in Volume I of the *International Encyclopedia of Unified Science*. Otto Neurath, editor-in-chief. Chicago: University of Chicago Press, 1958.
 A particularly lucid exposition of probability theory and its applications in science. A selection from this article is also reprinted in Danto, Arthur and Morgenbesser, Sidney, *Philosophy of Science*. New York: Meridian Books, Inc., 1960.

Richardson, M. *Fundamentals of Mathematics*. New York: Macmillan, 1958.
 Chapter 13 on "Probability and Statistics" contains a mathematical treatment of probability with numerous problems for supplementary work.

LIGHT AND
ELECTROMAGNETIC THEORY

The science of optics, the physical science of light, developed quite rapidly during the seventeenth century along with mechanics and astronomy. Newton, Huygens, Fermat, and many others made important advances in optics. Stimulated by the growing accomplishments of atomism, efforts were made to reduce optical phenomena to effects of mechanical motions of particles, but these attempts never completely succeeded. In the nineteenth century interest developed in the relationship of light to electricity and magnetism, and Maxwell's electromagnetic theory was successful in explaining almost all the properties of light known at that time.[1] It could be claimed by the end of the nineteenth century that most established optical theory had been reduced to electromagnetism. Developments of the present century have uncovered new optical phenomena, and new views of electricity and magnetism have emerged, and the reduction of optics to electromagnetism has never been quite completed. Scientists are convinced, however, that they are simply two aspects of the same underlying phenomena.

We shall first examine a few of the basic characteristics of light and then develop enough of the theory of electromagnetism to show how, by considering light to be an electromagnetic phenomenon, these basic characteristics can be accounted for. The unification of these two sciences is one of the most important chapters in pre-twentieth-century physics, for it marked the rise of a point of view that provided an alternative to the Newtonian mechanics of particles—a new point of view known as **field theory**. It also marked the elevation of electricity and magnetism from the status of interesting curiosities to one of fundamental importance in physical science and technology.

---

[1]One puzzle that was not explained by Maxwell's theory was the radiation and absorption of light and heat rays by different chemical substances in various regions of the spectrum.

HOW ILLUMINATION DIMINISHES WITH DISTANCE

The amount of illumination of a surface by a given point source of light is inversely proportional to the square of its distance from the surface (p. 99). This law can be understood by considering light as energy radiated in all directions and by utilizing a simple geometrical fact. Recognizing that the experience of seeing is due to a form of energy called light which passes from an observed object into the observer's eye (and not, as early philosophers had thought, a reaching out of the mind through the eye to "grasp" the object), it is appropriate to inquire whether the total amount of energy radiated in a given interval of time continues to spread outward unabated or not.

It is conceivable that light energy emanating from a concentrated source (e.g., a candle flame) would be diminished in total quantity so that the total energy that reaches a large sphere centered around the source would be less than that which reaches a smaller sphere concentric with it. This certainly happens when light is traveling in water. A mirror lowered into even the clearest water disappears from sight in less than a hundred feet, although in air the reflection from a mirror can be seen for at least twenty miles. Some light energy is also absorbed in air, but how can we determine whether light traveling in empty space is diminished in total quantity or not? While it is plausible that light energy is lost *en route*, perhaps being transformed into some other form of energy, it is also *conceivable* that light energy might not be conserved during transmission, but might even be augmented as it travels (the extra energy coming from heaven-knows-where). Because of our success with it, the most reasonable guide would seem to be the principle of conservation of energy. Consider the experimental implications of the hypothesis that light energy is not diminished or augmented while traversing empty space.

Imagine a series of concentric spheres surrounding a point source of light as shown in Fig. 9.1. If we represent the radius of any one of these spheres by the variable r, the surface area of such a sphere is given by the formula, $A = 4\pi r^2$. Call the total light energy leaving the source per second, L. If the light energy is undiminished as it moves outward and successively through the imaginary concentric spheres, the energy passing through each sphere is also L energy units per second. Examining a unit area (such as 1 cm^2) of each of the spherical surfaces, we must conclude that the amount of light energy falling on it becomes less and less for larger and larger spheres. This quantity, which is called the **illumination** and which we may denote by I, may be calculated by dividing the total energy per second by the total area, thus

$$I = \frac{L}{4\pi r^2} \qquad (9.1)$$

This equation is a consequence of our general hypothesis that the total light energy is undiminished while passing through empty space, and it expresses the law that the illumination on a screen of a given area is inversely proportional to the square of the distance of the screen from the source. (Since a flat screen is not everywhere equidistant from a given point-source of light, it is necessary to pick one point on it for distance measurement. It can also be shown that the same inverse-square relationships hold for flat surfaces as for spherical surfaces.)

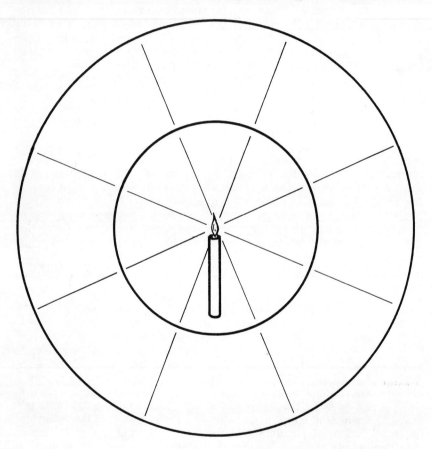

Figure 9.1 Illumination of Concentric Spheres by a "Point Source."

The inverse-square law for the illumination of surfaces by point sources, Eq. (9.1), has been very thoroughly confirmed by experimental test, so we are led to adopt, as a general principle, the notion that the total energy per second of the light emanating from a given source does *not* diminish as the light travels through empty space. If the source of light is so large that it cannot be regarded as a point-source, e.g., the sky or a ceiling filled with fluorescent tubes, the geometrical analysis becomes more complex, but it can still be carried out, and in these cases also, it supports the general principle we have adopted.

HOW FAST DOES LIGHT TRAVEL?

Scientists have speculated for many centuries whether or not the energy of light is transferred instantaneously from source to illuminated object. Galileo attempted to measure the speed of light in an experiment which involved two men stationed several miles apart on hilltops. Each was instructed to send a flash of light from a lantern when he received a similar flash from the other man. Although this method may be suitable for getting a rough idea of the speed of bullets, the lantern experiment failed to show any delay at all in the transmission of light. The experiment seemed to show that the speed of light was much greater than several miles per second.

The first demonstration that light did indeed require time for travel was made in 1676 by the Danish astronomer Ole Roemer (1644-1710). He measured the periods between eclipses of the largest and most rapidly revolving of the four satellites of Jupiter that Galileo had discovered. This particular satellite takes about 42 hours to make one journey around Jupiter, and it is eclipsed in the shadow beyond the planet during part of every revolution. The instant the satellite disappears can be accurately observed, permitting a very precise determination of its period. Roemer noted that the period of the satellite, so measured, was not exactly the same throughout the year. He explained the variation in the observed period by assuming that the light traveled from the satellite to the earth in a time which was proportional to the distance the earth was from Jupiter; that is, unlike most other astronomers, he assumed that light had a finite velocity.

On one occasion, when the earth was moving away from Jupiter (as at point A in Fig. 9.2), he predicted that, because of the earth's greater distance, on a certain date several months later (at point D), an eclipse of the satellite would be observed ten minutes later than had been predicted on the assumption that light traveled instantaneously. Observations confirmed his prediction, at least approximately so.

Roemer calculated, on the basis of a number of observations of this satellite, that light from it required about 22 minutes to cross the earth's orbit, a distance of some 300 million kilometers. If this is correct, then it must be concluded that light travels at the tremendous speed of 13.6×10^6 km/min or 2.27×10^8 m/sec. Astronomers were reluctant to believe Roemer's conclusion that the velocity of light was finite and measurable. Those who checked his observations obtained values as different from his as 3.74×10^8 m/sec, which

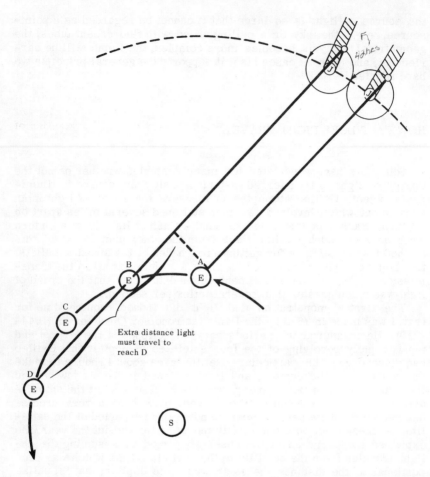

Figure 9.2 Positions of the Earth a Month Apart in Relation to Jupiter.

skeptics took as encouragement to seek other explanations. The percentage difference between these values is 39.3% of the larger. When confronted with discrepancies in measurements, it is usually advantageous to seek out the sources of error in the measuring instruments and estimate whether they are as large as the observed discrepancies or not. Without such analysis, the assumption of a constant speed of light cannot be reasonably questioned on the basis of these measurements.

More than 60 years after Roemer's work, an English astronomer, James Bradley (1693-1762), discovered another interesting phenomenon which also led to a value for the velocity of light. In seeking to detect the parallax of stars, which Copernicus had predicted but no one had yet observed, Bradley discovered that during each year the observed positions of all the fixed stars gradually shifted by a slight amount and then gradually returned to their original positions by the end of the year. The shifting was in the same direction for all stars, and the angular separation between particular pairs of stars did not increase or decrease, as Copernicus had predicted. Bradley concluded that this observed shifting could not be explained as a parallax effect. In order to aim the telescope at a given star, it was always necessary to tilt it slightly from the position determined by the geometrical positions of the earth and the star, and this tilting was always in the direction of the earth's motion around the sun.

After considering and rejecting many other possible explanations, Bradley finally realized that this shift in the direction in which stars were observed, called the **aberration** of starlight, must be caused by the motion of the telescope relative to the motion of the light from the star—the former moving by virtue of the earth's motion through space. (See Fig. 9.3 (a).)

Bradley's explanation may be understood by analogy with a familiar situation in which a person is walking rapidly with an umbrella through a vertically falling rain. (See Fig. 9.3 (b).) In order to achieve maximum protection, the walker tilts the umbrella forward so that its tip is ahead of his feet by a certain fraction of the height of the umbrella tip above the ground. This fraction should be equal to the ratio of the walker's speed to the speed of the falling raindrops. For example, if his speed of walking is one fifth the speed of the falling raindrops, he should tilt the umbrella so that its tip is ahead of his feet by one fifth the height of the umbrella tip. The top end of a telescope aimed at a star, located at right angles to the earth's motion, should be tilted ahead by a given fraction of its length—the same fraction as the earth's velocity is of the velocity of the star light.

The orbital velocity (in m/sec) of the earth's annual revolution around the sun is given by the ratio of the orbital circumference, $300 \pi \times 10^9$ m, to the period of revolution, $365 \times 24 \times 3600$ sec. The velocity is,

$$\frac{300 \pi \times 10^9 \text{ m}}{365 \times 24 \times 3600 \text{ sec}} = \frac{9.42 \times 10^{11} \text{ m}}{3.15 \times 10^7 \text{ sec}} = 2.99 \times 10^4 \text{ m/sec}$$

On the other hand, Bradley's observations showed that in order to keep a telescope aimed at a star from which the incident light was perpendicular to the earth's orbit, the telescope had to be tilted so that its end was shifted forward by 1/10,210 of its length, rather than pointed directly at it. According to Bradley's explanation this ratio 1/10,210 should be equal to the ratio of the velocity of the earth to the velocity of light. That is,

$$\frac{1}{10,210} = \frac{2.99 \times 10^4 \text{ m/sec}}{\text{velocity of light}}$$

Calculated from this equation, the velocity of light is 3.05×10^8 m/sec.

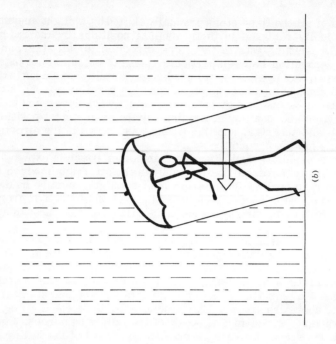

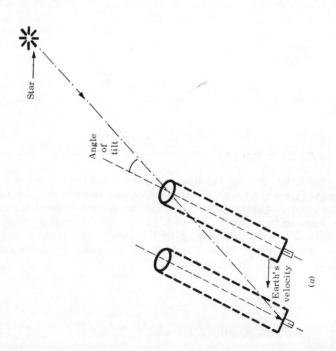

Figure 9.3 Bradley's Explanation of the Abberation of Star Light.

This result is certainly within a small percentage difference from the average of several determinations of the velocity of light by Roemer's method. The fact that so good an agreement was obtained by an independent method was certainly more impressive to the skeptics than a reduction in the percentage error by Roemer's method alone would have been. This illustrates the observation historians of science have made that disputes over minor variations in observational results are more often a sign of the appeal of an alternative conceptual scheme (in this case, instantaneous transmission of light) than they are grounds for doubting the validity of the method.

Further work on the velocity of light was not successfully undertaken until mid-nineteenth century. At that time, a return to Galileo's approach was initiated which made use of the reflection of flashes of light in a distant mirror, the reflected flash being compared with the original in order to detect the time lag. The first successful experiment using this approach was performed in France by A. H. L. Fizeau (1819-1896), but it was later improved upon by his close associate, J. B. L. Foucault (1819-1868).

To produce a rapid series of flashes, Fizeau employed a rotating disc, whose edge was serrated with evenly spaced teeth, on which light from a strong lamp was reflected by a glass plate. (See Fig. 9.4.) The flashes were focused by lenses and aimed at a mirror located 8633 meters away which reflected them back through the lenses to the same position on the rim of the rotating disc through which they originally passed. By rotating the disc at the right speed, each returning flash of light could be made to fall upon the adjacent tooth, instead of the empty slot through which it originally passed. The glass plate, used to reflect light through the disc to create the flashes, made it

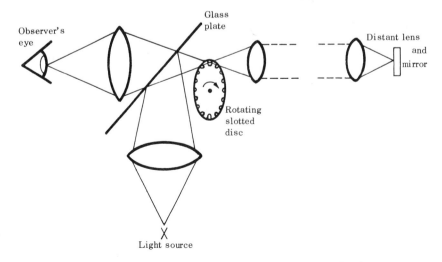

Figure 9.4 Fizeau's Apparatus for Measuring the Velocity of Light.

possible for an observer to look directly through the toothed edge of the rotating disc and determine whether the returning flashes were blocked or not.

Fizeau found that, when the disc which had 720 teeth, turned 12.6 times a second, the reflected light was blocked by the next *tooth*. At twice this speed, or 25.2 revolutions per second, the light came back through the *slot* next to that through which it originally passed. From either of these results, he was able to calculate the velocity of light as follows: The time for the light to return was $1/720 \times 25.2$ or $1/18,144$ second. Dividing the round trip distance of 2×8633 meters by this time, he obtained 3.12×10^8 m/sec as the velocity of light.

In Foucault's more accurate method, light—reflected over a much shorter distance—was displaced slightly by the rotation of the reflecting mirror. His measurement gave 2.98×10^8 m/sec, a value which is within 1% of the presently accepted value of 2.99790×10^8 m/sec. Both of these "terrestrial" methods, in confirming the validity of the astronomical methods, also served to confirm the average distance of the earth from the sun, which figured prominently in Roemer's and Bradley's calculations.

In this and the preceding sections we have seen the experimental determination of two basic properties of light, its diffusion rate, and velocity. We shall now turn to a consideration of theories concerning the nature of light.

IS LIGHT COMPOSED OF PARTICLES OR "WAVES"?

The inverse-square law of illumination can readily be accounted for by regarding light as composed of tiny particles which are "shot out" from a point source, uniformly in all directions. It is helpful to imagine a lawn sprinkler specially designed for spraying water droplets in all directions. Imagine further that gravitational force did not exist; we see that the spray would be uniform in all directions, and the amount of water collected on a surface in a given time interval would be inversely proportional to the square of its distance from the lawn sprinkler. The existence of a definite velocity magnitude for the transmission of light also tends to suggest that some kind of particles are being shot through space.

Another familiar law of optics is also easily explained on a particle model of light. As everyone knows, at least intuitively from everyday experience, a ray of light which strikes a mirror or any highly polished surface at a given angle "bounces off" in the same direction that a billiard ball would rebound from the cushion of the billiard table when striking it at the same given angle. Putting it more formally, the angle between the incident ray (corresponding to the path of the ball prior to impact) and the reflecting surface (corresponding to the cushion) is equal to the angle between the reflected ray (corresponding to the path of the rebounding ball) and the reflecting surface. (We have already noted this principle in connection with gas molecules colliding with a piston surface—see p. 213.)

The foregoing considerations strongly suggest that light may be regarded as consisting of myriads of tiny, luminescent particles or corpuscles. Such was Newton's theory of the nature of light. Today we more often hear of ''light waves'' and rarely of ''light particles'' (although the student may occasionally have heard of a photon or a quantum of light). Historically, a wave theory of light was developed by the Dutch physicist Christian Huygens (1629-1695) about the same time as, if not actually prior to, Newton's corpuscular theory. It is said that it was largely owing to Newton's overwhelming reputation that the wave theory failed to receive wide acceptance for over a century after it was first proposed.

In the remainder of this section, we will consider some of the optical phenomena which, because they were more readily explainable by a wave theory of light than by a particle theory, led to the revival and the universal acceptance of the wave theory of light.

First consider the familiar phenomenon of **refraction,** the bending of a ray of light as it traverses the boundary between two transparent media of different densities, such as air and water. Figure 9.5 represents an incident ray *IO* entering the water at point *O* and refracted in the direction *OR*. *I* and *R* are the points of intersection of the incident

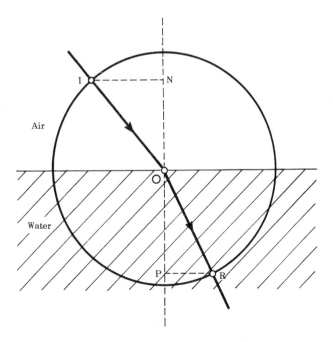

Figure 9.5 Diagram Illustrating Refraction of Light.

and refracted rays with an imaginary circle centered about O. (The radius is arbitrary.) The diameter of the circle is constructed perpendicular to the water surface, and the feet of the perpendiculars to this diameter from I and R are labeled N and P, respectively. No matter what the angle of incidence ($\angle ION$), the ratio of the distances IN/RP turns out to be constant for a given pair of media. This constant ratio is known as the **refractive index** of the second medium with respect to the first, and the fact that it is constant for all angles of incidence, given the two media, is known as **Snell's Law**. The refractive index of water with respect to air is 1.3, and that of glass with respect to air ranges from about 1.5 to 1.7, depending on the type of glass. (The refractive index for a pair of media may be inferred from their separate indices with respect to a third medium. The refractive index of one type of glass with respect to water is 1.6/1.3 or 1.23.)

Snell's law of refraction can be derived from either the corpuscular or the wave theory of light (although we shall not examine the derivations), but there is one crucial difference between these derivations. Under Newton's corpuscular theory the refractive index must be equal to the ratio, v_2/v_1, of the velocity of light in the *second* medium (water, in the case of Fig. 9.5) to the velocity of light in the *first* medium (air). In Huygen's wave theory the refractive index is given by v_1/v_2, the ratio of light-velocity in the *first* medium to that in the *second*—just the reciprocal of the value predicted from the corpuscular theory.

It might seem that this critical difference between a consequence of the corpuscular theory and the corresponding one of the wave theory could have led to an experimental test to decide between the two theories right away. Unfortunately techniques for accurately measuring the velocity of light were not yet sufficiently developed in the time of Newton and Huygens. It therefore remained for the French physicist Jean Foucault, almost two centuries later, to conduct the first decisive experiment comparing velocities of light in different media. Using his rotating-mirror technique, he showed that the velocity of light in air was *larger* than that in water by a factor of 1.3. This result agreed with the already known value, 1.3, of the refractive index of water with respect to air, and scored a definite victory for the wave theory which required that the velocity in air be larger than the velocity in water.

Even prior to Foucault's measurements of light velocities in different media researches were conducted on two other optical phenomena which eventually were recognized as favoring the wave theory. These were the phenomena of **diffraction** and of **interference**.

The discovery of diffraction actually antedates Newton's work in optics. Toward the middle of the seventeenth century, the Italian mathematician and physicist Francesco Grimaldi (c. 1618-1663) observed that, when a beam of light passes through a tiny hole, the area of light cast on a screen is slightly larger than would be expected on the assumption of straight-line light rays. Conversely, Grimaldi also observed, if a tiny obstacle (such as the tip of a needle) is placed in the beam of light, its shadow on the screen is slightly smaller than one would expect on the basis of straight rays. These empirical facts can readily be explained if we regard light as consisting of waves. They are analogous to the familiar facts that sound waves can be detected behind such obstacles as lamp-posts or tree trunks and also can be heard through openings that are not directly on a straight line between the source and the listener. Diffraction is the blurring of the edges of shadows by diffusion of energy into the shadow region, and it is characteristic of all kinds of wave motion. It is very difficult to imagine a mechanism or model by which the phenomenon of diffraction can be explained other than that of wave motion. But belief in the corpuscular nature of light was so firmly entrenched in the seventeenth and eighteenth centuries, that Newton and his followers persistently attempted (with partial success, it is true) to account for the phenomenon by the corpuscular theory.

The phenomenon of interference of light was discovered in 1802 by the versatile British scientist Thomas Young (1773–1829). His original experiment utilized a double-slit arrangement such as shown in Fig. 9.6. The two slits in the center screen are very narrow and close together. The slit in the screen on the left side, nearest to the light source, cuts out all but a very narrow beam of light. When this beam passes through the two slits in the center screen, it emerges as two overlapping trains of waves which form a pattern of bright and dark bands on the screen on the right side, farthest from the source of light. Such patterns are called interference patterns.

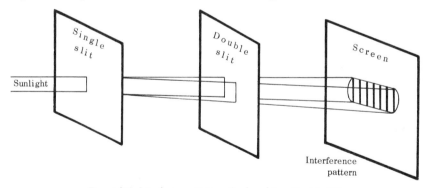

Figure 9.6 Interference Pattern Produced by a Double Slit.

The explanation of such interference patterns can be easily grasped by observing the pattern of ripples formed in a shallow tank of water when waves pass through two narrow openings. (An identical pattern is formed by two objects dipping slightly into the water surface and moving up and down together at the same frequency.) The moiré pattern of waves so formed shows radial lines of cancellation and reinforcement which correspond to the dark and light bands of the interference patterns. By using Huygens' method of drawing a series of concentric, evenly spaced circles around a point in each slit, a diagram is produced showing the same pattern as seen in the ripple-tank experiment just described (Fig. 9.7). Again it is difficult to explain interference phenomena on a particle model of light. Study of many other cases of interference patterns provides substantial support for the wave nature of light.

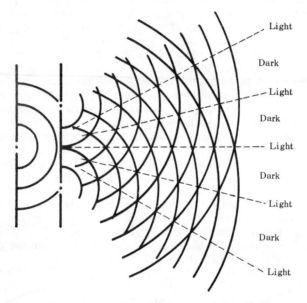

Figure 9.7 Huygens' Construction for the Double-Slit Interference Pattern.

Despite the support for the wave theory of light in the phenomenon of interference, Young's proposal to revive this theory met with violent protests from the corpuscular theorists (who constituted a vast majority of his contemporaries). It was not until 1815, when the French engineer Augustin Fresnel (1788–1827) independently rediscovered interference phenomena and made further experiments, that the wave theory began to gain wider acceptance. In 1850, with Foucault's measurements of light velocities in different media, the triumph of the wave theory seemed complete. The principal questions remaining were: What *kind* of wave is light? And what is the medium that carries this wave motion even in a vacuum and in the farthest reaches of the Universe?

We turn now to the subjects of electricity and magnetism, from which some answers to these questions were derived.

ELECTROSTATIC AND ELECTROMAGNETIC FORCES

Most people are familiar with the effects of static electricity, e.g., those experienced when, on a cold day, one removes an article of clothing made of synthetic fibers. The electric charges are produced by rubbing different substances together. Early scientists found that, when an object that has been charged by rubbing is brought near another also charged, the two objects may attract or they may repel each other, depending on the material of which they are made. If a piece of glass that has been rubbed with silk cloth is placed near a piece of amber rubbed with fur, they *attract* each other. But two pieces of silk-rubbed glass repel each other, as do two pieces of fur-rubbed amber. If two charged objects A and B attract each other, and A also attracts a third charged object C, then B and C repel each other. This explains why, in cold, dry weather hair that clings to the comb that combed it separates and why garmets made of synthetic fibers which cling before removal billow out in perfectly still air afterwards.

The principle of attraction and repulsion enabled scientists of the eighteenth century to classify all electrically charged objects into two groups such that any two objects of the same group *repel* each other, while any object of one group *attracts* any object of the other group. Charged objects of the two groups are evidently in two different states of electrification. Dufay called these states "resinous" (exemplified by silk-rubbed glass) and "vitreous" (e.g., fur-rubbed amber). Benjamin Franklin, working independently and being unaware of Dufay's terminology, designated the two states as **positive** and **negative** electrification, originating the nomenclature in use today. (Dufay's "vitreous" happens to be Franklin's "positive" electrification). To Franklin, who postulated a single type of "electric fluid," "positive" meant an excess of this fluid and "negative" meant a deficiency of it. Electrical-fluid theories are no longer held today, but we still use the terms "positive" and "negative," because they conveniently fit in with algebraic rules governing the product of signed numbers. From the modern standpoint, the choice as to which to call positive and which negative is purely a matter of convention, but one deeply entrenched.

Systematic experimentation with charged objects eventually led to Coulomb's discovery, nearly two centuries ago, of a quantitative relation between the amounts of charges and the force of attraction or repulsion acting between two objects. A ratio scale with which to measure the amount of charge on a metallized sphere became possible when it was recognized that one can take away half of the charge on a sphere by touching it momentarily with a second identical sphere that originally had no charge. If one assumes that the total charge on an object is made up of a large number of identical charges, all mutually repelling each other, then one can show by geometrical arguments that they will distribute themselves equally between the two spheres upon contact. By using many different initial charges and successive halvings by the above method, a ratio scale may be generated, if one has a standard way of generating a charge of one unit.

Coulomb discovered that the force between two electrical charges, measured on such a scale, is proportional to the product of the two quantities of charge and inversely proportional to the square of the distance between them. Stated as an equation, this law can be written:

$$f = K_1 \frac{q_1 q_2}{d^2} \tag{9.2}$$

where f is the force, q_1 and q_2 are the two charges—each of which may be positive or negative in sign, and d is the distance between the charges. The value of K_1, a proportionality constant, depends upon the units adopted. This makes it possible to adopt some convenient value for K_1 and then use Eq. (9.2) to establish the unit of charge.

Equation (9.2) bears a striking resemblance to Newton's law of universal gravitation. There is one important difference: the sign of f may be either positive or negative, depending on whether q_1 and q_2 are both of the same sign or one is positive and the other negative. In Eq. (9.2), a negative f implies a force of attraction while a positive f implies one of repulsion. In Newton's gravitation law (Eq. (3.13)), on the other hand, f is always positive and the force is always one of attraction.

The existence of two different states of electrification and their quantitative relation to force were well known by the late eighteenth century, but it was not until early in the present century that an adequate model explaining the physical basis for there being two, and only two, different states of electrification was developed. As everyone knows in this nuclear age, the accepted model of an atom of any substance contains a nucleus possessing a positive electric charge and one or more negatively charged electrons orbiting around it. In the normal terrestrial state of elements, the positive charge of the nucleus and the total negative charge of the surrounding electrons exactly counterbalance each other, thus producing an electrically neutral (or "non-electrified") state of matter. The electrons in the outermost orbits are rather loosely attached in many atoms, and can be removed under certain circumstances. One of these circumstances arises when two objects, made of suitable substances, are placed in close contact and rapidly moved with respect to each other—which is what happens when dry, human hair is briskly combed with a plastic comb. Whether an object becomes positively or negatively charged by rubbing depends on whether electrons are removed from the surface atoms of the object onto the material used for rubbing it or vice versa. Other circumstances under which the outer electrons are removed from some atoms (or atom groups) onto other atoms (or atom groups) include the following: (1) when salts, acids, and bases are formed from elements, and (2) when an electric current "flows" through a piece of metal such as a wire. Before attempting to describe the effects of moving charges quantitatively, it will be helpful to get a qualitative picture of how the electron model of electric currents works.

We all know that an electric current flows through a conducting wire "almost instantaneously." When we turn on a switch, the light goes on "instantly," even if it is located at the far end of a long corridor from the switch. In view of the present-day model of atoms, one might be tempted to think that an electric current consists of myriads of electrons rushing through the wire at a fantastic speed.

In a manner of speaking, this is correct. But we must realize that it is not any *single* group of electrons that travels through the length of the wire to produce an electric current. A few electrons are displaced from the atoms of the wire nearest to the negative pole of the electric source (e.g., a battery), these repel some electrons from an adjacent group of atoms, and these, in turn, repel other electrons from the next group of atoms, and so on down the line. It is this "chain effect," or pulse, that travels through the wire at a fantastic speed. The individual electrons themselves drift along very slowly. When a B & S No. 10 gauge, bare, copper wire is carrying its maximum safe current (35 amperes), the electron drift has an average velocity of only about 7×10^{-4} m/sec (less than 1 mm per second).

As an analogy, imagine a long train of railroad freight cars stopped at a station with the cars stretched apart so there is slack in the connections between them. The locomotive at the front end of the train is about to start backing the train. It first jolts the nearest car, which moves backward a little, jolting the next car backward slightly, and so on, and the jolt is very soon transmitted to the caboose, farthest away from the engine. The "pulse" of starting travels very rapidly through the train, but each car is still only creeping along at a snail's pace.

The point of the above analogy is to keep in mind that there are two kinds of "motion" involved: the slow drifting of electrons, and the rapid travel of an electric pulse. It is of great importance to distinguish clearly between these two motions. There is a very important effect of the drifting of electrons. Another force, separate from that described by Coulomb's Law, acts between *moving* charges. Forces of the Coulomb's-Law type, which are called **electrostatic** forces, are also acting between charges in motion. But when the moving charges are electrons flowing through wires (as compared with electron beams moving through a vacuum) the electrostatic forces cancel one another out, for there are equal amounts of positive and negative charge in each wire. Any force of attraction or repulsion that may act between two parallel wires, each conducting an electric current, is something different from the force between static charges. That a force exists between current-carrying wires may readily be demonstrated by the following simple experiment.

Two wires are mounted parallel to each other, one above the other, and connected to a battery or other source of energy so that electric charges move through them. A spring scale or balance is arranged to support one of the wires and measure the force between the two. (One such arrangement is shown in Fig. 9.8.) When a current (of like charges) is flowing through the two parallel wires in opposite directions (as in the figure), a force of repulsion is observed between them, but when they are connected so that the currents flow in the same direction, the force is one of attraction. Unlike the case of electrostatic forces, opposite currents repel and like currents attract.

Contrary to what we might expect on the basis of Eq. (9.2), forces between parallel wires do not follow an inverse-square law with respect

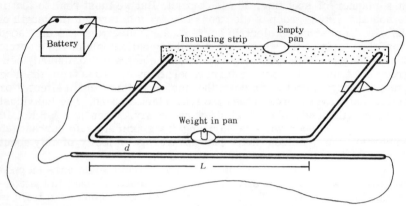

Figure 9.8 A "Current Balance" to Measure the Force Between Two Current-Carrying Wires.

to the distance between wires: the force is inversely proportional to the distance itself, and directly proportional to the length of the wires. It is also jointly proportional to the strengths of the two currents. (With different circuits than shown in Fig. 9.8, a pair of parallel wires *can* be connected so that different currents flow in the two wires.)

The proportionality relations we have just described are economically expressed by the formula, known as **Ampere's Law,**

$$f = K_2 \frac{i_1 i_2}{d} \cdot L \tag{9.3}$$

In this equation, the signs of i_1 and i_2 depend on the direction of the current. When the directions are opposite in the two wires, the two i's are of different signs, and thus f is negative; when the currents are in the same direction, the i's are alike in sign and f is positive. Consequently, the force given by Eq. (9.3) is one of *repulsion* when its sign is *negative* and is one of *attraction* when its sign is *positive*.

The force between moving charges, described by Ampere's Law, is known as a **magnetic** force, because magnets respond to it—either artificial ones made of iron or steel (including compass needles) or natural, lodestone magnets. A bar-shaped magnet brought near a wire that is carrying an electric current tends to rotate so that the bar is at right angles to the direction of the current. When the current is reversed, the magnet, if free to turn, will change its orientation by 180°. To understand better this peculiar effect on a magnet, it is helpful to examine the situation when an electric current is flowing in a loop of wire instead of a straight piece. The loop behaves like a bar magnet with the two faces of the loop corresponding to the two ends of the bar. If a bar magnet is broken into small pieces, each of these behaves as a magnet. So we can imagine (and even construct) a thin slice of a magnet that corresponds closely to the loop-of-wire "magnet" in shape. Conversely, we can place many loops of wire together to make a long tube (or a coil) which has the general shape of a bar magnet. (See Fig. 9.9.)

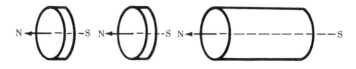

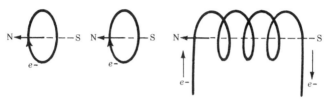

Figure 9.9 The Relationship of Circular and Bar Magnets to Loops and Coils.

To understand the relationship between electricity and magnetism more clearly, consider the implications of Eq. (9.3). A force exists between wires carrying currents, although the net electric charge on each wire is zero. Since the force must therefore be caused by the motion of charges, perhaps it is the moving charges themselves which are acted upon by this electromagnetic force. It is easy to show that this is indeed the case—a beam of electrons shot through a vacuum tube (such as a television picture tube) can easily be deflected by a magnet or by a current-carrying wire nearby. But is the motion of charges really the cause of electromagnetic force? In 1897, the American physicist, Rowland, showed that charged objects in motion *do* produce a magnetic force. He charged the rim of a disc and spun it rapidly, thereby causing a nearby compass needle to be deflected. It must be the case that charges in motion exert a force on each other over and above the electrostatic force between them, and we may expect that Eq. (9.3) is a consequence of a more basic law of charges in motion.

Such a law, governing the force produced by the relative motion of isolated charges, was worked out by Clerk Maxwell, the same man who contributed much to kinetic theory. When two charges moving in parallel directions are opposite each other (i.e., when a line joining them is perpendicular to their paths (see Fig. 9.10)), the force due to their motion is given by the following equation:

$$f_{\text{em}} = K_2 \frac{q_1 v_1 q_2 v_2}{d^2} \tag{9.4}$$

where v_1 is the velocity of charge q_1, v_2 the velocity of q_2, and d is the separation between the charges. Comparing this equation with Eq. (9.3), one would guess that $i = qv$. This would indeed be a possible definition of i, but other approaches are possible too.

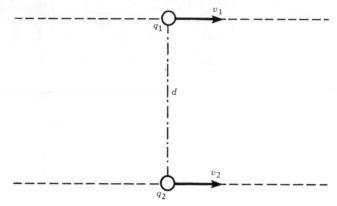

Figure 9.10 Position of Moving Charges for Equation 9.4.

This equation bears a much more striking resemblance to the electrostatic law, Eq. (9.2), than did the formula for the force between continuous streams of charges, Eq. (9.3). While it is extremely difficult to verify Eq. (9.4) directly by measuring the force between two charged objects in motion, there are many indirect consequences which are readily observable. By methods of integral calculus, Eq. (9.3) is shown to be a consequence of Eq. (9.4), as we expected. K_2 has the same value in both equations when the current in Eq. (9.3) is measured in charge units per second. It will suffice here to show in a general way how one might proceed to derive Eq. (9.3) from the more basic Eq. (9.4).

The strength of an electric current may be defined as the rate of flow of charges past a point. Since the strength of a current can be quantified conceptually at a single point, distance traveled need not be a part of the definition as would be implied in the possible definition we suggested above, $i = qv$. Expressing the point definition mathematically, we write,

$$i =_{Df} \frac{\Delta q}{\Delta t}$$

where Δq is that amount of charge which moves past a point in Δt sec.

A current may be regarded as a succession of small "packets" of charge, each of amount Δq. To examine the consequences of this definition we may bring distance back into consideration. If we denote by ΔL the distance traveled by such a moving packet of charge in the same time interval Δt, then

$$\frac{\Delta L}{\Delta t} = v, \text{ the velocity of the charge packets.}$$

Hence,

$$\Delta t = \frac{\Delta L}{v},$$ which, when substituted in the definition for i, gives

$$i = \frac{\Delta q}{\Delta L/v} = \frac{\Delta q}{\Delta L} v$$

Therefore,

$$(\Delta q) v = i \Delta L$$

from which substitutions can be made in Eq. (9.4) to yield

$$f_{em} = K_2 \frac{i_1 (\Delta L_1) i_2 (\Delta L_2)}{d^2}$$

as the magnetic force between two packets of charge when they are opposite each other. A similar but more complicated formula holds when they are not opposite each other. The techniques of integral calculus are required at this point to sum up the forces between each of the packets of moving charge in one wire and every one of the similar packets in the second wire. It is the sum of all these elemental forces that is given by Eq. (9.3). The fact that the total force is inversely proportional to d instead of d^2 is the result of the contribution of the whole of the current in one wire to the force on each moving charge in the other.

This discussion provides evidence that there is an intimate relationship between electrical and magnetic phenomena. We have pointed to the possibility of reducing magnetic theory to theories of electric phenomena and motion. The two phenomena warrant being treated in the single category of **electromagnetic** phenomena. Electromagnetic theory is a system of mathematical models, an electrostatic model and laws of motion combined to explain these phenomena.

We have seen two types of forces that act between electric charges. One, known as electrostatic force, acts between stationary charges. The other, which is designated as magnetic, but which may now more correctly be called electromagnetic, acts only between moving charges. These forces, represented by Eqs. (9.2) and (9.4), will henceforth always be distinguished by using subscripts on the f, thus: f_{es} for electrostatic force and f_{em} for electromagnetic force.

FORESHADOWINGS OF THE ELECTROMAGNETIC THEORY OF LIGHT

The two inverse-square laws, Eq. (9.2) for electrostatic force and Eq. (9.4) for electromagnetic force, having been established by the early part of the nineteenth century, a great deal of research was then devoted to determining accurately the two proportionality constants, K_1 and K_2. In 1856 two German experimenters, W. E. Weber and R. Kohlrausch, made a considerable advance in this respect. Not only did they succeed in determining the values of the constants with high precision, but they also noticed that, when the same unit of charge is used in each law, the ratio of the electrostatic constant, K_1, to the electromagnetic constant, K_2, was very nearly equal to 9×10^{16}. This number, they pointed out, is approximately the square of the velocity of light, which was known to be very nearly 3×10^8 m/sec. This important discovery raised the interesting question whether the ratio K_1/K_2 had this value merely by coincidence, or whether there was some fundamental connection between electromagnetic phenomena and light. This question was eventually answered by Maxwell when he developed his electromagnetic theory of light. But first, let us examine another rather surprising implication of that fact that $K_1/K_2 = 9 \times 10^{16}$.

Since K_1 is almost 10^{17} times as great as K_2, it would intuitively seem that the electrostatic force between two charges should be far greater than the electromagnetic force when they are in relative motion. How can we reconcile this with the fact that, in the laboratory, it is far more difficult to produce sizeable electrostatic forces than it is to produce strong electromagnetic forces? The latter forces can be built up to a strength of many newtons rather easily, but the former are barely measurable on the most sensitive balance. Could this intuitive expectation that f_{es} should be much greater than f_{em}, based on the value of K_1/K_2, be in error? Can we compare the electrostatic force Eq. (9.2) between two fixed charges on the one hand and, on the other, the electromagnetic force Eq. (9.4) between two moving charges which have the same separation and are equal respectively to the fixed charges? Assuming the same charges and separations for the two equations, we divide the two sides of Eq. (9.4) by the corresponding sides of Eq. (9.2) and cancel the q's and d's. We find

$$\frac{f_{em}}{f_{es}} = \frac{K_2}{K_1} v_1 v_2$$

solving for f_{em} by substituting the numerical value of K_1/K_2,

$$f_{em} = \frac{v_1 v_2}{K_1/K_2} \cdot f_{es} = \frac{v_1 v_2}{(3 \times 10^8)^2} \cdot f_{es} \qquad (9.5)$$

This result may be interpreted as confirming our intuitive expectation. For it tells us that if $v_1 = v_2$, the velocity magnitudes of the moving charges would have to be equal to the velocity of light for the electromagnetic force to be equal to the electrostatic force. The electron drift in currents that can be employed in ordinary conductors has velocities whose order of magnitude is 10^{-3} m/sec. Substituting this value for v_1 and v_2 in Eq. (9.5) we conclude that the electromagnetic force is only about $1/10^{23}$ of the electrostatic force *between the same charges.* How do we reconcile this conclusion with the fact that it is far easier to generate an electromagnetic force of several newtons than it is to produce an electrostatic force of comparable magnitude? The clue to answering this question lies in the italicized phrase in the previous sentence. For Eq. (9.5) compares the electromagnetic and the electrostatic forces that act between the same pair of charges. The relative ease with which a sizeable electromagnetic force can be produced, as compared with the difficulty of producing an equally sizeable electrostatic force, must mean that the number of electrons moving in a current is vastly greater than the number of electrons removed in ordinary laboratory procedures for producing an electrostatic force—such as rubbing one substance with another.

The above explanation seems plausible when we consider that an electric current is a chain of effects: the electrons in the atoms of one part of the wire repel those in an adjacent group of atoms, and these in turn repel the next set, and so on. A tremendous number of electrons is set in motion almost instantaneously—just as a single jolt imparted by the locomotive to the nearest car is rapidly transmitted to the next car, then to the next, and so on through a long train of freight cars. In rubbing a piece of glass with a silk cloth, on the other hand, because of the immobility of electrons in a nonconductor, no such chain reaction takes place, and only a few of the electrons in the outermost layer of atoms are displaced.

These consequences of the ratio K_1/K_2, interesting as they are, have not yet answered the question whether this ratio merely *happens* to have a value equal to the square of the velocity of light or whether there is some fundamental connection between electromagnetism and optics. A hint of such a connection is found in Eq. (9.5). We note that this equation may also be written as

$$\left(\frac{K_1}{K_2}\right) f_{em} = (v_1 v_2) f_{es}$$

We employ a kind of dimensional analysis—an approach introduced earlier in evaluating a suggested definition of the mechanical concept of temperature. (See p. 234.) The units of the quantities employed in this equation must satisfy the following relation:

(The unit of K_1/K_2) · (newtons) = (m/sec) · (m/sec) · (newtons)

Therefore K_1/K_2 must have the unit (m/sec)^2, that is, the units of velocity squared. We now attach the unit to the numerical value of K_1/K_2 and assert that

$$\frac{K_1}{K_2} = (3 \times 10^8 \text{ m/sec})^2$$

This result strongly suggests that it is not by coincidence that the value of K_1/K_2 is equal to the square of the velocity of light, so we

have increased the motivation to seek some more fundamental relationship between electromagnetic phenomena and light.

ELECTROMAGNETIC INDUCTION

An electromagnetic force acts between two current-carrying wires.
If one of these wires is free to move, its motion would give evidence
of the electromagnetic force between them. One of the major contributions of Michael Faraday (1791–1867) was his discovery of an effect
that is the inverse of the above. He found that when a relative motion
occurs between two current-carrying wires, an additional current is
induced in each wire over and above the existing current. The model
we have adopted of electron motion in a conductor permits us to explain currents induced in this way by employing the inverse-square
law for electromagnetic force as formulated in Eq. (9.4).

The following thought experiment allows us to isolate an induced
current from preexisting currents and to see how Eq. (9.4) applies to
it. Imagine that a sheet of metal placed parallel to a nearby current-
carrying wire is moved within its own plane. (See Fig. 9.11.) If the
electrons in the wire are flowing in the same direction in which the
metal sheet is being moved, the electrons in the metal sheet, according to Eq. (9.4), will be attracted toward the wire. The positively
charged nuclei of the metal sheet also are acted on by a force, but in
the opposite direction. They cannot move. But since some of the electrons are free to move, their motion could be detected by a current-
measuring instrument, the wires from which touch the opposite edges
of the metal sheet as shown in Fig. 9.11. The instrument and its wires
must not move with the sheet, for otherwise the electrons in them

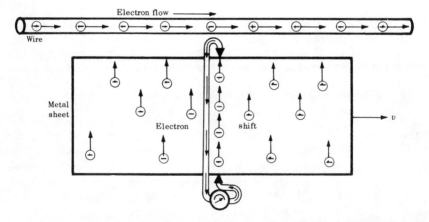

Figure 9.11 Induction in a Moving Sheet of Metal Near a Current-Carrying Wire.

would be affected by the motion in the same way as those in the sheet, and hence prevent the flow of any current through the instrument. We see how the inverse-square law for electromagnetic force (Eq. (9.4)) could explain the induction of a current in a moving sheet of metal.

Consider a variation of the above thought-experiment, in which the induced current flows through a wire. In place of the metal sheet, a short segment of wire is moved along a current-carrying wire. The short wire, while being moved, is always kept pointing toward the stationary wire and perpendicular to it. The motions of the electrons in the two wires would give rise to a force in accordance with Eq. (9.4). Evidence of this force could be obtained by means of a current-sensitive instrument connected to two parallel stationary wires with which the ends of the moving wire maintain contact, as shown in Fig. 9.12.

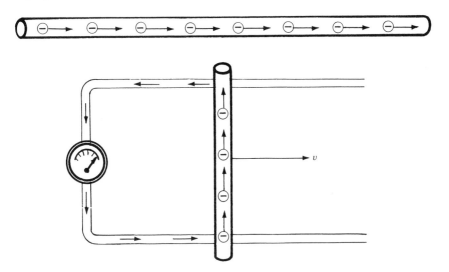

Figure 9.12 Induction in a Moving Wire Segment Near a Current-Carrying Wire.

In the above experiments, the induced currents would be extremely weak and very difficult to observe. Consider some experiments in which the induced currents are reinforced and hence made more readily observable. In the simplest of these experiments, two segments of wire are connected at their ends to form a rectangular loop with a current-sensing instrument as part of the loop, as shown in Fig. 9.13. When this loop is rotated around an axis perpendicular to a neighboring current-carrying wire, electrons in the two segments experience forces in opposite directions, both of which contribute to the same circulating current. The student should determine the directions of the forces during a complete revolution of the loop, in order to see that the induced current reverses its direction once in every half-revolution.

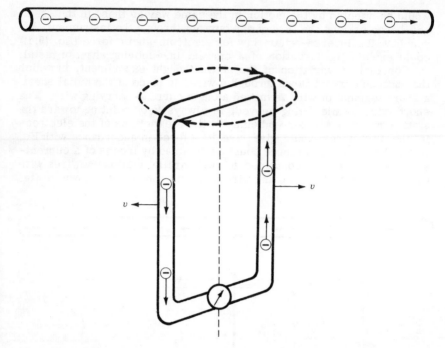

Figure 9.13 Induction in a Single Rotating Loop Near a Current-Carrying Wire.

Further reinforcement of the induced current can be effected by replacing the long, straight, current-carrying wire by a current-carrying loop that surrounds the loop in which a current is to be induced (Fig. 9.14). When a current flows in the outer loop, and the inner loop rotates around an axis perpendicular to two sides of the current-carrying loop, the effect is a virtual doubling of that in the previous experiment. In each of the segments of the rotating loop *parallel* to the axis of rotation, the electrons experience a force which is the sum of the two forces due to the sides of the outer loop *perpendicular* to the axis of rotation. In the rotating loop, the forces are such as to produce a circulating current whose direction reverses every half-revolution. The same effect is produced if the outer, current-carrying loop is rotated instead of the inner loop. The reinforcement can be multiplied many more times by using many current-carrying loops.

A still more practical way for observing an induced current consists of an extension of the above, using two coils each containing several dozen turns of wire. In this way, we need not employ such strong currents and such sensitive instruments as would be required actually to carry out the preceding experiments. Although we have been discussing rectangular loops to make it easier to identify the direction of the induced current, it turns out that circular loops or

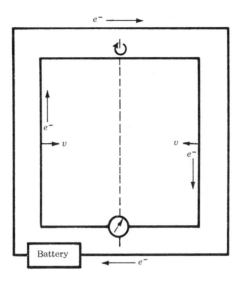

Figure 9.14 A Double-Loop Experiment for Induction of the First Type.

coils do just as well. The ends of one of the coils should be connected
to a battery so that a continuous current flows through it, and the ends
of the other coil should be connected to a current-sensing instrument
such as a galvanometer. From the previous experiment, we would expect that, if the two coils are placed near each other, face to face, and
one of them is rotated around an axis parallel to its faces (Fig. 9.15),
a current should be induced in the coil not connected to the battery.
Such is indeed the case. With this apparatus, there are several other
ways in which a current can be induced. A variety of relative motions
of the coils besides those described above will result in induced currents. In principle, all cases of induction based on relative motion
can be explained by means of Eq. (9.4), although the details of such
explanations would often be very difficult to work out.

There is another interesting technique for producing an induced
current which cannot be explained by Eq. (9.4), even in principle. If
the two coils are placed face to face, both stationary, whenever the
connection of the coil to the battery is either made or broken, the
galvanometer connected to the other coil registers a momentary induced current. The direction of these momentary induced currents
differs when making and breaking the battery connection to the first
coil. It is not necessary to switch the current completely on and off;
any change in the strength of the current will result in an induced
current in the second coil while the change is taking place. Such
changes in current strength imply changes in the drift velocity of
electrons. Since Eq. (9.4) takes into account only the *average* drift
velocity of electrons, it is clearly insufficient to explain effects which

are caused by *changes* in electron velocity. How may electromagnetic theory be extended so as to account for these effects?

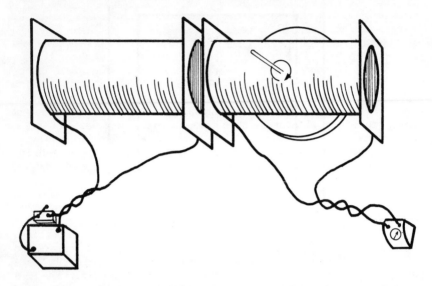

Figure 9.15 Two Coils Arranged for Induction Experiments.

The second type of electromagnetic induction just discussed differs from **induction of the first type** in that it requires an acceleration of charges, i.e., $\Delta v/\Delta t \neq 0$. Experiments confirm that the strength of current induced in this way depends on the rate of change of the current as well as on the physical dimensions and relative positions of the coils. For a given physical arrangement,

$$i_{\text{induced}} = K \frac{\Delta i}{\Delta t} \tag{9.6}$$

Recalling that $i = (\Delta q/\Delta L)\,v$ (Eq. (9.5)), we can translate the right-hand member of Eq. (9.6) into terms which express the motions of charges in the first coil. $\Delta q/\Delta L$ is the amount of charge per unit length that is free to move in a wire. Denote it by q_L, and write,

$$i = q_L v$$

Therefore, $\Delta i = \Delta(q_L v)$. But q_L is a constant for a given wire, so we obtain $\Delta i = q_L \Delta v$, whereupon Eq. (9.6) becomes

$$i_{\text{induced}} = K q_L \frac{\Delta v}{\Delta t} = K q_L a \tag{9.7}$$

where a is the acceleration of the charges in the first coil.

Charges are set in motion in the second coil as a result of the acceleration of charges in the first coil, impling that a force has been generated between the charges in the two wires. This suggests that a *third* force law would explain the observed interaction of *accelerated* charges and that Eq. (9.7) might be derived from it. From Eq. (9.7) we infer that, in this interaction—called **induction of the second type**— the force on each electron in the second coil would be directly proportional to the acceleration of the charges and the amount of charge per unit-length in the first coil. We would also expect this force to diminish with increased distance between coils, but Eq. (9.7) gives no basis for determining how it might be related to distance. It might appear desirable to express such a law in terms of isolated charges, one of which is accelerated relative to the other. There is, however, a much more efficient way of explaining induction in general and, indeed, all electromagnetic phenomena—an approach which avoids explicit dependence on force laws. The principal value of force laws, even the first, seems to lie primarily in clarifying the idea that all electrical and magnetic effects are ultimately due to the attractions and repulsions of charged particles on each other.

If was Faraday and Maxwell, primarily, who succeeded in developing this new approach with its great conceptual power and remarkable simplicity of the equations involved. These equations employ, as variables, Faraday's concepts of **electric** and **magnetic fields**. The idea of changes in magnetic fields form the basis for a unified explanation of the two kinds of induction. Maxwell, in particular, by applying these equations to the relations between magnetic fields and electric fields, was able to deduce that electromagnetic effects are propagated with the velocity of light. In a subsequent section, we shall see for a particular case how his reasoning may be carried through to this conclusion.

ELECTROMAGNETIC INDUCTION AND THE FIELD CONCEPTS

Faraday, Maxwell and other nineteenth-century theorists conceived of electric and magnetic effects as being propagated through the medium of an all-pervading elastic "substance," known as the **aether** (sometimes called the **luminiferous aether** because it was supposed that light waves were also propagated in it). The aether was the last of the "subtle fluids," examples of which we first encountered in the case of Aristotelian elements and later in phlogiston, and in the "funiculus" postulated by the anti-vacuists (or plenists) to explain the mercurial barometer. Like its forerunners, the aether was postulated as a substance having precisely those properties needed to account for phenomena—in this case electrical phenomena that were observed in an otherwise empty space. We find ourselves today in the interesting position of having kept the properties but disposed of the substance which was supposed to possess them. Abstract field concepts and mathematical equations serve as well or better for holding these properties together in a theory as does a purely imaginary substance.

Field concepts today may most simply be characterized as convenient abbreviations for complex force laws. Equation (9.2) may be rewritten by introducing the abbreviation, $D = q_1/d^2$, so that it becomes

$$f_{es} = K_1 D q_2 \qquad (9.8)$$

By employing the more inclusive abbreviation, $E = K_1 q_1/d^2$, we obtain

$$f_{es} = E q_2 \qquad (9.9)$$

Since E and D are related by the equation, $E = K_1 D$, it may be difficult to see at the outset why both of these concepts should be needed. We shall see in the next section that having both E and D, and also a pair of magnetic-field concepts, brings out theoretical relationships which would otherwise have been concealed.

In the elastic aether theory of the nineteenth century, D was conceived of as the physical shift or **displacement** of the aether under the influence of a charged object. We may get a rough idea of this conception by considering, as a two-dimensional analogy of the aether, a rubber sheet stretched taut horizontally. Such a sheet would undergo a downward displacement everywhere if some heavy object were placed on it. If a little ball were placed anywhere else on the sheet, it would tend to roll toward the heavy object. We could describe the situation by saying that the heavy object was "surrounded by a field," and the displacement of the rubber sheet at any point from its original flat condition was a measure of the ball's tendency to roll. But another way in which the "strength" of this field could be measured at a given point is to determine the slope or inclination of the sheet at that point. The value of E, called the **electric field strength,** was somewhat similarly conceived as a measure of the **gradient** of the force that would be exerted on a unit-charge at any given point in the elastic aether. The force on a charged object at a given point could be determined either from the displacement at that point and the charge on the object, or from the gradient (electric field strength) at the point and the charge.

Today, D and E, as abstract field concepts, are still called the "displacement" and "electric field strength," respectively, although the aether, in terms of which they were originally conveived, has been discarded. They are vector quantities, so that associated with every point in space is a direction and a magnitude for each of these variables. Used with Eqs. (9.8) and (9.9), the magnitudes of these variables enable us to determine the force on a given charge q_2. To determine the direction of such a force requires other considerations besides the magnitudes of D and E. An essential feature of these field variables is that they depend only on the charge q_1 and its position relative to the point in question, and not on charge q_2. The directions and magnitudes of D and E at any point express a disposition for any charge, q_2, to be acted upon, if it were there, by a force of magnitude $K_1 D q_2$ or, equivalently, of $E q_2$. They serve to predict the effect of a fixed charge q_1, located elsewhere, on any charge that could be placed at the point in question. The economy of expression and the conceptual flexibility made possible by these field concepts should be apparent.

For electromagnetic force, Eq. (9.4) may also be abbreviated by means of either of two field concepts. Let $H = q_1 v_1/d^2$ and $B = K_2 q_1 v_1/d^2$, whereupon the magnitude of the force is given by

$$f_{em} = K_2 H q_2 v_2 \qquad (9.10)$$

or

$$f_{em} = B q_2 v_2 \qquad (9.11)$$

H is known as the **magnetic-field gradient** and B the **magnetic-flux density**. Since $B = K_2 H$, we regard H and B as analogous to D and E, respectively. These variables serve to predict the effect of a moving charge on any other moving charges that might be momentarily located in its vicinity.

So that these field concepts serve in determining the direction of electric and magnetic forces as well as the magnitude, it is necessary that a direction be associated with each of them as well as a magnitude. At any point in space, D and E have the same direction, and H and B have the same direction. With regard to D and E, their direction at a given point is taken as the direction of the force that would be experienced by a positive charge located at that point. This means that the force on an electron would be in the opposite direction from the direction of D and E at the point where it is located.

With regard to H and B, their direction at a given point is taken to be the direction of the force that would be exerted on the north-seeking pole of a magnet, if placed at that point. In the vicinity of a current-carrying wire, a magnet, such as a compass needle, will take a position at right angles to the wire. The direction of H and B at a point near a wire will always be tangent to the circle passing through that point, centered on the wire and lying in a plane perpendicular to it. The direction of H and B is at right angles to the electromagnetic force on a moving charge whose magnitude is given by Eqs. (9.10) or (9.11). (See Fig. 9.16.)

A convenient rule for remembering the directions of H and B near a current-carrying wire, known as the **left-hand rule**, is as follows: If one grasps the wire with his left hand so that his thumb points along the wire in the direction in which the electrons are moving, his fingers will encircle the wire, pointing in the direction of circles around the wire along which the directions of H and B would be oriented at every point.

Can we apply the above field concepts to the phenomena of electromagnetic induction? We begin by considering an example of the first

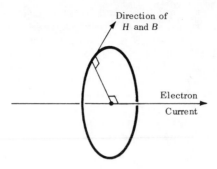

Figure 9.16 Direction of the Magnetic Field
Around a Current-Carrying Wire.

type of induction so that we may use the electromagnetic-force law in
its abbreviated form, Eq. (9.11). The most direct application we have
made of the force law to induction so far is in the experiment involving
a single wire segment moving through a magnetic field. (See Fig.
9.17.) The electromagnetic force on an electron in the moving wire
segment may be expressed as

$$f_{em} = Bq_2 v_2$$

where B is the magnetic-flux density at the point where the electron
under consideration is located, q_2 is the charge of the electron and v_2
is the velocity of the moving wire. (The student should check that the
circular direction for B shown in the figure agrees with the left-hand
rule.)

In anticipation of finding relationships between electric and magnetic fields, it should be noted from Eqs. (9.9) and (9.11) that an electric field strength, E, moving with the wire, and equal to Bv_2 in magnitude, would generate force of the same magnitude on the electron as
the stationary magnetic field does. They would be completely equivalent if E were directed toward the stationary wire as shown in Fig.
9.17.

What consequences develop from this conclusion? Although the
magnitudes of B and E will vary along the moving wire segment, we
may consider a portion of the wire segment whose length l is so
small that B and E do not vary appreciably within this portion. The
induced current represents a certain amount of energy expended.
Recalling that the energy expended (or work done) in moving any object is equal to the force applied multiplied by the distance moved
(p. 205), we write the following equation for the work done by the electric field in moving an electron through a portion of the wire of
length l:

$$W_e = Eq_2 l$$

where q_2 is the charge of the electron. Equivalently, we take the magnetic field as the agent responsible for the work done on the electron and write,

$$W_e = (Bv_2) q_2 l$$

Equating these two expressions gives us,

$$Eq_2 l = Bv_2 q_2 l$$

Divide both sides by q_2 and substitute for v_2, $\Delta d / \Delta t$, where Δd is the distance the wire segment moves while an electron is traversing the portion l in time Δt. This gives us

$$El = B \frac{\Delta d}{\Delta t} l$$

Referring to Fig. 9.17, we note that $(\Delta d)(l)$ is equal to the area swept out by the small portion of wire l during time Δt (as it moves to the right through the distance Δd). Denoting this area by Δa, the equation above becomes,

$$El = B \frac{\Delta a}{\Delta t} \tag{9.12}$$

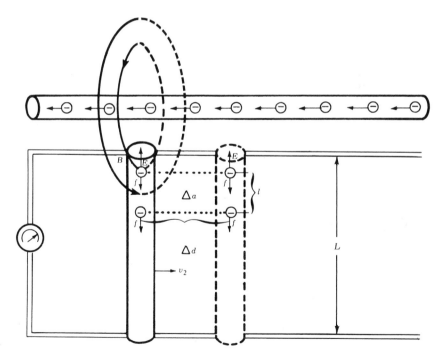

Figure 9.17 A Moving Wire Segment in a Magnetic Field.

It may be surprising that area enters into the theory of interacting electrons, but it should seem more plausible considering that we are using field concepts which represent properties of the space surrounding charges. Since Eq. (9.12) would hold for any small portion of the wire segment, we can imagine writing a similar equation for each such small portion and then adding them together to obtain the following equation,

$$\sum El = \sum B \frac{\Delta a}{\Delta t}$$

In the successive terms of the sum on the left, we have different values of E and of l. We replace each of the individual values of E by the average value for the entire wire segment which we write $\overline{E}$. So the left-hand member of the above equation becomes $\overline{E}\Sigma l$ or simply $\overline{E}L$, where L is the total length of the wire segment. The right-hand member of the above equation becomes $B\Sigma\Delta a/\Delta t$. Noting that $\Sigma\Delta a$ is the area swept out by the entire wire segment in time Δt, we designate that quantity as $\Delta\Sigma a$, or more simply, ΔA. This is the amount by which the area of the entire loop formed by the moving wire segment and the wires connected to the galvanometer changes in Δt seconds. With these new notations, the above equation becomes

$$\overline{E}L = \frac{\overline{B}\,\Delta A}{\Delta t} \tag{9.13}$$

This equation implies that a magnetic field through a wire loop that is changing in area is equivalent to an electric field moving along with a wire segment, and thus not changing relative to it, which is what was found by the first type of induction experiments.

The same approach can be used to explain the induction of a current in a loop of wire of fixed area rotating in a steady magnetic field. (See Fig. 9.18.) The area of the loop itself does not change with time, i.e., $\Delta A/\Delta t = 0$, so Eq. (9.13) would lead us to predict no induced current. We know that an induced current is produced (except at that instant when the loop is passing through the plane of the wire carrying the current), so if Eq. (9.13) is to serve for this case some reinterpretation is called for.

In the experiment with the moving wire segment, the direction of motion was perpendicular to that of B, and the loop whose area was changing was always perpendicular to B. This suggests that in the rotating-loop experiment instead of the conventional area of the loop (i.e., as viewed perpendicular to the loop itself), we should consider the area of the loop as viewed from the direction in which B points. This would be the same as the area of the shadow of the loop thrown on a plane perpendicular to B. (See Fig. 9.19 (a).) This projected area, which is designated by A_p, changes with time so that $\Delta A_p/\Delta t \neq 0$. Experiments show that, with ΔA_p substituted for ΔA, Eq. (9.13) does indeed hold for the rotating loop, provided L is taken as the total length

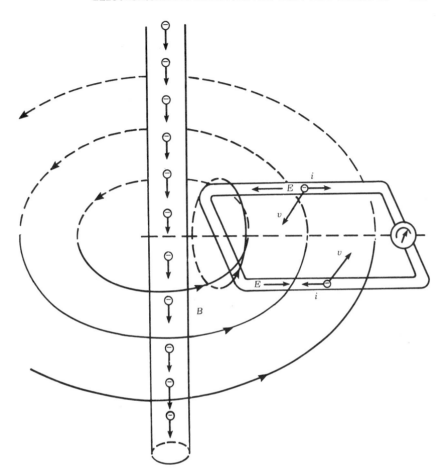

Figure 9.18 A Rotating Loop in a Magnetic Field.

of the two sides of the loop parallel to the axis of rotation. Such a conclusion prompts us to seek a more fundamental explanation as to why the projected area of a loop should be relevant to electromagnetic induction. Why do the area involved in Eq. (9.13) and the direction of B have to be perpendicular to each other?

In the analysis of the rotating-loop experiment, the perpendicularity of area and magnetic field was achieved by considering a shadow of the loop—or, more technically, its projection onto a plane. Is it possible that we could achieve the same end by considering the component of B which is perpendicular to the loop itself? From this point of view, it is the component of B rather than area which changes as the loop rotates. The question is, whether $B(\Delta A_p)$ is equal to $(\Delta B_p) A$, where the subscript p denotes a projection.

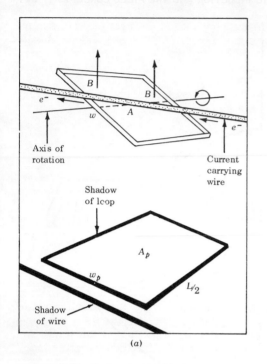

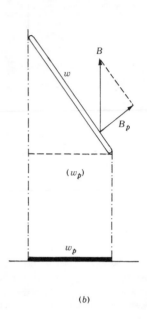

(a)

(b)

Figure 9.19 (a) The Rotating-Loop Experiment Showing the Shadow of the Loop.

Figure 9.19 (b) Analysis of Rotating-
Loop Projection and Perpendicular
Magnetic-Field Component.

From Fig. 9.19 (a) we can see that as the loop rotates the length
of its projection $L/2$ remains unchanged. ΔA_p depends only on the
variation in the width w_p of the projection. Referring to Fig. 9.19 (b),
we find that the two triangles shown—the one having B and B_p as sides
and the other w and w_p as sides—are similar triangles. We infer that
their corresponding sides are proportional. This means that,

$$\frac{w_p}{w} = \frac{B_p}{B}$$

Since the length of the loop and its projection are both equal to $L/2$,
we may multiply the left member of this equation by $(L/2)/(L/2)$. So the
above equation implies that

$$\frac{A_p}{A} = \frac{B_p}{B}$$

Multiplying both members by the denominators, we obtain

$$BA_p = B_pA$$

We may apply this equation to any positions in the rotation of the loop. Choose two, one only slightly rotated past the other, and designate the projected areas as A_p and A_p' and the components of the field strength B_p and B_p' respectively. We use the above equation for the first position and a primed version of it, $BA_p' = B_p'A$, for the second—there being no primes on B and A because they are constant. Subtracting the first equation from the second, we obtain

$$B(A_p' - A_p) = (B_p' - B_p)A$$

or

$$B(\Delta A_p) = (\Delta B_p)A$$

This result gives us an alternative to Eq. (9.13)

$$\overline{EL} = \frac{(\Delta B_p)A}{\Delta t} \tag{9.14}$$

In place of Eqs. (9.13) and (9.14), a single equation may be written which reduces to either of them under the conditions respectively appropriate to each. The expression $\Delta(BA)$, which means $B'A' - BA$, becomes $B(\Delta A)$, when B is constant and $(\Delta B)A$ when A is constant. We therefore write, as a more general equation for induction in a loop,

$$\overline{EL} = \frac{\Delta(BA)}{\Delta t} \tag{9.15}$$

where B and A must be perpendicular to each other (typically perpendicular components or projections), and L represents the total length of the wire segments which remain perpendicular to B.

This equation should be tested further to discover how general it is, employing as many different induction experiments as possible. Consider one illustrating induction of the second type. Imagine a pair of rectangular wire loops, one just inside the other. We connect a battery to the outside loop and a galvanometer to the inside loop as shown in Fig. 9.20. Now, whenever we either connect or disconnect the battery, the flux density B inside the outer loop changes rapidly. When this happens, currents are induced in the inner loop, and measurements confirm that these currents are proportional to the rate of change of B with time. The amounts of the induced currents are attributable to induced field strengths given by Eq. (9.15), where L is now equal to the perimeter of the inside loop. It is an indication of the power of the field concepts, that when they were introduced to represent Eqs. (9.2) and (9.4) more concisely, they led to a single equation which explains both first and second types of induction, whereas Eq. (9.4) could only explain the first type and Eq. (9.2) could explain neither.

Equation (9.15) is known as Faraday's Law, and it covers a very large variety of induction experiments, many of which were first tried by Faraday himself. He found that in whatever way he changed the area of a wire loop in a magnetic field, his law held. The law also proved valid for experiments in which the flux density perpendicular to a loop was changed, as well as for experiments in which combinations of both kinds of changes were made.

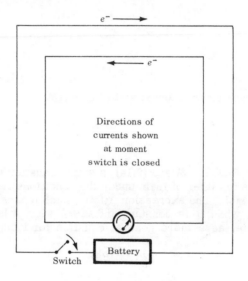

Figure 9.20 A Double-Loop Experiment for Induction of the Second Type.

Faraday noted that Eq. (9.15) does have some restrictions on its applicability. It does not apply without some qualifications to the first induction experiment we considered on p. 298, the case of the moving sheet. (See Fig. 9.11.) If the loop in that experiment is taken to consist of the straight line which crosses the metal sheet from one contact point to the other, the connecting wires and the instrument, then no change occurs in either the area of the loop or the flux density. Therefore Eq. (9.15) would not account for the induced current. In order that Eq. (9.15) be applicable here, it is necessary to consider a particular narrow strip of the moving sheet itself as a part of the loop. As this strip moves, it sweeps out an area, ΔA, and the induced current is proportional to $\Delta A/\Delta t$. So Eq. (9.15) holds on this interpretation of the experiment.

Faraday invented a piece of apparatus similar in principle to the moving-sheet idea, in which a disk revolved freely with one edge between two poles in a magnet. (See Fig. 9.21.) A contact was mounted so that a galvanometer could be connected to the edge of the disk protruding between the poles of the magnet, the other connection being made to the axle. Whenever the disk in this apparatus is turned by an external force, a current is indicated by a galvanometer connected across the two wires.

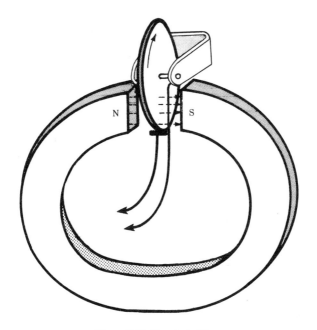

Figure 9.21 Faraday's Disc.

Theoretical exploration:

9.1 The student should attempt to explain why it is that, conversely to the phenomenon described above, when a current is passed through such a disk by way of the same contacts, a motion of the disk results. ■

It is well to recognize that there may be occasions for considering induction phenomena without a loop actually being present. In such situations, if we are to use Eq. (9.15), which refers to the area of a loop, we must seek some plausible way of imagining a loop whose presence would leave other things unchanged. We will see one instance in the next section in which this approach can be successfully followed.

HOW FAST DOES AN ELECTRIC PULSE MOVE
ALONG A WIRE?

Maxwell made use of field concepts in developing the entire mathematical formulation of Faraday's field theory of electromagnetism.

Perhaps his most direct contribution to technology stemmed from his prediction, based on this mathematical theory, that rapidly changing currents could produce waves, now known as radio waves, which would travel through space with the velocity of light. Let us look at the general line of reasoning Maxwell employed. When applied to a simple, imaginary experiment, his main arguments may be easily understood, although in their original, more general form they are likely to appear extremely abstruse to the mathematically unsophisticated.

Consider two long parallel wires and a battery which can be connected across the ends, as shown in Fig. 9.22. At the moment it is connected, even though there is not a complete circuit, we may expect a surge of electrons being drawn out of one wire in through the positive terminal of the battery and being pushed out through the negative terminal into the other wire. At that instant, the electrons at the far ends of the two wires will still be unaffected. A starting pulse moves down the wires, as electrons in motion set others in motion—analogous to the starting pulse transmitted from car to car of a long railroad train. It is the very rapid passage of this flurry of electron agitation whose velocity we wish to calculate. (The velocity with which the electrons themselves travel through wires is very small indeed.)

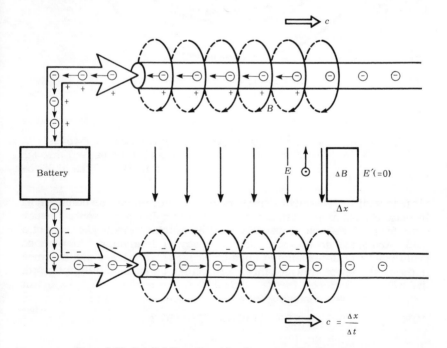

Figure 9.22 Parallel Wires Just After Connecting Them to a Battery.

The electrons already in the wire will be accelerated whenever the pulse reaches them. Because of the acceleration of these charges, we should expect an induction effect of the second kind to occur. Consider a point in the plane of the wires somewhere between them. Initially the flux density is zero at this point, but after the starting pulse passes by, the flux density will have a value B, which could be determined by summing the effects of all the electrons that are accelerating in both wires.

To make use of Faraday's law (Eq. 9.15) for inferring something about E from a knowledge of B, imagine a rectangular wire loop around the point we have been considering, as shown in Fig. 9.22. This loop must be imagined small enough so that, at a given instant, the value of B is essentially the same throughout its area. Because B is changing, there would be a tendency for electrons to be set in motion in every segment of the loop. In Eq. (9.15), $\overline{E}L = \Delta(BA)/\Delta t$, we take $\overline{E}$ to be the average of E all around the loop, L as the perimeter of the loop, and Δt as the time interval from the instant the flux density attains the value B at the left side of the loop to the instant it becomes B at the right. This time is the time it takes the starting pulse of current to traverse a distance equal to the horizontal width of the loop, Δx. We express this fact as follows: Using the letter c to represent pulse velocity, so as not to confuse it with electron drift velocity, v, we write,

$$c = \frac{\Delta x}{\Delta t}$$

As we develop the equations relating the field variables in this situation, we seek ways of having them involve c, which we are to calculate.

Evaluate the quantity $\overline{E}L$ for the loop. The effect of the moving pulse is that it builds up an excess of electrons on one wire and creates a dearth of electrons on the other. A spreading electric field, E, is created in the wake of the pulse so that there would be an upward force (see Fig. 9.22) on any electron which should happen to lie in the space between the wires.

As the pulse, in its movement from left to right, passes the left wire-segment of the loop, the spreading electric field would tend to produce a clockwise flow of electrons around the loop, if there really were one. As the pulse passes the right-hand segment, the electric field would act in the same direction on both sides, so the current would cease. The tendencies for currents to form in the two horizontal sides of the loop always cancel each other, because the electrons in one would experience forces conducive to a clockwise current and in the other, forces conducive to a counterclockwise current. The total current induced in the loop is that induced in the left-hand segment while the pulse traveling down the wires passes by this segment. Although in applying Eq. (9.15) to the present situation, $\overline{E}$ is the average of the values of E around the loop and L is the perimeter (since all four wire segments are perpendicular to B), actually the only effective portion of the loop is the left-hand wire segment, whose length we may denote by Δy. For this segment $\overline{E}$ is simply E, and the rest of the perimeter may be ignored, so $\overline{E}L$ reduces to $E\,\Delta y$. Writing the latter expression as the left-hand member, and recalling that, when loop area is constant, $\Delta(BA)$ may be rewritten as $(\Delta B)\,A$, Eq. (9.15) becomes,

$$E\,\Delta y \; = \; \frac{(\Delta B)\,A}{\Delta t}$$

E, we note, is just the amount by which the electric-field strength changes as the pulse moves from one side of the loop to the other. We replace E by ΔE and divide both members of the above equation by A, obtaining

$$\frac{\Delta E\,\Delta y}{A} \; = \; \frac{\Delta B}{\Delta t}$$

We replace A by $(\Delta x)(\Delta y)$, and cancel the Δy's, so the above equation becomes much simpler and more symmetrical:

$$\frac{\Delta E}{\Delta x} \; = \; \frac{\Delta B}{\Delta t} \tag{9.16}$$

This equation expresses **Maxwell's Second Law** as applied to this experiment. In its complete generality, this law specifies the relationship between E and B for each of the three components of B. It is postulated to apply whether or not there is a wire loop in the space being studied, so it should have something to say about our imaginary experiments. A simple transformation of Eq. (9.16) yields an expression for c: $\Delta x/\Delta t = \Delta E/\Delta B$. This result does not yet put us in a position to compute the value of c. We must follow still further the mathematical ingenuity of Maxwell.

Theoretical exploration:

$$\left\{ \begin{array}{l} \dfrac{\Delta E_z}{\Delta y} \; - \; \dfrac{\Delta E_y}{\Delta z} \; = \; \dfrac{\Delta B_x}{\Delta t} \\[3ex] \dfrac{\Delta E_x}{\Delta z} \; - \; \dfrac{\Delta E_z}{\Delta x} \; = \; \dfrac{\Delta B_y}{\Delta t} \\[3ex] \dfrac{\Delta E_y}{\Delta x} \; - \; \dfrac{\Delta E_x}{\Delta y} \; = \; \dfrac{\Delta B_z}{\Delta t} \end{array} \right.$$

9.2 The three equations above express the relation known as Maxwell's Second Law. Subscripts x and y are used to indicate components in the directions of the Δx and Δy, shown in Fig. 9.22, and subscript z to indicate the direction perpendicular to the plane of the figure. Maxwell developed these equations in order to give a more general and abstract formulation of Faraday's empirical law, Eq. (9.15). In order to show how these three equations reduce to Eq. (9.16) for the experiment we are analyzing, the student should determine the answer to the following questions: In the plane of the loop we have imagined, which of the quantities, B_x, B_y, and B_z, are zero and which are not changing with time? Which of the three components of E are zero in the plane of the loop? $\Delta E_z / \Delta y$ is the slope (or gradient) of the graph of E_z plotted against y. Which of the gradients in the equations above are zero in the plane of the loop? Substitute zeros in the appropriate places in the general statement of Maxwell's Second Law to see that it reduces to Eq. (9.16). ■

Maxwell's Second Law relates the space rate of change (or gradient) of the electric-field strength at any point in space to the time rate of change of the magnetic flux density at that point. Maxwell intuitively reasoned that there should also be a realtionship holding the other way round; that is, relating the space rate of change of the magnetic field to the time rate of change of the electric field. (There was a strong feeling at the time that the relationships between electric and magnetic fields probably were symmetrical.) Suppose one postulated, corresponding to Eq. (9.16), that

$$\frac{\Delta B}{\Delta x} = \frac{\Delta E}{\Delta t}$$

Multiplying the two members of this equation with those of Eq. (9.16), $\Delta E / \Delta x = \Delta B / \Delta t$, yields

$$\frac{\Delta B \, \Delta E}{(\Delta x)^2} = \frac{\Delta E \, \Delta B}{(\Delta t)^2}$$

Because multiplication of the field variables is commutative, i.e., $\Delta B \, \Delta E = \Delta E \, \Delta B$, this equation, in turn, yields

$$\left(\frac{\Delta x}{\Delta t} \right)^2 = c^2 = 1$$

But c, the magnitude of the pulse velocity, depends on the system of units employed, e.g., meters and seconds or miles and hours, so our new postulate must be wrong.

It is at this point that the field variables D and H become indispensable. They provide an alternative way of describing electric and magnetic fields, so we write a different postulate corresponding to

Eq. (9.16) as follows:

$$\frac{\Delta H}{\Delta x} = \frac{\Delta D}{\Delta t} \tag{9.17}$$

This says that the x-gradient of H equals the time rate of change of displacement, what Maxwell called the **displacement current**.

Does the use of this equation in conjunction with (9.16) avoid the difficulty just encountered? Multiplying the corresponding members of these two equations, we obtain,

$$\frac{\Delta E \, \Delta H}{(\Delta x)^2} = \frac{\Delta B \, \Delta D}{(\Delta t)^2}$$

whence,

$$\frac{(\Delta x)^2}{(\Delta t)^2} = \frac{\Delta E \, \Delta H}{\Delta B \, \Delta D}$$

or

$$\left(\frac{\Delta x}{\Delta t}\right)^2 = \frac{\Delta E}{\Delta D} \cdot \frac{\Delta H}{\Delta B}$$

Because $E = K_1 D$ and $B = K_2 H$, and because $c = \Delta x/\Delta t$, this last equation is equivalent to

$$c^2 = K_1 \cdot \frac{1}{K_2} = \frac{K_1}{K_2}$$

Since it has already been seen that K_1/K_2 is equal to the square of the velocity of light (p. 296), we see that, as a consequence of Eqs. (9.16) and (9.17), we would have to conclude that the velocity c of the propagation of a pulse down a pair of wires is equal to the velocity of light. Equation (9.17) is a special case of the set of equations known as **Maxwell's First Law** (stated fully below), so this result is a consequence of Maxwell's First and Second Laws.

MAXWELL'S "DISPLACEMENT CURRENT": A CLUE TO RADIO WAVES

It is instructive to examine the approach Maxwell took in arriving at his first law, because it had no direct experimental support. He argued that a changing electric field (such as that between the two wires in the situation just analyzed) must itself constitute a kind of current. As soon as the battery is connected, electrons flow into it from the wire connected to the positive terminal and also flow out from the battery into the other wire. The electrons cannot get across the space between the wires, so the current quickly comes to a halt. It seemed to Maxwell that, in some sense, there ought to be a complete circuit if there is a current. While the current flows, an electric field is being built up between the wires. Maxwell proposed that this spreading field could be regarded as a special kind of current which, like an ordinary current, produces a magnetic field. So far as the production of a magnetic field is concerned, it is as though, in the situation described, there was momentarily a complete circuit of wire carrying a current.

Maxwell, who saw field concepts as physical deformations of the aether, chose to call this imaginary current a *displacement current*, meaning a progressive shifting of the aether, and he defined displacement current as the time rate of change of D. Maxwell's First Law, in its general form combines, for a given point in three-dimensional space, the displacement current with the ordinary current of electrons. The three equations for this law, expressing the relation of the space rate of change of the magnetic field to the components of the total current, are:

$$\begin{cases} \dfrac{\Delta H_z}{\Delta y} - \dfrac{\Delta H_y}{\Delta z} = \dfrac{\Delta D_x}{\Delta t} + i_x \\[2ex] \dfrac{\Delta H_x}{\Delta z} - \dfrac{\Delta H_z}{\Delta x} = \dfrac{\Delta D_y}{\Delta t} + i_y \\[2ex] \dfrac{\Delta H_y}{\Delta x} - \dfrac{\Delta H_x}{\Delta y} = \dfrac{\Delta D_z}{\Delta t} + i_z \end{cases}$$

where i_x, i_y, and i_z are the three components of the electron current, if such exists at the point in question.

Theoretical exercise:

9.3 Following the pattern illustrated in Exercise 9.2, the student should verify that these equations reduce to Eq. (9.17) for the loop we have imagined in our parallel-wire experiment (Fig. 9.22). ∎

Maxwell's laws lead to the theoretical prediction that a pulse of electric and magnetic fields moves with the speed of light through the space in the neighborhood of a pair of wires. Maxwell also showed that this was true of all pulses moving through conductors and that these pulses leave the vicinity of the conductors and travel through space indefinitely with the velocity of light. In the case we have considered, the pulse of electromagnetic fields moves off past the ends of the wires, except for a portion of the energy which is reflected when it reaches the end and returns along the wires.

Taking advantage of the tendency for pulses to reflect at the ends of wires and oscillate back and forth, Heinrich Hertz, a German physicist, was later able to measure the velocity of electromagnetic pulses, in a manner somewhat analogous to Fizeau's technique for measuring the speed of light. He was also able to detect oscillating electric currents in appropriately shaped conductors at considerable distances from the wires in which charges were being forcibly accelerated back and forth, demonstrating the transmission of electromagnetic waves through space. This confirmation gives us good experimental reason for accepting Maxwell's First Law, which had been so imaginatively conceived.

Practical means of transmitting and receiving electromagnetic waves of this type were subsequently developed commercially by Guglielmo Marconi, an Italian engineer, and others for purposes of radio communication. Techniques for molding messages of these radio waves have recently been developed to such an extent by the television industry that detailed moving pictures in color can be sent at the rate of 50 frames a second. In radio telephony we learn that hundreds of simultaneous conversations can be sent and received by a single transmitter and receiver.

Not only have the technological advances based on the discovery of radio waves been a boon to industry and society, but these same developments have also opened new techniques for scientific study in many fields, including radio astronomy, meteorology and X-ray crystallography. These indirect contributions may well outweight the direct.

METHODOLOGICAL REVIEW

One of the most basic metaphysical problems in the history of science concerns the question whether forces (gravitational, electrical, or otherwise) between two objects should be regarded simply as the action of one body on another separated by a distance, in which the intervening space plays no part, or whether they should be regarded as the result of a modification by one body of the properties of a medium pervading all space which, in turn, acts on the second body. This is known as the problem of action at a distance *vs* action by an intervening medium, and the aether controversy is certainly the most prominent example in the recent history of science.

The controversy over the aether is not unlike the problem which arose in connection with the spherical-shell models of the universe developed by the Greek astronomers. The shells provided a medium which held the planets and stars in place and gave them their respective motions. When Kepler abandoned these spherical shells and introduced eliptical orbits, he claimed he was merely using them as a mathematical device for calculating the positions of the planets. He was forced to sidestep the metaphysical question, "What keeps celestial objects in orbit?" Newton, taking an entirely different concept of space, answered the metaphysical question with his concept of a universal gravitational force. For Newton, space put no constraints at all on the movement of objects and the planets and satellites acquired their orderly behavior by virtue of a God-given motion of their own which balanced exactly the gravitational force.

The success of this action-at-a-distance point of view in astronomy was such that we find the whole development of science in the seventeenth and eighteenth centuries involved in building theoretical models based on atomic and mechanical conceptions. Most scientists, principally on the authority of Newton, conceived of light as particles in motion until the end of the eighteenth century. The development of the wave theory of light, when it finally acquired recognition through the experiments of Young, Fresnel and others, raised the serious question of what it is that undulates in light waves. (Someone has said that the luminiferous aether was invented so that the verb "to undulate" could have a subject.)

The aether did not become a matter of serious scientific study, however, until Faraday's and Maxwell's concepts of electric and magnetic fields were developed. The early laws of electricity and magnetism, e.g., the force laws of Coulomb and Ampere, were formulated in terms of action at a distance, paralleling Newton's law of gravity. With inverse-square laws in mechanics, optics, electricity, and magnetism, there did seem to be a great ubiquity in the Newtonian approach. The explanatory power of field concepts in the growing science of electromagnetism definitely led physics, in the latter part of the nineteenth century, away from action at a distance and toward belief in an all-pervading medium capable of exerting some constraint on an object—especially on a charged object.

It would seem that physical science has been vacillating between action at a distance and action through an intervening medium, and the fact that the physics of the twentieth century brought back the idea of light as particles, when Albert Einstein discovered that wave theory could not explain the action of a photoelectric cell, fits this pattern. At the same time that it has adopted Einstein's photons, modern physics has retained field concepts. This, to a considerable extent, is also because of Einstein's work.

Einstein's special theory of relativity, in which the velocity of light became a universal constant, put Maxwell's electromagnetism in more systematic form, and his general theory of relativity replaced Newton's gravitational force with curvature of space, a field concept not unlike the electromagnetic distortions of the aether. On this view, planets are kept in their orbits by the curvature of space, somewhat like a marble going round and round inside a salad bowl. Curved space required a new geometry, for it became clear that Euclidean geometry, which had been taken for granted, would have to be replaced by one of the new non-Euclidean geometries in the new field theory of gravitation.

Field concepts are also embodied in particle physics. Photons, as light particles are called, are still governed by Maxwell's Laws. Even the well-established particles of physics such as electrons, protons, and other constituents of atoms have come to be regarded as possessing wavelike properties. For these wavelike particles, a new theory of wave mechanics has been developed in which all matter and energy is, in principle, simultaneously wavelike and particlelike.

In modern physics, all matter is regarded as basically electrical in character. Because of this the interaction between any two objects, even when they appear to touch, becomes a case of action at a distance. But the space between particles is filled with fields and waves to which are attributed the repulsive forces that make balls bounce and make the ground support us.

When we look at the classical theories which entail action at a distance, we see now that they tacitly assigned to space the properties of Euclidean geometry, such as are implied in the Pythagorean Theorem, the formula for the area of a sphere, and the theorem concerning the proportionality of the sides of similar triangles. These Euclidean properties of space have crept into physical science everywhere, and some of the most basic laws, such as the inverse-square laws, probably rest just as much on such geometrical assumptions as they do on the experimental evidence that was available.

The geometrical theorems themselves are based on certain basic assumptions regarding space, including the famous postulate of parallels which states that one and only one line can be drawn through any point parallel to a given line. Non-Euclidean geometries, in which this postulate is replaced by the postulation, either of no parallel lines at all, or of more than one parallel line, were developed at the end of the nineteenth century. These geometries have proved to be logically just as sound as Euclidean geometry, showing that a choice of a geometry must be made in developing a scientific theory, whether it is recognized as such or not. Scientific theories are tested by experiments; geometries must be experimentally tested along with them.

In the final analysis, the aether controversy reduces to a difference in linguistic convention, because scientific theories attribute certain properties to space no matter whether we regard it as filled with aether or not. The feeling that some substance must be present to possess these properties is merely a linguistic habit—the converse of the linguistic habit we also have of attributing properties to concrete objects. Useful as this first habit may have been in the historical development of electromagnetic theory, we find now that we can use field properties for computation without concluding that they are properties of existent objects. This means that metaphysical controversies concerning the actual existence of objects or properties named in scientific theories need not be resolved in order for the theories to be useful in science. When it comes to the evaluation of a scientific theory, we have as criteria the four qualities we have mentioned in previous chapters: simplicity, scope, precision, and fruitfulness in leading to new and useful ideas.

The theories developed in this chapter, like most of those in earlier chapters, have met these criteria very well, and earlier theories which have not met these criteria have nearly all been forgotten. We have tried to make plausible the process of theory formation, but in the journey we have taken through scientific thought, we too, like Newton, have stood on the shoulders of giants: Copernicus, Kepler, Galileo, Newton, Dalton, Mendelyeev, Faraday, and Maxwell. It is hoped that the viewpoint of their shoulders enables the student to see further than he otherwise could into the continuing scientific revolution in which he lives.

PROBLEMS

1. Consider the following anecdote:

    The physics professor asked a student in his class to tell him what electricity is. The student answered, "I am very sorry, I knew it, but I have forgotten now." At this the professor remarked, "This is a great tragedy! The only person in the world who ever knew what electricity is has now forgotten it."
    a. How would you defend the professor's contention that no one knows what electricity is?
    b. Suppose the student's answer had been, "Electricity is the interaction of charged particles." What rejoinder or further question could the professor have given which would represent the point of view expressed in the anecdote.
2. A hydrogen atom has a proton for a nucleus whose positive charge is 2×10^{19} coulombs and an electron orbiting around it whose charge is the same as that of the proton in magnitude. The radius of the smallest orbit of the electron is 53×10^{-11} m, and that of its next principal orbit is 32×10^{-10} m. Calculate the force of attraction in newtons on the electron in each case and the work in newton-meters it takes to raise it from the first to the second orbit. This is also the energy carried by the photon emitted when the electron falls from the second to the first orbit.

    In the m.k.s. system of units, charge is measured in coulombs and the electrostatic- and electromagnetic-force constants have the following values:

$$K_1 = 1.113 \times 10^{-10} \ \frac{\text{newton-m}^2}{\text{coulomb}^2}$$

$$K_2 = 10^{-7} \frac{\text{newton-sec}^2}{\text{coulomb}^2}$$

3. Assume the velocity of light is 3×10^8 m/sec and the charge on the electron as given in Problem 2.

    a. Find the magnitude of the force in newtons (and its direction) on one electron due to another electron 1 cm away. Repeat when it is 10^{-8} cm away.

    b. Two electrons are moving past each other in opposite directions so that their relative speed is 2/3 the velocity of light. Calculate the total force (electrostatic plus electromagnetic) between them, if their distance apart is 1 cm. Repeat for 10^{-8} cm.

    c. The mass of an electron is 9×10^{-31} kg. Calculate the gravitational attraction between two electrons 1 cm apart. Repeat for 10^{-8} cm apart.

    d. Compare the three kinds of forces at the two distances.

SUPPLEMENTARY READINGS

Boorse, Henry A. and Motz, Lloyd. *The World of the Atom*, Vol. I. New York: Basic Books, Inc., 1966.
    Selections 5 (Huygens), 6 (Newton), 21 (Faraday), 22 (Maxwell), 23 (Crookes), 25 (Michelson and Morley), and 28 (Thomson) are recommended original scientific writings for this chapter.

Conant, James Bryant and Nash, Leonard K. (eds.). *Harvard Case Histories in Experimental Science*. Cambridge, Mass.: Harvard University Press, 1957.
    Case 8, "Development of the Concept of Electric Charge," gives the development of electrical science up to the discovery of Coulomb's Law.

Cullwick, E. Geoffrey. *The Fundamentals of Electro-Magnetism: A Restatement for Engineering Students and Others of Physical and Theoretical Principles in Accordance with Modern Scientific Thought*. New York: Macmillan, 1939.
    Pages 120–140 leading up to the relativistic equivalence of electricity and magnetism can be read without calculus. The text as a whole assumes familiarity with calculus but avoids the customary vector analysis.

d'Abro, A. *The Rise of the New Physics, Its Mathematical and Physical Theories* (2 vols.) (formerly titled "Decline of Mechanism"). New York: Dover Publications, Inc., 1951.
    Especially recommended are Chapters 9, 10, and 11 on mechanistic, field, and phenomenological theories, and Chapters 18 and 19 on light and electromagnetic theory.

Einstein, Albert and Infeld, Leopold. *The Evolution of Physics: The Growth of Ideas from Early Concepts to Relativity and Quanta.* New York: Simon and Schuster, 1954.
General exposition of the development of field theory showing its crucial significance, as well as that of the velocity of light, for modern physics.

Faraday, Michael. *Experimental Researches in Electricity.* (Originally published in 1839, recently republished as one of the *Great Books of the Western World* by Encyclopaedia Britannica.)
An eminently readable account of the work of a great experimenter.

Jaffe, Bernard. *Michelson and the Speed of Light.* Garden City, N.Y.: Doubleday (Anchor Books), 1960.
Reviews the methods of measuring the speed of light and takes the reader a considerable distance into the evolution of relativity.

Macdonald, D. K. C. *Faraday, Maxwell, and Kelvin.* Garden City, N.Y.: Doubleday (Anchor Books), 1964.
Brief, well-illustrated biographical sketches of three great scientists.

Magie, William F. *A Source Book in Physics.* New York: McGraw-Hill, 1935.
Includes selections from the original writings of most of the scientists discussed in this chapter.

Newton, Isaac. *Optics, or a Treatise of the Reflections, Refractions, Inflections, and Colours of Light.* 4th ed. (1730). New York: Dover Publications, Inc., 1952.
Newton at his most readable.

Orear, Jay. *Fundamental Physics.* New York: John Wiley & Sons, 1961.
Chapter 8 presents a different and equally instructive derivation of Maxwell's First Law and the velocity of an electromagnetic wave.

Physical Science Study Committee. *Physics.* New York: Harcourt, Brace, 1965.
A text for high schools exhibiting the process of inquiry into fundamental questions. See Part II, "Optics and Waves," and Part IV, "Electricity and Atomic Structure." The illustrations and experiments described in the accompanying laboratory guide are especially recommended.

Pierce, John R. *Electrons and Waves.* Garden City, N.Y.: Doublday (Anchor Books), 1964.
Recommended for further study of electromagnetism.

Polyani, Michael. *Science, Faith and Society.* Chicago: University of Chicago Press, 1964.
In this edition of a 1945 lecture, Polyani discusses in a new foreword, the implications for recent history of his views on scientific creativity—an extremely thought-provoking document.

Rogers, Eric M. *Physics for the Inquiring Mind: The Methods, Nature, and Philosophy of Physical Science.* Princeton, N.J.: Princeton University Press, 1960.
See Chapters 33, 36, 37.

Shapley, Harlow (editor). *Source Book in Astronomy 1900-1950*. Cambridge, Mass.: Harvard University Press, 1960.

See selections 63 and 64 by de Sitter and Einstein.

Skilling, Hugh H. *Exploring Electricity*. New York: Ronald Press, 1948.

Treats many of the practical aspects of electricity as well as basic theory.

Webster, David L. "Electricity," *Encyclopaedia Britannica*. Chicago: William Benton, Publisher, 1961, volume 8, pp. 153-211.

A lucid survey of the subject. The section on "Special Relativity" is very appropriate.

Williams, L. Pearce. *Michael Faraday, A Biography*. London: Chapman and Hall, 1965.

An authoritative and sensitive life history of one of the most outstanding experimental scientists.

EPILOGUE

It was a great three hundred and eighteen years for physics—from the publication of Newton's *Philosophiae Naturalis Principia Mathematica* to Einstein's three epoch-making papers in volume 17 of the *Annalen der Physik* (1905). Measured in terms of the number of man-years devoted to scientific investigation or the number of scientific reports and treatises written, this period could be reckoned as far more productive than the 1400 years from Ptolemy to Copernicus. By similar measures, Einstein's papers may well antedate the still-unknown discoveries of the 1980's by a greater amount of scientific thought than Newton's *Principia* antedated him. It has been estimated that more than 90 percent of all the scientists who ever lived are alive today.

Today's army of scientists have lived and worked with a post-revolutionary science although their basic education in physics was classical. They embrace both the classical period we have studied and modern science. We cannot attempt in this volume to give the student a view of modern physical science; for that he must turn elsewhere. However, a few words about the revolution of the early nineteen hundreds seem needed, if only to dispel the notion that old methods of thought were suddenly abandoned in the rush of new ideas.

What was abandoned was confidence in the absolute truth of existing theory. The scientists who were shaken by Einstein's disclosures had been educated in a world view that demanded to know absolutely the truth about the construction of the world. They attached to Newton's highly successful model a degree of certainty we have attempted to avoid by methodological analysis. How did the structure begun by Copernicus, Kepler, Galileo, and Newton and so ably extended by Dalton, Faraday, Maxwell, and many others begin to crumble?

For quantum mechanics, there is little dispute. In 1900 Max Planck, in Germany, was investigating the distribution of wavelengths in heat radiation. It had been discovered that the theory was inconsistent. One law worked for long wavelengths and another for short wavelengths, but neither agreed with experiments over the whole spectrum. Tackling the problem from the point of view of electromagnetic theory, Planck made a breakthrough using the theory Hertz had worked out for the electromagnetic radiation created by an oscillating electric current in a pair of wires (a dipole). Planck postulated that heat was radiated by Hertz' dipoles. Then he could derive a formula for the entire heat-radiation spectrum. However, to give a physical interpretation of the formula, he had to assume that the emission and absorption of energy occurred only in whole numbers of a small unit. These quanta, or smallest amounts of energy that can be radiated or absorbed, are not noticeable in ordinary radiation measurements, but Planck assumed that energy does not exist in any amounts except multiples of a quantum. Thus it was postulated that energy, like matter, was atomized, or quantized—to use the term that Planck introduced. By plausible adjustments of his theory Planck was able to find an expression for the absolute probability of each wavelength in the spectrum.

One of Einstein's 1905 papers extended Planck's quantum to the transmission of light, in the form of particles he called photons. Another set forth the principles of the special theory of relativity, and the third explained Brownian movement. Although serious problems remained for many years, such as the problem of quantum electrodynamics, which Feynnman, at the California Institute of Technology, helped solve nearly fifty years later, modern physics was off on a new set of models which left Newtonian and Maxwellian physics in the position of being still very good for many purposes but definitely in second place.

The quantum of energy, or action, as Planck preferred to define it, emerged from a most unimpressive problem in physics by the classic method of building a mathematical equation to fit experimental data and then trying to find a physical explanation for the equation. Other problems cropped up concerning the difficulty of explaining line spectra in gaseous emission and absorption, X-rays, and radioactivity; and the world inside the atom was opened up for study. The atom came to be conceived as a system of electrically charged and neutral particles with enormous energy locked in its nucleus.

The achievements of quantum mechanics linked with those of relativity theory have been revolutionary in both concept and practice. As a consequence of military applications of the new physics, control of the use of nuclear weapons is one of the major problems confronting civilization. The peaceful uses of atomic energy may hold one key to this problem, but other keys must be developed in the social sciences and humanities. Modern physical science needs to be understood because of its influence, but more importantly, because as one of the greatest achievements of the human mind, it must serve as a guide in the needed development of new science.

INDEX